The Nature of Perceptual Adaptation

THE NATURE
OF PERCEPTUAL
ADAPTATION

by Irvin Rock

BASIC BOOKS, INC., PUBLISHERS

NEW YORK • LONDON

© 1966 by Irvin Rock
Library of Congress Catalog Card Number: 66-26218
Manufactured in the United States of America
Designed by Sophie Adler

To Peter and Alice

Preface

It seems to have become a custom for authors of textbooks or other scientific works to explain, in the preface, why they have written the book. My original reason for doing so was the belief that I had something to say about a related set of topics, all of which were concerned with the problem of perceptual adaptation in one way or another. Since undergraduate days I have been intrigued by the problem, first investigated by Stratton, of whether the world would ultimately appear to be right side up if the retinal image were erect rather than inverted. My dissertation was concerned with this problem. Shortly thereafter I began work on a problem which is relevant to perceptual adaptation, namely, the relationship between vision and touch. A few years later I became interested in a question analagous to the one studied by Stratton, namely, whether objects in the world would ultimately appear normal in size if the entire retinal image were magnified or minified.

During this period, interest in the problem of perceptual adaptation was revived by the work of Erismann and Kohler at Innsbruck and of Richard Held, then at Brandeis. New and dramatic findings were reported and new techniques were developed. Empirical data on adaptation began pouring into the literature at such a rapid rate that a summary of current findings made one month could easily become obsolete within the next few months. As I began to set down my thoughts, it became increasingly clear to me that—transcending my original purpose of reporting my ideas concerning certain specific problem areas—it was necessary for someone to raise the questions about perceptual adaptation that arise when one considers the findings in the light of the already existing body of knowledge and theory in the field of perception as a whole. There was little evidence that the findings on adaptation were being considered in relation to what was already known about the very perceptual functions expected to undergo change during exposure to distorting optical devices.

This brings me to a further reason for writing this book, one which also became clear to me only after I began to work on it. The problems in perception are concerned with how things look, with the realm of sensory appearances. Whatever the difficulties of getting at this essentially private world, we must face the fact that this is, nevertheless, the subject matter we wish to explain in perception. Therefore, when an observer looks at the world through prisms that yield curved retinal images of objectively straight lines, we must explain: (1) why these lines now *appear* curved and (2) why they begin to *appear* less curved or even straight as the observer continues wearing the prisms. If, instead, we talk about the observer's *behavior* while wearing the prisms, we will not be focusing on the relevant problem or, to say the very least, we will not be focusing on the same problem.

Partly because of the strong positivistic bias in contemporary psychology and partly because of enchantment with the concepts and language of modern engineering and information theory, it appears that many investigators in the field of perceptual adaptation are not willing to talk about perception *qua* perception. For example, in adaptation to prismatic displacement of the image, the fundamental question, I should think, is where do objects appear to be located—and what change, if any, in such apparent locations occurs over time. Yet many workers in this field prefer to speak of the disruption of sensory-motor coordination by the prisms and the re-establishment of such coordination via continued exposure to prisms. While it is true that proper coordination is often a sign of correct perceptual localization, it is by no means necessarily the case. Furthermore, this emphasis makes it difficult to deal with measures that do not seem to entail coordination—for example, judgments of when a target, the position of which is varied by the experimenter, appears straight ahead. As a rule there are satisfactory objective methods for ascertaining what the observer *sees*, and these methods are often quite different from those which are concerned with his motor coordination. Therefore, the emphasis in this book is on how the world appears, and is, in view of the neglect (or disdain) for such an approach in the current literature, a major justification for writing it. I hold the deep conviction that one of the ever-present dangers in contemporary psychology is the tendency to avoid dealing with its unique problems on their own terms, either by hiding behind the skirts of a hardheaded philosophy of science or by prematurely borrowing the paraphernalia of the natural sciences. No explanation of the changes that occur in prism adaptation is going to be satisfactory if it fails to address itself to the question of why things *look* different following exposure to prisms—assuming of course that it has been established in any given case that there is such a perceptual change.

This book should be viewed as an early attempt to grapple with what I believe are the central problems in this relatively new field of perceptual adaptation, rather than as an attempt to systematize an existing body of knowledge. In most cases the factual data are not yet clearly established. I have not hesitated to speculate, on the assumption that only by so doing can we truly advance our understanding of perception. No doubt I am quite wrong about some of these speculations, and in at least one case (concerning the perception of curvature) I find myself quite unsure and even surprised by my own conclusions. I would be satisfied in the long run, even though many of my speculations prove wrong, if my analysis of the problems proves correct.

The question of consistency has troubled me a great deal. Having tackled each type of adaptation separately—e.g., regarding tilt, displacement, size, etc.—and dealt with each on the basis of logical considerations and the evidence at hand, the larger question arises: Is the theory developed to deal with one type of adaptation consistent with that developed to deal with other types? I believe it is, but the careful reader will surely give this question much thought.

The reader should be forewarned that this is a difficult book, primarily because it is often necessary to stop and think through an example in order to visualize what is being described. For instance, if I refer to how the scene appears to move when a subject wearing left-right reversing prisms moves his head, this requires some thought. The need to do this is *not* a sign of the reader's intellectual limitations—I would be suspicious of anyone who can read non-stop through such material.

A word concerning the "bias" of the author is perhaps in order. There is often a desire on the part of those in fields related to psychology to categorize a psychologist as "Behaviorist" or "Gestaltist," etc. I'm afraid I will have to disappoint such readers, for although my training was strongly influenced by Gestalt psychologists, my approach here is to deal with each problem on its own intrinsic merits. If my belief in the goal of explaining the phenomenal experience of perception or in the importance of relational determination can be considered Gestalt-oriented, then my belief in the modifiability of perception can perhaps be considered empiristic. The theory I propose is in some respects Helmholtzian, but, on the other hand, it is embedded in a Gestalt-like theory of memory traces.

One further point of clarification here concerns my use of the term "information." It will be evident that the theory of adaptation to which I subscribe is based on the notion that what we find out via perception concerning the spatial properties of the world can influence the way things subsequently appear. How we gain such sensory information and how it can affect subsequent perception is discussed at length, but at this point I wish to make clear that I am not using the term "information" in the sense employed in computer engineering or "information theory." There it is used to mean the quantitative reduction of alternatives from which decisions or choices must be made. What I mean by information in the context of perceptual adaptation is essentially this: When the world appears distorted on first viewing it through prisms, information essential to adaptation consists of perceptual data which indicate that the world is not the way it appears.

There are many people whose help has been invaluable in the writing of this book. I learned a great deal from interchange with students, particularly those in seminars on perceptual adaptation conducted during 1963 and 1965. I am particularly indebted to Arien Mack, with whom I have discussed virtually every aspect of the problem of perceptual adaptation over a period of several years, and I have profited immensely from our discussions. For reading the manuscript and making helpful suggestions, I am very grateful to Drs. Sheldon Ebenholtz, Lloyd Kaufman, Carl Zuckerman, Edward S. Tauber, Sidney Morgenbesser, John Ceraso, Julian Hochberg, Charles Harris, and Arien Mack. I am indebted to Drs. William Feinbloom and Thorne Shipley for advice and help concerning optical apparatus. For typing, proofreading, and other less tangible but nonetheless vital forms of encouragement and support, I am grateful to my wife, Sylvia Rock. Finally, I wish to acknowledge with appreciation support of my research on perceptual adaptation in the form of a grant from the National Science Foundation.

I. R.

New York
August 1966

Contents

The Nature of Perceptual Adaptation

Introduction

CHAPTER ONE

Preliminary Comments

This book is intended as a monograph on a particular problem area in the field of perception, namely, adaptation to optical transformations of the retinal image. The transformations are brought about by viewing the world through optically refracting or displacing elements such as prisms, lens systems, or mirrors. The kinds of transformations that have been studied and that will be discussed in this monograph are: inversion or tilting of the retinal image, alteration of the direction or rate of movement of the image across the retina with movements of the head, minification or magnification of the image, lateral displacement of the image, and unequal displacement of different parts of the image resulting in alterations of curvature. Initially, as one might expect, viewing the world through a device that distorts the retinal image results in distortions of perception. By "adaptation" is meant a change in the direction of normal perception. If adaptation were complete, the world would appear precisely as it did before it was viewed through the distorting device. It would look exactly as it looks to us.

While this book is primarily addressed to experimental psychologists and advanced students, it will also be of interest to all those who are concerned with the nature of perception. To make it possible for the non-

1

psychologist or non-specialist to follow the argument, several steps have been taken, namely: technical matters concerning apparatus and the like have been kept to a minimum, sub-topics not essential to the main argument have been relegated to an addendum at the end of chapters and can be bypassed with impunity, and an attempt has been made in the following pages to supply certain necessary background information. In order to get an overview of the main ideas presented in Chapters 2–7, the reader may find it helpful to examine in advance the summaries of each of these chapters.

A basic knowledge of vision will not be necessary to follow the discussion. An understanding of the stages of the visual process as schematically pictured in Figure 1–1 is all that the reader will require. All non-essential

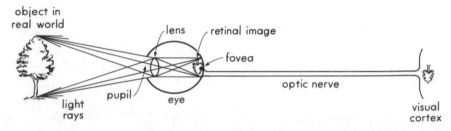

Figure 1–1

details about the eye and the brain have been left out. Light rays radiate outward in all directions from every point on an object. (It is difficult to illustrate this in a diagram, and therefore only two such points are indicated.) A very small segment of these rays is intercepted by the pupillary opening of the eye, and, of course, only these can affect vision at any given moment. Intercepted rays pass through the refractive, transparent media of the eye such as the lens. Those rays with a common origin are focused on a single point at the back of the eye. Rays from different points in space will be focused on different points at the back of the eye. The light-sensitive tissue on which these light rays are focused consists of cells that make up the retina. Hence, when I speak of the "retinal image" or merely of the "image," I mean the focused light on the retina which, taken all together, can be said to be a picture of the object in the real world. (I am, therefore, *not* using the term "image" in the sense of a mental representation unless I specifically say so.) In this respect the eye *is* like a camera, the retina being analogous to the light-sensitive film. The retinal image is inverted and left and right are reversed with respect to objects in the real world which, again, is true of the image registered on the film in a camera. The fovea is a small region of the retina, near the center, where vision is clearest. That point in space which is fixated falls on the fovea. The retinal image may sometimes be referred to as the proximal stimulus in contradistinction to the external object in the world, the distal stimulus.

Each cell of the retina stimulated by light transmits signals via nerve fibers which together make up the optic nerve and optic tract. These fibers pass through certain brain structures, and eventually the excitations are relayed to the surface layers of the occipital lobe at the rear of the brain, the visual cortex. The important facts for our purposes about the manner in which these excitations arrive at the visual cortex are these: The relative position of retinal points to one another is more or less preserved, thus yielding a cortical "image" or "map" of the retinal image (and hence, also, a map of the external scene represented), although this cortical "image" is certainly not a perfect replica of the retinal image. The cortical representation has the same orientation as the retinal image, namely, inverted and left-right reversed in relation to objects in the world.

Most workers in the field of perception assume that it is the events in the visual cortex and surrounding areas—supported, to be sure, by the action of the rest of the brain—that underlie our visual experiences. Some may take the neutral position of psychophysical parallelism, that concomitant with every sensory experience there is a corresponding event in the brain, but most psychologists assume, I believe, that the brain event is primary and *causes* the phenomenal experience. (By "phenomenal experience" is meant "subjective awareness" and, when referring to sensory events, is synonymous with "perceptual experience.") The realm of brain events is more inclusive than that of subjective experience. Every experience requires an underlying brain event, but the reverse is not the case.

Hence, it would seem that an explanation of perceptual phenomena calls for a statement of what is going on in the brain, particularly in the visual cortex and related areas. I agree with this in principle, but must add a very important qualification, namely, that there are good reasons why advances in our understanding of perception (or all of psychology, for that matter) will, at first, be of a non-physiological nature. One reason is that otherwise we would be forced to leap prematurely to an inappropriate level of analysis. In physics, for example, all explanations may ultimately come down to the behavior of the atom, but it would be absurd to try to explain the behavior of a falling body in such terms without first having developed the laws of motion on a descriptive, macroscopic level. Similarly, in perception it would be absurd to try to explain a phenomenon such as the moon illusion [1] in terms of neural firing without first trying to subsume it under some more general psychological law or body of knowledge. As a matter of fact, without such descriptive laws the brain physiologist does not know what kinds of neural processes to look for. A second reason is that we know very little about the working of the brain, so that even where it *is* appropriate to seek a physiological explanation, we would be severely limited in what we could say about any psychological problem if we had to state our explanations, at this time, in specific neurophysiological terms. It may, therefore, be desirable to imagine what might be going on in the brain to account for perceptual experience, but to do so in very general terms. By analogy, it was once a useful theory in physics that all matter consisted of elementary particles, without specifying the nature of such particles.

In seeking to account for adaptation, therefore, I will aim at uncovering the relevant psychological principles and do no more than suggest in general terms the nature of the underlying brain events. One explanatory construct I will make use of is the memory trace, by which I mean an aftereffect or residue of some kind in the brain, resulting from a previous experience, which endures over time and "represents" that previous experience. This definition avoids any specific neurophysiological assumptions as to the nature of the trace, yet clearly acknowledges that, ontologically, it is a physiological entity. Ultimately, therefore, it should be possible to reduce statements we make about the trace to statements about the neurophysiological events constituting the trace.

The theory of adaptation I will espouse in this book has to do with the acquisition of memory traces of a particular kind. The theory assumes that these memory traces can affect subsequent perception. How is this possible? We certainly cannot answer this question in terms of physiological events having to do with the memory trace, but it is possible to attempt an answer in very general terms. When I look at any familiar object, such as a printed word, I immediately experience it as familiar and meaningful. It is virtually impossible to "see" it as a mere form, devoid of meaning. The same is true when I hear a word. I cannot divorce the sound from its meaning. Yet, logically, the familiarity and meaningfulness can hardly reside in the visual or auditory stimulus. After all, the first time we saw or heard that same word it was not meaningful. Hence

---

[1] The apparently larger size of the moon over the horizon than at the zenith.

the familiarity and meaning derive from past experience and, if so, if the past is to have an effect in the present, that experience must be carried in the form of a memory trace. Therefore there is no escaping the conclusion that the meaning we experience as *in* the percept is based upon a contribution from a memory trace. The trace in some way interacts with the stimulus, enriches it, and the result of this apparently instantaneous process of which we are completely unaware is the experience of a familiar, meaningful word "out there."

In the above example, the memory trace affects how a stimulus looks (or sounds), but not in respect to its strictly perceptual qualities. That is to say, the word looks familiar and meaningful, but the *shape* is not altered by the trace. The subjectively experienced shape of the letters and indeed of the entire word is the same whether the word is familiar or is being seen for the first time. Can a trace affect the perceptual aspect of the way a stimulus appears? I believe there are cases of this sort, although the matter cannot be decided merely on the basis of logical analysis. For example, it seems plausible that the reason why I see Figure 1–2 as three-dimensional is because of a contribution from memory traces.

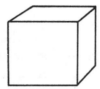

Figure 1–2

The stimulus is, after all, two-dimensional. Based on experience in daily life with three-dimensional cubes, memory traces are deposited which contain two components, the two-dimensional projection of the cube, which looks like Figure 1–2, and the three-dimensional structure of the cube. The actual cubes seen in daily life appear three-dimensional because cues of depth are present, such as retinal disparity. Later on, when only the two-dimensional picture is seen, it arouses that same two-dimensional component of the memory trace, which in turn arouses by association the three-dimensional component of the memory trace. That component somehow enters into the total organization which underlies the perceptual experience of the stimulus as a cube. Thus, just as in the case of recognition and meaning, the trace contributes something instantaneously that is not *in* the stimulus, such that the quality in question appears as if it were "out there" in the stimulus. This then is the way in which I believe the memory trace can affect perception.[2]

Historical Background

The earliest interest in the problem of optical transformation grew out of the realization that the retinal image was inverted. A controversy developed as to whether the inversion of the retinal image was necessary for upright vision. As a result of this controversy, the question arose whether an optically re-erected image must necessarily yield *inverted* vision. A similar question was later raised in connection with the location of objects with respect to the self. Helmholtz performed an experiment in which he viewed the world through a wedge prism, the immediate effect of which was to displace all objects to one side.[3] The question at issue was whether objects would continue to appear displaced (implying that the eyes must necessarily be directed straight ahead if an object which is straight ahead is to be correctly localized) or whether the observer would in time begin to locate objects correctly again (implying that perceived location is the result of a learning process).

The important impetus to work on the problem of adaptation, however, was the experiment by George Stratton at the end of the nineteenth century.[4] Stratton wore a lens system which caused the retinal image to be re-erected. He sought an answer to the question posed above. Could that now upright image yield upright vision? He believed it was possible. His procedure, findings, and interpretation will be thoroughly explored in the next chapter. In the sixty-odd years since then, the experiment has been repeated several times.

In 1933, Gibson set out to study the question of adaptation to displacement of the image using a technique similar to that used by Helmholtz.[5]

---

[2] I am indebted to Hans Wallach, whose thinking and empirical work on this subject have influenced me greatly. For supporting evidence see H. Wallach, D. N. O'Connell, and U. Neisser, The memory effect of visual perception of three-dimensional form, *J. exp. Psychol.*, 1953, **45**, 360–368.

[3] H. von Helmholtz, *Treatise on physiological optics* (Trans. from the 3rd German ed.; J. P. C. Southall, Ed.), Vol. III, New York: Dover, 1962.

[4] G. M. Stratton, Some preliminary experiments on vision without inversion of the retinal image, *Psychol. Rev.*, 1896, **3**, 611–617; Upright vision and the retinal image, *Psychol. Rev.*, 1897, **4**, 182–187; Vision without inversion of the retinal image, *Psychol. Rev.*, 1897, **4**, 341–360 and 463–481; The spatial harmony of touch and sight, *Mind*, 1899, **8**, 492–505.

[5] J. J. Gibson, Adaptation, after-effect and contrast in the perception of curved lines, *J. exp. Psychol.*, 1933, **16**, 1–31.

(Margaret Wooster had already conducted a careful experiment along these lines in 1923.[6]) Two findings which came out of the Gibson study had a profound effect on the subsequent history of the adaptation problem. When viewed through a wedge prism with base left or right, vertical straight lines appear curved. Gibson's subjects reported that such lines appeared less curved following a period of inspection and, on removing the prisms, straight lines now appeared somewhat curved in the opposite direction. Wundt had made similar observations some years earlier.[7] The second finding was that the same effects were obtained if the viewer inspected *truly* curved lines *without* a prism (rather than straight lines made to appear curved by a prism).

This last finding led Gibson to believe that the adaptation effect had nothing to do with learning, in the sense of acquiring information as to the true properties of objects in the environment. In the case of adaptation to an inverted or disoriented image, the observer might be expected to obtain information that objects which at first appeared inverted or tilted were not. In the case of displacement, the observer might be expected to learn that objects which at first appeared in particular positions were actually, say, 10 degrees to the left of such positions. In the case of prismatic curvature of straight lines, the observer might acquire the information that apparently curved lines were actually straight. But, if adaptation were based upon such information, there should not be any effect of viewing truly curved lines, since all available information would merely confirm the fact that they were curved. Inasmuch as they did appear less curved over time, this was a change in a non-veridical direction. It therefore seemed gratuitous to assume anything more was going on in the prism situation than in the situation in which the curved lines were seen directly, since the prism produces the same proximal stimulus, namely, curved image lines. Another fact which led Gibson to this conclusion was that in his experiments with prisms the subject for the most part remained stationary and, for reasons to be discussed later, had little or no information available as to the effects of the prisms. Hence there was little difference between viewing a straight line through the prisms and viewing a curved line directly.

These findings, therefore, led Gibson to seek an explanation in a very different direction. In another study he had discovered that tilted lines

[6] M. Wooster, Certain factors in the development of a new spatial coordination, *Psychol. Monogr.*, 1923, **32**.

[7] W. Wundt, Zur Theorie der raumlichen Gesichtswahrnehmungen, *Phil. Stud.*, 1898, **14**, 11.

tend to appear somewhat less tilted following a period of inspection, and vertical lines seen afterwards appeared slightly tilted in the opposite direction.[8] Both cases (curvature and tilt) suggested to Gibson some tendency of perception to approach the norm, a process of normalization (i.e., curved lines straightening out and tilted lines straightening up, so to speak). Ultimately Köhler and Wallach demonstrated that it was possible to derive Gibson's effects as special cases of a more general effect they discovered, the figural aftereffect.[9] Figural aftereffects are characterized by a tendency of contours to appear displaced from their actual position in a direction away from the locus in the retina of a previously inspected contour. A straight line in displacing away from the locus of a previously inspected curved line would tend to appear curved in the opposite direction. The Gibson and Köhler-Wallach hypotheses will be discussed in more detail in later chapters. Suffice it to say now that the phenomena being studied and the explanations proposed are in the nature of changes believed to occur in the neural medium as a result of the continued presence of contours in specific retinal-cortical positions. The subject typically is instructed not to move his eyes during the inspection period so that the stimulus pattern falls in a particular place on the retina. These effects are, therefore, quite analogous to other well-known effects of continued fixation, such as successive color contrast. In the case of color contrast, "adaptation" means that the inspected color appears increasingly less saturated, presumably because of the fatiguing of the retinal cells being stimulated. Upon removal of the inspected stimulus, the observer experiences the complementary color in precisely that region of the field where the inspected stimulus had been located, a negative after-image.[10]

These developments had the effect of deflecting attention away from the problem of perceptual adaptation to distortions created by prisms and lens systems. Yet it is hardly evident that adaptation such as Stratton and Helmholtz had in mind can be reduced to the kind of effects discovered by Gibson and Köhler and Wallach. It is difficult to imagine how a contour-displacement or normalization theory could do justice to systematic change in the perceived location of all objects in the field. In fact, it would seem more plausible on the face of it that adaptation to a re-erected image or to a displaced image, if it occurred, would be based on learning or ac-

[8] J. J. Gibson and M. Radner, Adaptation, after-effect and contrast in the perception of tilted lines. I and II, *J. exp. Psychol.*, 1937, **20**, 453–467; 553–569.

[9] W. Köhler and H. Wallach, Figural after-effects: an investigation of visual processes, *Proc. Amer. Phil. Soc.*, 1944, **88**, 269–357.

[10] Some evidence has recently appeared that suggests that normalization is not entirely restricted to the region of the retina stimulated during inspection.

quiring information that things were not as they at first appeared to be. Despite Gibson's findings, adaptation to prismatic curvature and tilt might prove to depend upon information acquired through commerce with the environment that lines which appeared curved or tilted were not. Normalization or figural aftereffect explanations are not mutually exclusive of those based upon the acquisition of information. For purposes of brevity, I will henceforth refer to adaptation based on learning or acquiring information as prism adaptation in contradistinction to normalization or displacement effects generated simply by continued exposure to certain stimulus patterns, which I will call configurational adaptation.

It was not until the work of Erismann and Ivo Kohler in Austria became widely known that interest in prism adaptation revived.[11] These investigators studied the long-term effects on perception of wearing distorting prisms and mirrors. They reported evidence of marked perceptual changes, including a type of change they called a situational aftereffect (to be discussed in Chapter 6), which by its very nature could not be understood on the basis of the configurational-type of adaptation. The work of Held also played a major role in the revival of interest in prism adaptation.[12] His research focused on adaptation to prismatic displacement, with an attempt to establish the crucial role of bodily movements initiated by the observer. He was also the first investigator to distinguish experimentally beween prism adaptation and the configurational type of aftereffect.

At this writing, interest in the problem of prism adaptation is rapidly accelerating. A new sub-field of perception has emerged, one that seems destined to play an increasingly important role in the development of our understanding of perceptual phenomena. Current research is aimed at gathering information on the extent of adaptation, if any, to the various

[11] The original monograph was published in 1951 and has now been translated. See I. Kohler, The formation and transformation of the perceptual world (Trans. by H. Fiss), *Psychol. Issues,* 1964, **3**, No. 4, 1–173.

[12] Specific references to experiments by Held and his colleagues are given in the appropriate context in subsequent chapters. The papers launching their work on adaptation to prisms were: R. Held and N. Gottlieb, A technique for studying adaptation to disarranged hand-eye coordination, *Percept. mot. Skills,* 1958, **8**, 83–86; R. Held and A. Hein, Adaptation of disarranged hand-eye coordination contingent upon re-afferent stimulation, *Percept. mot. Skills,* 1958, **8**, 87–90. More general statements are given in R. Held, Adaptation to rearrangement and visual-spatial aftereffects, *Psychol. Beitr.,* 1962, **6**, 439–450; R. Held, Exposure-history as a factor in maintaining stability of perception and coordination, *J. nerv. ment. Dis.,* 1961, **132**, 26–32; R. Held and S. J. Freedman, Plasticity in human sensorimotor control, *Science,* 1963, **142**, 455–462; R. Held, Plasticity in sensory-motor systems, *Scient. Amer.,* 1965, November, 84–94.

types of distortion, the length of exposure period required to produce adaptation, and the conditions which are necessary and sufficient to yield adaptation, among other subjects. Although some of this research is theoretically oriented, for the most part there has not been adequate analysis of the nature of the particular perceptual function under examination. That is to say, before it is possible to inquire meaningfully about the probable effects of distortion, it is necessary to have some understanding of the basis of the perceptual experience under ordinary conditions. For example, unless we have some idea about the determinants of perceived direction under normal conditions, we will have no idea how to approach the problem of prismatic alteration of direction. Unless we have some notion as to why the world appears stationary despite the fact that the image displaces across the retina with every movement of the head, we will have no point of departure for exploring the problem of why the world seems to move when lenses are worn, etc.

Methodological Considerations

How can it be determined whether an adaptive change has taken place? The most obvious answer is to ask the observer how the world appears to him at various times during the course of exposure to the distorting optical device. This is essentially what Stratton did except that he himself was the observer. This method yields valuable data, but it has certain limitations. One is that phenomenal descriptions are often somewhat unclear or ambiguous. For example, there has been much disagreement as to whether or not Stratton's introspective reports attest to adaptation to inversion. Furthermore, the observer might grow so accustomed to the new state of affairs that he no longer is aware of how it actually looks. Yet "growing accustomed" is not necessarily the same as genuine adaptation. A further limitation of introspective report is that it is not quantitatively precise. Imagine that an observer has been exposed to prismatic displacement for a period of time. What we would like to know is whether objects appear displaced by as much as the prism causes them to be displaced and, if not, to what extent they do appear to be displaced. To find this out, we need some method of actual measurement, one which compares the way things look following a period of experimental exposure with the way they looked at the outset.

There are two different ways of making such a before-after comparison and both have been used in recent years. The most obvious way is to require the observer to make a perceptual judgment at the time he first looks through the optical device and then to require him to make that same type of judgment following a period of exposure. For example, at the time of putting on wedge-prism spectacles, the observer is asked to point to a visual target. Presumably he would make an error equal to the angular displacing effect of the prisms. Following a period of viewing through the spectacles, he is again asked to point to a target. If any adaptation has occurred, he will now point somewhere between the location he pointed to at the outset and the actual location of the target. The before-after difference in degrees is therefore a measure of the magnitude of adaptation.

There is, however, one problem connected with this method.. During exposure the subject will generally become aware of the manner in which the optical device distorts his perception. When given a test, he may try to discount this distorting effect in order to give the "right answer." Thus both genuine adaptation and efforts at discounting the effects of distortion in a test lead to the same outcome, namely, perceptual judgments which are either veridical or in the direction of being veridical. Related to this is the fact that, even at the outset of the exposure period, information may be available to the observer as to the distorting properties of the optical device; if so, the "before" or pre-exposure test does not accurately reveal the perceptual distortion created by the device. Hence the base-line value against which any change is to be gauged becomes difficult to evaluate.

These difficulties are avoided by conducting both the pre- and post-exposure tests without the optical device. Genuine perceptual adaptation should change the way the relevant stimulus is perceived, even in the absence of the optical device. For example, if the prismatically curved images of objectively straight lines have come to signify straight lines (assuming complete adaptation), then we should expect that this would be revealed with or without the optical device. With the optical device, a truly straight line whose image is curved appears straight. Without it, a line which is actually curved by that amount (whose image is, therefore, also curved) should appear straight. In short, following adaptation, whatever the experience yielded by the particular proximal stimulus rendered by the optical device, that proximal stimulus without the device should yield the same perceptual experience. If, therefore, adaptation to prismatically created curvature is complete, in the test following removal of the prism, the observer should select a curved line when asked to indicate what line appears straight. If presented with an actually straight line, he should see it as curved in the direction opposite to the curvature induced by the prisms, and this result has been called a negative aftereffect.

The advantage in conducting the post-exposure test without the optical device is that the observer would not be inclined to correct for distorting effects if he is now viewing the world with his naked eye. He has absolutely no reason to think any correction is necessary if no device is in front of his eyes. Furthermore, an adaptation effect will be revealed by a non-veridical judgment (e.g., the selection of a curved line as representing a straight line) which the observer obviously would, if anything, be trying to avoid. Hence, the actual error made becomes impressive evidence of the change that must have occurred in the observer's nervous system. There are, however, two related problems connected with this method. One is that adaptation may in part be tied to (or conditional upon) the stimulus features of the experimental apparatus. The "feel" of the spectacles may be a factor in leading to the altered significance of stimuli. This can perhaps be dealt with by requiring the observer to wear the spectacle frame with lenses or prisms removed. The other problem is that it often takes time to remove the distorting apparatus, so that the post-exposure measure in this case cannot be as quickly obtained as when it is taken with the device on. Speed is a factor to the extent that adaptation wears off rapidly when the exposure period ends. In the light of the possibly rapid "wearing off" of adaptation, it may be desirable to take only one or, at most, only a few measures in the post-exposure test, thus necessarily reducing the reliability of the measure.

It might be well to make explicit a problem that arises in attempting to measure adaptation, namely, that a matching or subjective equating procedure cannot be used. For example, if we want to know how tilted a standard line appears following exposure to prisms, we would learn nothing by having the observer indicate when another line appears to have the same tilt as the standard. No doubt the observer would do this with accuracy but the question would remain: How tilted do both lines appear? If an objectively tilted standard line, via adaptation, now appears vertical, the observer would select an equally tilted comparison line when asked to match the tilt of the standard, and yet that tilted comparison line would appear vertical. (Failure to grasp this point has been dubbed the El Greco Fallacy in our laboratory in honor of those art historians who believe El Greco painted elongated figures because he suffered some visual defect and saw his figures that way. If he saw figures elongated, it would apply to his painted figures as well. Therefore he would paint figures in their correct proportions but see his painted figures as elongated. If, perchance, he painted a figure as elongated, he would then have to see it as even more elongated than he painted it and it would not match his perception of the figure he was reproducing.)

The problem is to find out how something appears to the subject. Verbal description of a test object may serve the purpose where labels exist for various points along the sensory dimension under investigation (e.g., colors, curvature, direction), but often the information provided in this way is too inexact. Where there is a unique point along the sensory dimension, the observer can be asked to indicate when a variable stimulus looks as if it is at that point—for example, when a color appears achromatically neutral, when a line appears straight or vertical, or when a target appears straight ahead. Another alternative is to have the observer respond in a different modality, as, for example, pointing at a visual target (provided the pointing hand and arm are not visible) or indicating the visual size of an object by matching it tactually.

One other methodological problem worthy of mention has to do with whether exposure to the optical device must necessarily be continuous or can be intermittent. By intermittent I mean exposure periods separated by intervals during which the observer is permitted to see the world normally. The question is whether intermittent exposure can lead to a cumulative effect or whether the effect of one exposure will be completely eradicated by the subsequent exposure to normal conditions of stimulation. Investigators such as Stratton, guided by intuition, have scrupulously avoided intermittent exposure. Those few experimenters who have used this method have done so chiefly in an attempt to increase the amount of adaptive change. Thus far, the typical experiment on adaptation is concerned with whether a significant effect can be obtained or whether different conditions of exposure yield different effects over an arbitrarily selected time period. Because of the lack of experimental evidence bearing on this question, it is not possible to say much that might illuminate the difference between intermittent and continuous exposure. The question is raised here as a way of drawing attention to an almost unexplored area of adaptation research.

The Meaning and Significance of the Adaptation Paradigm

One might ask whether the term "adaptation" is appropriate for the kind of effect under discussion. As noted above, in the case of classical sensory adaptation, there is a gradual diminution of sensation based on a fatiguing of the sensory cells stimulated. In the case of an optically altered image, what is presumed to occur is not so much a diminution of sensation as diminution of the perceived distortion. In both cases, however, there is a change in the phenomenal effect of stimuli such that upon removal of the exposure-stimulus, the world will be experienced somewhat differently than before. Classical adaptation is perhaps more nearly the same as the kind of normalization effects studied by Gibson in that, in both cases, the perceptual experience approaches a neutral point following exposure (i.e., a colored stimulus appears less saturated, almost achromatic; a tilted line appears less tilted, almost vertical). In adaptation to optical distortion, the perceptual experience, however, approaches veridicality, not neutrality. The term "adaptation," therefore, might be appropriate in the sense of change in the direction of effectively coping with the environment.

The significance and importance of research on perceptual adaptation is that we can study perception in the process of undergoing change. We can vary conditions at will and obtain quantitative data. This has generally not been possible in the traditional experimental approaches to the role of past experience in perception. There are few experiments on human adults that reveal any genuine alteration of perception due to past experience. It is a reasonable assumption—although admittedly one that might ultimately prove incorrect—that if perception is alterable in the adult, then those conditions which lead to the change may be identical to the conditions which account for the development of perception. Even if this assumption should prove incorrect, which I doubt, at very least we stand to learn about the relative plasticity of certain perceptual functions and a great deal about factors underlying certain perceptual experiences. The meaning of these comments will become clearer in subsequent chapters.

Adaptation to a
Disoriented Image

CHAPTER TWO

Upright Vision from an Inverted Image

Ever since it was discovered that the retinal image is inverted, men have wondered why it is we experience the world as upright. As I shall try to make clear, this is not a real problem, but, stated in more general terms, the relationship between the orientation of the image on the retina and the perceived orientation of the scene is still not understood despite a long history of speculation and experimentation. No theory advanced to date does justice to the nature of this relationship, and the experimental work on adaptation to an abnormally oriented image has thus far failed to provide a clear answer to what actually happens to perception.

We can begin our discussion with the question: How is it possible for an inverted image to yield upright vision? The question presupposes that the orientation of the image on the retina (a fact concerning the image as a physical object) and the perceived orientation of the scene (a fact in the realm of phenomenal experience) are in the same universe of discourse. The presumption is that the image and the perception are inverted with respect to one another. In point of fact, the image is inverted with respect to the physical objects it represents, including the physical body of the observer, but it makes no sense to say it is inverted with respect to the phenomenal "up" and "down." It is implicit in the question that ex-

15

ternal objects in the scene ought to appear upside down with respect to the observer because their images are inverted with respect to the observer. But this compares phenomenal objects with the physical self, whereas the proper comparison is between phenomenal objects and the phenomenal self. To the extent that the observer sees his own body, its image is also inverted, so that there is no basis for phenomenal objects to appear inverted with respect to the phenomenal body of the observer, and in point of fact, of course, they don't. For the sake of the argument, I am assuming here that the phenomenal body is the visually perceived body.

There are different meanings of "right side up" and "upside down" which will be clarified later in the chapter, but the meaning that is under discussion now is concerned with how things appear to be oriented with respect to the observer (or egocentric orientation). After all, the same problem of how an inverted image yields upright vision can be raised even if the observer were lying in a supine position. If he then reads a book held overhead in a horizontal plane, the words would appear "right side up" although, in relation to the body, the retinal image of the words would be upside down. A further clarification is that terms such as "upright" are generally applied to familiar objects that have distinctive upper and lower parts—for example, trees, people, or the printed words in the above example. If the bottom of a word is seen as uppermost, then it is said to appear "upside down" or "inverted." But clearly the broader question at issue here concerns any and all objects, whether familiar or not. The question is why any object whose image is inverted is not seen inverted. In this broader sense, "upright" implies that the orientation of an object in relation to the self is perceived veridically and "upside down" implies that such orientation is perceived non-veridically, 180° reversed. For example if, for the supine observer, an arrow aligned with the long axis of the body points toward the feet, perception would be upright if the arrow is experienced as pointing toward the feet (despite the fact that its image points in the other direction), and it would be upside down if the arrow is experienced as pointing toward the head. The point I am trying to bring out here is simply this: Since the arrow's orientation in relation to the observer is correctly represented by the inversion of both the image of the arrow and the image of the observer's own body, there is no reason to think perception should be inverted merely because the entire image is.[1]

[1] It is true that, were we to see our own retinal image, it would appear inverted with respect to everything else we see, but in this case the image itself becomes a phe-

Suppose the question is put in this way: Why does stimulation of, say, the upper portion of the retina signify a "down" phenomenal direction when it ought to signify an "up" direction? I would then ask: Why "ought" any particular retinal region signify any particular phenomenal direction? The naïveté of the question can be brought out by considering the problem at the level of the brain.[2] Suppose the visual cortex were located on top of the brain—that is, in the position where the sensorimotor cortex is located. It would no longer make any sense to expect, a priori, a particular region of the visual projection area to signify a particular phenomenal direction. No cortical region would be regarded by us as "up" or "down," for the entire visual cortex would lie in a horizontal plane. Yet, if the visual cortex were located in that position, no student of neurophysiology would consider it a problem that "up" and "down" could be represented. Phenomenal facts of this kind must derive from neural relationships, and we should not necessarily expect to find a one-to-one correspondence between the physical geometry of the brain and the geometry of phenomenal space. Hence, the problem of why vision is upright when the image is inverted is not a real problem.

Must the Image Be Inverted?

The real question is whether it is necessary that the image be inverted for upright vision. Having concluded that there is no reason why an inverted image should not yield upright vision, and taking into account that the image *is* inverted and our vision *is* upright, one might well conclude that there is some good reason why this relationship must obtain. I will argue that an inverted image is not necessary for upright vision. Over the last few centuries theories to explain the necessity of an inverted image have continued to appear. Only recently, a half century after Stratton published his work, an eminent authority on vision, Gordon Walls, wrote a monograph in which he ardently defended this very propo-

---

nomenal object whose orientation can be compared with that of other phenomenal objects. However, the *perceived* orientation of the *image* cannot be of any consequence. We do not see our image, and only the most sophisticated individuals even know about its orientation.

[2] The philosopher Descartes, troubled by the uprightness of vision from an inverted image, speculated that the cortical "image" was right side up, that is, that the fibers from the retina to the brain crossed from top to bottom and left to right, etc. This was before it was known that the cortical pattern of excitation representing the retinal image is *not* reinverted.

sition.[3] I will discuss Walls' reasoning later on. It was precisely because psychologists did believe an inverted image was necessary for upright vision that Stratton launched his now classic experiment on adaptation to a re-erected image.[4] Although his experiment is well known, his logical analysis of the problem has either been neglected or insufficiently understood. His argument, which is more or less identical with an analysis made by Berkeley in 1709, forms a central thesis of this monograph.[5]

As noted, when we inquire about the phenomenal uprightness of the entire scene, we are referring to its perceived orientation in relation to the observer. It is phenomenally upright if the sky is experienced in the same direction with respect to the ground as the head is with respect to the feet and, conversely, if the ground is experienced in the same direction with respect to the sky as the feet are with respect to the head. Now, inasmuch as the retinal images of all objects including the visible body will suffer the same fate if the entire image is physically inverted (as it is under normal circumstances), then the phenomenal things to which the image gives rise will be in an upright relationship to the phenomenal self.

The head, which is painted [by which Berkeley means imaged on the retina] nearest the earth, seems to be furthest from it; and on the other hand, the feet, which are painted furthest from the earth, are thought nearest to it. Herein lies the difficulty, which vanishes if we express the thing more clearly and free from ambiguity, thus: how comes it that, to the eye, the visible head, which is nearest the tangible earth, seems furthest from the earth, and the visible feet, which are furthest from the tangible earth, seem nearest the earth. The question being thus proposed, who sees not the difficulty is founded on a supposition, that the eye, or visive faculty, or rather the soul by means thereof, should judge of the situation of visible objects, with reference to their distance from the tangible earth? Whereas it is evident the tangible earth is not perceived by sight; and it hath been shown in the two last preceding sections, that the location of

[3] G. L. Walls, The problem of visual direction, *Amer. J. Optom.*, 1951, **28**, 55–83, 115–146, 173–212.

[4] G. M. Stratton, Some preliminary experiments on vision without inversion of the retinal image, *Psychol. Rev.*, 1896, 3, 611–617; Vision without inversion of the retinal image, *Psychol. Rev.*, 1897, 4, 341–360, 463–481. Particularly relevant to the discussion below is an article by Stratton which usually is not cited: Upright vision and the retinal image, *Psychol. Rev.*, 1897, 4, 182–187.

[5] G. Berkeley, *An essay towards a new theory of vision,* London: J. M. Dent, 1910. Stratton's argument is identical to Berkeley's only with respect to the question under discussion, namely, his reason for believing an inverted image is not necessary for upright vision. It is this argument that is central to this book, not Stratton's theory of the origin of upright vision and not Berkeley's theory of the derivation of visual space from tactual space. In fact, I will defend the very opposite hypothesis concerning the relationship between vision and touch.

visible objects is determined only by the distance they bear from one another; and that it is nonsense to talk of distance, far or near, between a visible and tangible thing.

If we confine our thoughts to the proper objects of sight, the whole is plain and easy. The head is painted furthest from, and the feet nearest to the visible earth; and so they appear to be. What is there strange or unaccountable in this? Let us suppose the pictures in the fund of the eye, to be the immediate objects of the sight. The consequence is that things should appear in the same posture they are painted in; and is it not so? The head which is seen seems furthest from the earth which is seen; and the feet which are seen, seem nearest to the earth which is seen; and just so they are painted.

But, say you, the picture of the man is inverted, and yet the appearance is erect: I ask, what mean you by the picture of the man, or, which is the same thing, the visible man's being inverted? You tell me it is inverted, because the heels are uppermost, and the head undermost? Explain me this. You say, that by the head's being undermost, you mean that it is nearest to the earth; and by the heels being uppermost, that they are furthest from the earth. I ask again, what earth you mean? You cannot mean the earth that is painted on the eye, or the visible earth: for the picture of the head is furthest from the picture of the earth and the picture of the feet nearest to the picture of the earth; and accordingly the visible head is furthest from the visible earth, and the visible feet nearest to it. It remains, therefore, that you mean the tangible earth, and so determine the situation of visible things with respect to tangible things: contrary to what hath been demonstrated [earlier]. The two distinct provinces of sight and touch should be considered apart, and as if their objects had no intercourse, no manner of relation to one another, in point of distance or position.[6]

In this passage, Berkeley is talking about the perceived orientation of another person in relation to the ground, but his argument would have been even stronger if he had referred to sight of portions of the observer's own body. Suppose the image is re-erected and is physically upright as in the Stratton experiment. Here, too, all images retain their directional relationships to one another. The upper part of the image of a tree and the upper part of the image of a house are in the same direction as the upper part of the image of the observer himself. In short, what the image provides us with is the relationship of direction of one thing to another, and this relationship is not changed at all when the orientation of the image as a whole changes. Hence in order to have upright vision it does not appear to be necessary that the image be inverted, and Stratton sought to prove this by wearing an optical apparatus which re-erected the image.

[6] Ibid., pp. 65–66.

Why Does an Optically Re-erected Image Appear Upside Down?

As anyone who has ever looked through a microscope or astronomical telescope knows, however, a device which rotates the image by 180° does lead to a phenomenally upside down world. Thus, at the outset Stratton saw things upside down (and, needless to add, left-right reversed as well). But this simple fact does not follow from the analysis outlined above. With respect to what can the entire visual field be said to appear inverted? Many people, on hearing this question, feel the answer is rather obvious. The visual field is inverted with respect to the gravitational-proprioceptive sense of up and down. A little thought will show, however, that this is not an answer at all. We do, of course, experience the various parts of our body via proprioceptive sensations. We also sense the direction of gravity. The vestibular mechanism in the inner ear is particularly important in this respect. In addition, we feel pressure on whatever region of the body is in contact with the ground, as the feet in standing upright; we feel a pull when we lean over, etc. If the observer wearing the optical device is upright, can we say that his visual world is experienced as inverted with respect to the direction of gravity? If gravity is sensed as pulling toward the feet (by virtue of the sensations referred to above) and if the visual feet are seen on the visual ground (because the image of the feet is in contact with the image of the ground), then where is the contradiction? Only by assuming some intrinsic relationship between the sensed direction of gravity and particular retinal directions would this answer be tenable—that is, if the direction of gravity were linked with the direction "lower-retina-to-upper-retina." This is theoretically possible but is hardly obvious and is not what was meant by saying the visual field appears inverted with respect to the direction of gravity.

It is possible, however, to demonstrate that gravity is irrelevant to the perception of inversion that follows from looking through an inverting lens. Suppose the observer is lying in a supine position. Gravity is now pulling at right angles to his body. Wearing the optical device, however, things will still appear inverted although it may not be as immediately obvious as when the observer is upright. (It is irrelevant whether the observer *realizes* his perception is right side up or upside down. What matters is whether the perceived orientation of things in relation to the self is veridical [upright] or not veridical [upside down].) A book held in its normal position in relation to the observer would appear egocentrically upside down and could not easily be read. Now in this situation it is not possible to argue that the inversion is with respect to gravity, because the direction of gravity is orthogonal to the up-down axis with which we are concerned.

Can it be argued that it is the sense of position of parts of the body via proprioceptive sensations, not the reaction to gravity, that is crucial? Our supine observer would, of course, continue to have these sensations. If the felt head is the "top" and the felt feet the "bottom," can we explain the experienced inversion in terms of the upside-down relation of the visual book to the proprioceptive body image? As Berkeley points out in the quotation cited above, we cannot speak of the relationship of direction between objects each of which is given in a different sense modality. It would only be correct to say that the head is felt to be at one "end" of the body, the feet at the other, and the abdomen in between. Similarly, the visual head is imaged at one end, the visual feet at the other. Regardless of the over-all orientation of the visual image, therefore, the feet can be felt to be in the same place as the visual feet unless one wishes to postulate that there is some link or association between the proprioceptively given feet and a particular retinal direction, in this case the upper retina.

This brings us to Stratton's answer to his own question: With respect to what can the entire visual field be inverted? In his experiment he had the impression that visual representations persisted in their old form rather than coming immediately into line with the new perception. In other words, the visual direction which had previously been "down" remained so, despite the presence of objects such as the sky in that region. The only explanation he could find for this fact was in terms of the role of other sense modalities, particularly touch. As a result of a lifetime of experience, associations develop between particular proprioceptive sensations and particular visual sensations. For example, proprioceptive stimulation of the left hand is associated with visual objects on the left side of the field. Since objects in this perceived direction usually stimulate the right portion of the retina, an association is established between touch sensations on the left and stimulation of the right retina. Each signifies the same location of an object in space.[7] Hence, if an object is grasped with the left hand, the observer will imagine it to be located visually in a place associated

[7] Obviously a hand would not always stimulate the same region of the retina even if it were always kept on the side of the body. It depends upon the position of the eyes and of the head. Hence Stratton's argument would have to be modified in such a way that the proximal stimulus "location" entails a particular patterning of stimuli (retinal position, eye position, and head position in the case of vision; hand position, arm position, etc., in the case of proprioception).

with a particular visual "local sign," namely, one associated with stimulation of the right portion of the retina. "Local sign" refers to some hypothetically distinctive property of each sensory point which makes it possible to distinguish one such point from another, for example distinct retinal points. With an inverting lens, the felt object, physically on the observer's left, will excite cells of the retina on the left side. Therefore, a visual location will be suggested by the felt object which is at odds with the one actually perceived. In short, inverting the image abolishes intersensory harmony (experiencing one object in one location) and intersensory disharmony constitutes what we mean by experienced inversion of the field. The visual location suggested by stimulation of other sense modalities will not be the same as the visual location given by the actual retinal stimulation. In Stratton's own words:

However that may be, the facts in the present case are more accurately described when we say that the discord was not between tactual directions and visual directions but between the visual directions suggested by touch and the visual directions given in the actual sight. The real question then is: Why did touch-perceptions so persistently suggest visual images whose positions and directions were in discord with the actual scene? The answer is found, I think, in the familiar doctrine of "local signs" in touch and in sight, and in the further assumption that a system of correspondence exists whereby a sign in one sense comes to be connected with and to suggest a particular sign in the other sense. . . . A perception in one sensory field suggests, therefore, in terms of the other sense an image in that place whose local sign is most strongly associated with the local sign of the original perception.[8]

The inverted position of the retinal image is not essential to "upright vision" for it is not essential to a harmony between touch and sight, which, in the final analysis, is the real meaning of upright vision. For some visual objects may be inverted with respect to other visual objects, but the whole system of visual objects can never by itself be either inverted or upright. It could be inverted or upright only with respect to certain non-visual experience with which I might compare my visual system—in other words, with respect to my tactual or motor perceptions.[9]

One can readily understand why Stratton would be led to this answer. The entire visual field can only be inverted with respect to something else, and it is plausible that he would feel that that something else would have to be sensory. However, the notion of intersensory disharmony as an explanation of perceived inversion requires careful analysis. If by disharmony is meant a disruption of the unified impression of an object's

[8] Stratton, op. cit., 1897, p. 472.
[9] Ibid., pp. 475–476.

location which one usually obtains via vision and touch, it is not clear
whether such a theory could explain the inverted location of objects which
are not touched. There could be no direct contradiction between the location of the visual image of a chimney and any particular proprioceptive
sensation. Perhaps Stratton would argue that tactile-proprioceptive stimuli
are ever-present, thus continually creating expectations as to where the
various parts of the body would appear, and even if the body is not visible,
the direction of external objects is somehow judged in terms of the visualized directions evoked by the felt body. (Does this mean that visual
orientation would not be present for a totally anesthetized observer?) In
any case, the theory becomes much more complicated than it at first appeared if it is to do justice to the perception of external objects experienced only by vision.

When Stratton says that visual images are suggested whose positions
and directions are in discord with the visual directions given in actual
sight, he is accurately describing what anyone will experience in looking
through an inverting device. For example, the feet will appear in a position and orientation at odds with the position and orientation in which
they are visualized. When he attributes this to intersensory disharmony,
it is because he is at a loss otherwise to explain how the "old" representation or visualization continues to be present. Yet if he ties this imagery to
specific retinal locations—in which I believe he is correct—why does he
need a conflicting sense modality to evoke such imagery? To be concrete,
if the feet have usually stimulated the upper retina, then Stratton would
say that an association develops between the tactile-proprioceptive complex of sensations from the feet and the location of the visual image of
the feet on the upper retina. Presumably the association is between the
felt feet and the seen feet in a certain visual location. As a result, tactile
stimulation from the feet will now trigger a memory trace of the upper
retinal local sign which in turn, I take it, will trigger a memory image of
the feet in a certain location. If so, why is the tactile stimulation from the
feet necessary? Any visual stimulus which strikes the upper retina should
even more directly evoke the visual memory of the feet. What his description calls for is an explanation of how the visual imagery of the feet can
continue to be evoked by the upper retina when at the same time they
now are directly imaged on the lower retina. The assumption of an association between upper retina and visually perceived feet is sufficient. This
way of approaching the problem will be clarified and amplified later in
the chapter. (Of course, where the position of a part of the body is highly
variable, as is true of the hands, one might say that there would be no

single association between proprioceptive and visual local signs. Each distinct hand position would be associated with a specific pattern of visual stimuli representing location. In that event, Stratton would be correct, proprioceptive stimuli *would* be necessary to evoke the relevant visual imagery which is now at odds with the actual visual location of the part of the body.)

It might be objected that perhaps the only things associated are tactile-proprioceptive sensations and sensations of retinal excitation in particular positions (leaving out the visual content of what is seen and therefore visual memory images of such content). I fail to see how such a theory could deal with the problem of experienced inversion. According to this view, tactile stimulation of the feet would lead to the expectation of *some* visual stimulation striking the upper retina, so that whatever object was imaged there would suffice and there should be no conflict. Obviously then, the conflict depends upon expecting to *see the feet* in that location.

Stratton realized that intersensory disharmony cannot simply mean feeling something in one place and seeing it in another, because he grasped the point made by Berkeley that localizations from different modalities are not *directly* commensurate. Hence he clearly states that feeling leads to visualizing, and it is this visualizing that is at odds with the inverted visual stimulation. If one accepts the argument presented here, that touch is not always needed to trigger the visualizing process, then it becomes clear that this sort of explanation of visual inversion is *in fact* a visual one, i.e., an explanation in visual terms.

As to the problem of intersensory conflict in Stratton's experiment, I believe he was correct in explaining such conflict in terms of associations previously formed between specific "local signs" in each modality. Therefore, the necessary new associations can be acquired during exposure to the optically transformed scene, thus abolishing the intersensory conflict. Apparently this did happen in Stratton's experiment. As noted, I agree with Stratton that the initial conflict is based on the translation of the sound or touch experience into a visualized location which is then at variance with the actually seen location. There is good reason for believing that the intersensory relearning which goes on during the wearing of the device, prior to a possible visual adaptation to inversion, consists in coming to reinterpret the felt or heard location in such a way that it now conforms with the actually seen location.[10] In that event, the intersensory

[10] The evidence for this claim will be presented in subsequent chapters, and the problem of the relationship between vision and proprioception in Stratton's experiment will be taken up again in Chapter 7.

conflict would disappear, but vision would remain inverted. It is the visualized location, based on retinal local sign, which must change for visual adaptation to an inverted image to take place, not the visualized location based on the local sign from another modality.

An attempt to deal theoretically with the problem raised by Stratton has come from those who believe the main issue is that of motor adaptation, such as Ewert,[11] Snyder and Pronko,[12] and Smith and Smith.[13] In Stratton's report he describes how, at the beginning of the experiment, he had great difficulty in performing motor activities. This difficulty gradually diminished with time. If one wishes to focus on motor performance as an index of uprightness or normalcy, then the problem of adaptation reduces itself to one of learning sensory-motor coordinations. While the problem of sensory-motor learning is an important one, it would be unfortunate to reduce the problem of perceptual adaptation to motor learning. In the case of perceptual adaptation, we want to know whether the scene appears upright or inverted. It is quite possible for the scene to appear inverted but for the observer nevertheless to become extremely adept at performing all motor tasks wearing the lens system. In fact, Stratton did fairly quickly learn to overcome difficulties in performance while at that stage continuing to experience the scene as inverted. The same is true of others who repeated his experiment. Conversely, it is at least logically possible to imagine perceptual adaptation taking place without practice of motor tasks. It is an interesting question whether the motor problem might then no longer exist—in other words, perceptual adaptation (the world appearing upright again) might, ipso facto, obviate motor adaptation in that the subject would direct his movements appropriately, based on where things appeared. In all probability, however, activity of the observer plays a role in perceptual adaptation (for reasons to be covered later), but even so, this does not require the belief that motor adaptation is equivalent to perceptual adaptation.

It is true that perceptual adaptation can be difficult to assess. Snyder, who wore an inverting lens system for a month, became so accustomed to it that he could ride a bicycle with ease. When asked how the world appeared, he was puzzled and found it difficult to answer. Clearly he had gotten used to inversion, to the point where it was no longer in the center

[11] P. H. Ewert, A study of the effect of inverted retinal stimulation upon spatially coordinated behavior, *Genet. Psychol. Monogr.*, 1930, 7, 177–363.

[12] F. W. Snyder and N. H. Pronko, *Vision with spatial inversion*, Wichita: U. of Wichita Press, 1952.

[13] K. U. Smith and W. M. Smith, *Perception and motion*, Philadelphia: Saunders, 1962.

of his awareness. Nevertheless, one can think of certain operations by which an unequivocal answer to whether perceptual adaptation has occurred can be obtained. For example, one could present a vertically moving luminous dot in a darkened room and ask the observer whether it appeared to be moving up or down. Certain other methods have been employed which will be described later. The operations by which perceptual adaptation can be gauged are not the same as those for determining motor adaptation.[14]

To sum up, we have thus far considered various answers that have been given to the question posed in this section. All of these answers are of a *non*-visual nature, and we have rejected them all. Before yielding to such seductive explanations of the visual by the non-visual, is it not incumbent upon us to seek an answer within the visual modality proper? At this point, however, it will be well to consider Gordon Walls' reason for believing that no visual adaptation is possible, that an inverted image *is* necessary for upright vision.[15] Walls' thesis is based upon an analysis of the representation of the image at various stages along the visual pathway from retina to cortex. As noted in the previous chapter, it is now known that every location on the retina has a corresponding region of maximum excitation in the visual cortex, that is to say, there is a point-for-point representation of the retinal image in the pattern of excitation reaching the visual projection area in the brain. To be sure, there is considerable distortion of the geometry of distance relationships between retinal points in this cortical "image," but still the spatial relationships present in the retinal image are at least topologically preserved in the cortical "image." Therefore, Walls reasoned, stimuli impinging on the fovea will give rise to cortical excitation in a region which "represents" foveal or central vision; stimuli from the lower retina will give rise to cortical excitation in a region which "represents" peripheral vision in the upper part of the field,

---

[14] Taylor has recently proposed a more sophisticated behavioral theory of adaptation, in which perception is defined as a state of readiness for actions directed toward objects in the environment that affect the sense organs. In my opinion, the advance here over earlier, behavioristically oriented theories is in the recognition of the field of perception as a discipline in its own right (mental phenomena are acknowledged to exist and to be the legitimate subject matter of scientific inquiry) and in the realization that, although related, motor adaptation and perceptual adaptation are not one and the same thing. Taylor claims that perceptual change is based upon motor adaptation— the re-establishment of conditioned responses to the altered stimulation via the reinforcement of successful performance. See J. G. Taylor, *The behavioral basis of perception,* New Haven: Yale Univ. Press, 1962.

[15] Walls, op. cit.

and so forth. These relationships are built into the nervous system.[16] Therefore, by actual neuro-anatomical arrangement the lower retina must yield perception of objects located phenomenally above those which stimulate the upper retina, and so forth.

In my opinion, there is a fallacy in Walls' reasoning. It is, perhaps, plausible to suppose that excitation of the fovea will give rise to an object located centrally in the momentary field, and excitation of the lower retina might plausibly be expected to give rise to objects located in the periphery on the basis of the cortical mapping of the retinal image. But is there any logical necessity for expecting that stimulation of the lower retina (or lower visual cortex) must be tied to any *particular* peripheral direction in phenomenal space? In what way is that region tagged "up" by virtue of its location in the cortical "image"?

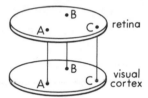

Figure 2-1

In Figure 2-1, it is supposed that the relative position of retinal points A, B, and C with respect to each other and with respect to a center-to-periphery schema is preserved in the cortical "map." But if perception is governed by what is given in the cortical map, what are we entitled to predict? Unless maps are oriented (to pursue the metaphor for a moment), they can only tell us where things are in relation to each other; they cannot tell us anything about the direction of places with respect to our own location. In the same way, we cannot tell whether B is up, down, left, or right with respect to A, and similarly for C. It is irrelevant that B arrived from the upper retina and C from the right side of the retina.

Walls was led astray on this crucial point by the fact that, ordinarily, objects that impinge on the lower retina and excite the lower cortex are located above the observer's eye and are experienced as "up." But suppose the lens system of the eye worked in such a way that an object above

---

[16] Walls' argument in the monograph under discussion was aimed at those empiricists who believe that in retraining vision (as, for example, with inverting lenses or the like) virtually anything can be accomplished because no basis exists in anatomy for determining the spatial aspects of vision. In this respect, he was clearly correct.

the eye stimulated the upper retina. Everything Walls says about the projection system would still be true: The excitation would still travel to a particular locus in the projection area, one near the top of the cortical "map." Yet for perception to be veridical, this point would have to be experienced as "up." [17]

There is one further argument to consider. When the head is turned rapidly to the side, the eyes automatically turn in the opposite direction. This compensatory reflex serves the purpose of minimizing or preventing displacement of the images of objects in the field or, otherwise expressed, of permitting the observer to continue fixating the same point in space. It is based upon a reversed image. Similarly, movements of the two eyes necessary to fixate objects at varying distances would seem to be geared to a reversed image. Thus, to change fixation from a far to a nearby object requires convergence, but this is only true if the images are reversed. If they are not, divergence would be required.[18] It would appear, therefore, that certain aspects of visual behavior have evolved in relation to a reversed image. This fact, however, does not mean that an inverted, reversed image is necessary for upright vision, only that certain visual-motor responses will be interfered with if the image's orientation is altered.

Statement of a Hypothesis

Although—in the light of Berkeley's argument—the absolute orientation of the entire retinal image ought not to be of any consequence for perceived orientation, the fact is that throughout life it does have a specific orientation. If a record of this specific orientation were to be left in the nervous system, that record might be the basis for the awareness of inversion upon viewing the world through a re-erecting lens system. To illustrate, a point seen as moving in the direction forehead-to-chin or "downward" has always been represented by a retinal image moving up-

---

[17] The preservation of the relative position of points from retinal image to cortical "map" might also plausibly be expected to yield an immediate apprehension of shape— for example, the image of two lines at a certain angle to one another would yield two corresponding cortical lines of excitation at a certain angle to one another and thus yield the perception of two lines at a certain angle to one another. Walls might be correct in saying that the experienced angle between the two lines would be given by the projected lines of excitation in the visual cortex, but how would each line's direction relative to the self be experienced? There is no reason to believe that a vertical retinal line giving rise to a (more or less) vertical cortical line must be experienced as phenomenally vertical, at least from what is now known about the neuro-anatomy of the visual system.

[18] I am indebted to Lloyd Kaufman for this observation.

ward. A memory trace might be laid down which would be faithful to
that upward retinal-cortical direction and which would be associated
with the sense of downward egocentric direction. If such a trace existed
(or, rather, trace-complex, since similar traces are deposited throughout
life), then it might serve as a correlate of perceived egocentric orientation. The direction of the image of a moving point or the orientation of
the image of an object would be perceived in terms of how it compared
with the trace. Hence, if the image is now reinverted, its orientation is at
odds with that of the trace, and it is on this basis that we experience the
entire scene as upside down. The existence of such a trace-complex would
also explain another fact, namely, that orientation can be veridically perceived even when an isolated object is seen in an otherwise homogeneous
field or when a stationary observer cannot see any portions of his own
body. Under such conditions, orientation can hardly be based upon the
directional relationship of the object to the visible body.

The existence of the kind of trace described above brings about a state
of affairs such as Walls thought to be innately "given." That is to say, for
an adult, the lower region of the visual cortex signifies the egocentrically
uppermost part of the field, the upper region of the visual cortex signifies
the egocentrically lowermost part of the field; similarly with respect to
the left visual cortex and the rightmost egocentric field and the right visual
cortex and the leftmost egocentric field. Before proceeding, however, it is
necessary to restate the hypothesis more carefully. In and of itself, excitation of any point in the visual cortex does not signify any particular
experienced location in space relative to the observer. Such localization
depends upon eye position and head position as well as retinal position
(see Chapter 4). What I wish to suggest is that a particular *direction*
within the neural substrate, say downward, is correlated with a particular
egocentric direction, namely upward. Of two points, A and B, if A excites
the substrate below B, A will be experienced phenomenally above B—
"above" in an egocentric sense, not necessarily in respect to the "up" of
objectively perceived space. (If the observer were standing on his head,
the egocentric "above" would now actually be in the downward direction
of space.) More specifically, the egocentric "above," "below," "left," and
"right" refer to directions that are experienced in relation to the head.
For example, when I say A is experienced as egocentrically above B, I
mean it is sensed as being in the same direction in relation to B as the
forehead is to the nose, or the nose to the chin. When I say a line is experienced as egocentrically vertical, I mean it is experienced as parallel
to the sagittal axis of the head, and so forth. The retinal-cortical directions

bear a fixed relationship to the head but not necessarily to the trunk. The eyes do not change their orientation to the head to any appreciable extent. If the head is tilted with respect to the trunk, it is nevertheless still the case that a line stimulating a vertical retinal direction will be experienced as egocentrically vertical (parallel to the sagittal or vertical axis of the head); if the image of a point displaces downward along a vertical retinal direction, then even with the head inverted, the point will be seen to move egocentrically "upward," i.e., toward the top of the head. Therefore, it seems correct to tie the retinal-cortical directions to head-defined egocentric orientations only. Nevertheless, since the observer is generally aware of the position of the head with respect to the trunk, he will be able to take it into account and thus will also be aware of the orientation of the object with respect to the trunk or entire body.

Henceforth the term "egocentric" will be used as defined here, to refer to the orientation of objects in relation to the "above," "below," "left," and "right" sides of the head. It will be helpful to think of the objects whose egocentric orientations are being specified as lying in a plane perpendicular to the observer's line of sight. Egocentric orientation then has to do with direction in this plane, either of a line, of two or more points, or of a moving point, insofar as such direction can be related to the "sides" of the head. It is not necessarily the case that the observer is consciously aware that he perceives the orientation of objects in relation to the "sides" of his head. For example, lying supine in bed, a person will orient a book so as to make the text egocentrically upright. He is aware that the book is "upright" in this position in the sense that the upper side of the words is in the "12 o'clock" position, but probably he is unaware that this is based on the directions given by his head. The subjective "meaning" of egocentric orientation is even more difficult to spell out in the case of animals or human infants, because it is even more unlikely that they would relate an object's orientation to the "sides" of the head. It is possible that for animals the meaning of egocentric "above" or "below" would derive from anticipated direction of movement. For example, when a quadruped sees an insect on the ground moving in the egocentrically "upward" direction, this would mean it experiences the insect as moving in the direction of its own customary forward locomotion. When a cat sees the top of a fence on which it is walking as egocentrically "vertical," it means that it is seen to lie in the straight-ahead direction of locomotion. Anticipated direction of movement probably enters into the meaning of egocentric orientation for human adults as well.

It is important to make clear that the hypothesis of a trace that is faithful to the specific orientation of the image (henceforth to be referred to as the stimulus-copy aspect of the trace) is intended to deal with the question posed earlier as to what basis might exist for perceiving the entire optically-transformed visual field as inverted or tilted. It also serves to explain veridical apprehension of the egocentric orientation of visually isolated objects in daily life.[19] But the trace hypothesis should not be interpreted to mean that egocentric orientation is entirely learned or entirely a function of such stimulus-copy traces. To the extent that the body is represented in the visual field, egocentric orientation is directly given precisely as is implied in Berkeley's argument. Therefore, if no such traces existed (as in the case in the newborn human infant), the potential for veridical perception of egocentric "up" and "down" is present immediately, regardless of the orientation of the image. Perhaps the neonate looking at the world through inverting lenses would not see things above his head as "up" and those below as "down" (since that implies an immediate appreciation of "up" and "down"), but by the same token there would be no misperception of such directions either. If an infant inspected an object while, at the same time, seeing portions of its own body, one might say that the object's egocentric orientation would be given—for example, a doll's orientation to the self could be veridically perceived—but at the outset this would not have much, if any, meaning. For the adult, however, where a lifetime of experience has resulted in establishing the egocentric significance of each particular direction in the substrate, the situation is different. As already noted, if point A is above point B in the neural substrate, it signifies a direction relative to B which is experienced as egocentrically "below." With the inverting lens device, a point A in the environment which is egocentrically above B will yield that same cortical excitation. Hence, at the outset, the observer will experience A below B when it is above B.

I believe that Stratton was actually reporting this fact when he experienced visual representations as persisting in their old form. He realized

[19] It has recently been discovered that there are cells in the visual cortex that respond only when the retina is stimulated by lines at a particular orientation (D. Hubel and T. Wiesel, Receptive fields, binocular interaction and functional architecture in the cat's visual cortex, *J. Physiol.*, 1962, **160**, 106–154). Hence the mechanism for detecting lines and discriminating their orientation is now revealed. Beyond that, though, I do not believe this discovery has any immediate relevance for the problem under discussion. I have assumed that the difference in the orientation of lines does not have to be learned. But the perception of a line as egocentrically vertical, horizontal, or tilted cannot be assumed to be given merely because different cortical cells respond depending upon the orientation of the image. It is plausible to believe that this phenomenal "meaning" of the orientation of a line is a function of prior experience.

that the conflict was between this "old form" of visual representation and the newly given visual position of objects, but he felt that some explanation was required for the persistence of the prior visual directionality. In other words, he knew that the upper retina was continuing to signify "down" relative to the lower retina, and the only way he could find to explain this fact was in terms of intersensory associations of local sign, that is, that touch sensations from a part of the body continued to bring to mind a visual localization different from the one actually given. What I have suggested is that visual memory alone can more directly explain why the upper retina continued to signify "down" provided we are willing to make the assumption that the memory trace, considered from the standpoint of its faithfulness to specific features of the proximal stimulus (in this case its orientation in the neural substrate), has psychological consequences.

The situation for the observer who first puts on the inverting device is one of conflict between direction as it ought to be perceived in terms of the relational information provided by the image and the now invariant information provided by the adult brain. To illustrate, suppose the observer looks at a luminous figure A in an otherwise dark room. He will see it inverted, V, with respect to himself. This means he experiences the apex as pointing downward, in the direction his chin is from his forehead. Now, if the room lights are turned on, and behind the figure is a mirror, then he will see his own face in the mirror. It, too, will appear inverted. With respect to the mirrored face, the A is not inverted. The apex points toward the forehead. Hence, as far as the visible self is concerned, the figure is not inverted egocentrically. The conflict is perhaps even more clearly illustrated by considering the perceived orientation of the mirrored image of the face alone. It is experienced as egocentrically inverted. That experience ought to be impossible, as the head *defines* egocentric orientation. It can only happen because the upward direction in the neural substrate has come to signify the direction "forehead to chin" so strongly that it can override the directly given visual information that this is not the direction "forehead to chin" but rather "chin to forehead."

There is some fragmentary evidence that is difficult to interpret on the basis of the analysis I have presented. Schlodtmann [20] elicited pressure phosphenes in a few young subjects who were blind from birth. Apparently they were able to localize the phosphenes correctly with respect to the self despite the control provided by the contralateral relationship

[20] W. Schlodtmann, Ein Beitrag zur Lehre von der optischen Lokalisation bei Blindgeborenen, *Arch. f. Ophth.*, 1902, **54**, 256–267.

between the region stimulated and the perceived location. One would not imagine that a subject would report a subjective point of light as being in an "up" direction when the experimenter pressed the lower portion of the eyeball unless the perception were quite genuine. Assuming Schlodtmann was correct in believing there was no opportunity to learn the direction signified by any particular locus of retinal stimulation, there never having been any prior visual experience other than that of diffuse light, the conclusion that such direction is given innately would seem to be warranted. Yet it cannot be based upon the position of the spot of light relative to the visible body because nothing but the spot is seen. In view of the great importance of this finding and because only a few subjects met Schlodtmann's stringent criteria concerning prior blindness, the experiment should be repeated. However, it may prove very difficult to find cases of total congenital binocular blindness where pathways from retina to cortex are unimpaired such that pressure phosphenes are elicitable.

Experiments on direction have also been performed with animals. Some of these, such as were done by Sperry [21] and his collaborators, entailed inverting the eyes of mature amphibia by surgery (an ideal procedure from the standpoint of not restricting the field of view!). As such, they are similar to Stratton's experiment in that they raise the question of adaptation to a reoriented image. The animals tested consistently followed and snapped in a direction opposite to that of the moving lures, and there was no evidence of any change over time. Similar results were obtained in an experiment by Stone in which the surgery was performed during the embryonic stage, so that it is clear that for certain animal species the location of objects with respect to the self is given innately and does not seem to be subject to adaptation.[22] These experiments, strictly speaking, are concerned with the experienced location of a point with respect to the observer (discussed under the heading of radial direction in Chapter 4) and not with the directional relation of points within a frontal plane, which is the essence of egocentric orientation.[23] More directly relevant to

[21] R. W. Sperry, Effect of 180 degree rotation of the retinal field on visuo-motor coordination, *J. exp. Zool.*, 1943, **92**, 263–279.

[22] L. S. Stone, Functional polarization in retinal development and its re-establishment in regenerating retinae of rotated grafted eyes, *Proc. Soc. exp. biol. Med.*, 1944, **57**, 13–14; Polarization of the retina and development of vision, *J. exp. Zool.*, 1960, **145**, 85–93.

[23] Therefore, the experiments of Sperry and probably the Schlodtmann experiment as well are concerned with a different problem. The problem under discussion now is that of egocentric orientation. To contrast the two phenomena, consider a short line located in the frontal-parallel plane. The line, if vertical, will be perceived as parallel to the long axis of the head (egocentric orientation). Regardless of where the line is

egocentric orientation is the finding that newly born guppies and newly hatched praying mantises circle in the direction of vertical stripes that are rotated around them.[24] Hence one might say they veridically discriminate "leftward" from "rightward" at birth.

Concerning all evidence of this type in lower organisms, it is possible to argue that we are focusing on the question of *behavioral* response to direction and not the perception of direction. The salamander may innately respond to stimulation of its lower left retina by swimming to its upper right but not have the experience of direction analogous to ours. In lower species there is a more direct connection between optic fibers and motor centers than there is in man. One can readily grasp the adaptive value of a built-in mechanism for responding behaviorally to stimuli located in different directions with respect to the animal. Assuming, however, that direction is given innately in some or all species, this does not imply that in man it is not also subject to learning. In fact, as will be brought out in Chapter 4, there is now a considerable body of data suggesting that adaptation to prismatically altered radial direction does occur, and in a fairly short time. Therefore, nativistic and empiristic theories may not be mutually exclusive on this particular question. Although the evidence on adaptation to a rotated image is far more equivocal, I am going to adopt the same argument, namely, whether or not an inverted image innately signifies upright vision for some or all species, it is in principle possible for an image in any orientation to yield upright vision.

An Experiment on the Egocentric Orientation of a Line

To summarize, I have suggested that: (1) the question of the uprightness of vision has to do with perceived egocentric orientation, not direction defined in terms of the up and down of space, (2) in the adult human observer, the egocentric "up" and "down," "left" and "right," are a function of memory traces that remain in specific orientations in the visual neural substrate, being copies of the specific orientations of images that occur in

in the frontal plane, it will retain this apparent orientation so long as its tilt does not change. But if it is to the observer's left, its radial direction is quite different from when it is, let us say, directly below his head. As I will try to make clear in Chapter 4, complete specificity of radial direction would seem to depend, among other things, upon a discrimination by the nervous system of the up-down, left-right egocentric orientations, so the two problems are not unrelated, and that is why this evidence is considered here.

[24] I. Rock, E. S. Tauber, and D. P. Heller, Perception of stroboscopic movement: evidence for its innate basis, *Science*, 1965, **147**, 1050–1052.

daily life, and (3) this stimulus-copy aspect of the memory trace is associated with phenomenal egocentric directions as defined by the "sides" of the phenomenal head. Concerning (1) I have already hinted at the distinction I have in mind, but it will be helpful at this point to clarify it further. Often when we speak of "vertical," "up" and "down," "above" or "below," we have in mind directions in phenomenal space, namely, the direction perpendicular to the earth, toward the sky (or ceiling), toward the ground (or floor), respectively. We are becoming clearer about the determinants that govern perception of the vertical and horizontal of space, namely, proprioceptive-vestibular cues based on gravity and the cues provided by the visual frame of reference. Now, it is true that when the observer is upright, the perceived vertical of space is aligned with, or identical to, the direction perceived as parallel to the head, the egocentric "vertical." But if the observer is tilted, his egocentric vertical and the vertical of space are now phenomenally distinct. In the past, this distinction has either not been clearly drawn or it has been neglected. In the experiment described below, an attempt was made to demonstrate that we do experience egocentric orientations as distinct from the vertical and horizontal directions of space, to determine the accuracy and consistency with which they are perceived, and to demonstrate that the necessary and sufficient condition for their perception is the orientation of the image on the retina.

The basic plan of the experiment was to require the observer to judge the orientation of a luminous line with respect to the sagittal and left-right axes of his head while lying on his back (supine position) on a table in a totally dark room. The line rotated about a vertical axis in a horizontal

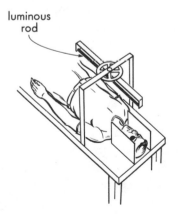

luminous
rod

Figure 2–2

plane above the observer's eyes (see Figure 2-2). It was exposed at successive 5° intervals until the observer indicated that its position was correct. Under these circumstances it may be concluded that gravity did not play any role in the judgments. The line remained in the same relation to the force of gravity at all times, namely, in a horizontal plane, and therefore no position of the line was distinguishable from any other with respect to gravity. For this reason judgments of the line's orientation could have nothing to do with the perception of the direction of the line relative to gravity, but could only be a function of its egocentric orientation. The possibility that touch or proprioception influenced the judgments in any other way was eliminated by preventing the observer from lifting his arms from the table. Furthermore, since the room was completely dark, it may be concluded that the judgments were not influenced by any visual frame of reference.

It was also decided to eliminate the possibility that the judgments were based upon or improved upon by cues from eye movements. If the observer were allowed unrestricted eye movements during the time of observation of the line, he might sweep his eyes along its length, thereby providing himself with a possible cue as to the orientation of the line with respect to his head. As noted above, one purpose of this experiment was to show that perceived egocentric orientation depends upon the orientation of the retinal image and not upon any other stimulus conditions. The following procedure was, therefore, adopted. The line could be made to flash on briefly (approximately two-tenths of a second). Prior to each exposure of the line, the observer was given a signal to fixate a small, luminously painted spot exposed at the center of the line. Shortly after the observer fixated, the line was exposed.

Finally, the observer was allowed to use only one eye, the other eye remaining blindfolded throughout the experiment. It is possible that binocular vision might provide cues to the orientation of the line: A double image of the line produced by far or near convergence might be a cue, because the width between the images would be maximum for the egocentric sagittal and zero for the egocentric left-right direction of the line. Details of the procedure have been previously reported.[25]

A word should be said in advance about how the results are to be interpreted. The hypothesis that the egocentric orientation of a line can be perceived under the conditions of this experiment does not set any exact criterion to be met for its acceptance or rejection. What the hypothesis

[25] I. Rock, The perception of the egocentric orientation of a line, *J. exp. Psychol.* 1954, **48**, 367–374.

really amounts to is the contention that observers will be able to accomplish this to the extent that their judgments of the direction of the line will
not simply be random. In other words, it is by no means necessary and, in
fact, it is impossible to predict the degree of accuracy with which this task
can be accomplished. Whether or not the judgments are random can be
determined by comparing the central tendency of settings to the vertical
with those of the left-right orientation.

All observers were able to judge the egocentric orientation of the rod
with considerable, but by no means perfect, accuracy and consistency.
The mean settings ranged from 1.5° to 9.0° clockwise or counter-clockwise
(taking the sagittal plane of each subject's head as 0°) for the sagittal,
and from 1.5° to 14.0° clockwise or counter-clockwise (taking the horizontal plane of each subject's head as 0°) for the left-right orientation. The
standard deviations (SDs) ranged from 2.0° to 6.5° for the sagittal and
from 2.3° to 12.2° for the left-right settings, with average SDs of 4.0° and
5.5°, respectively. This means that retinal orientation does—within the
limits of this accuracy and consistency—determine the egocentric orientation of a visual line. The extent to which the settings are determined by the
vertical and horizontal retinal coordinates, and are not merely random, is
brought out by the fact that the mean vertical and mean horizontal settings
are approximately 85° apart. The variability is such that this difference is
highly significant.

The results confirm the assumption of the dependency of perceived
egocentric orientation on orientation within the neural substrate, but also
show that this holds only within certain limits of accuracy. The mean settings for many observers do not precisely coincide with the sagittal and
left-right axes of the head. Furthermore, the size of the SDs points up the
fact that for a given observer there is a range of retinal orientations within
which any one may be the proximal stimulus for a line which appears
parallel to one of the axes of the head (sometimes there is a considerable
range of uncertainty for an observer even during a given trial). Some observers showed a range of 25° or more from their extreme clockwise to
their extreme counter-clockwise settings.[26]

As noted earlier, the hypothesis that a correspondence would be found
between retinal-cortical orientation and perceived egocentric orientation
was not based on any of the facts now known about retinal projection or
the cortical representation of the retinal image. Rather, it was based on
the hypothesis that, via past experience, specific retinal orientations could

[26] There is quantitative and qualitative evidence that the observers found it more
difficult to make the left-right setting than the sagittal setting.

signify specific egocentric orientations because of the more or less un-changing relationship of eye to head orientation. The results show that, while a fairly close correspondence between retinal orientation and phe-nomenal orientation to the head obtains, it is not a precise correspondence. This bears out the objection raised to the position taken by Gordon Walls, because by contrast the correspondence between the objective and the phenomenal orientation of two lines *to each other* is precise. Small differ-ences in the orientation of a line relative to another line are readily per-ceived, and this we may assume *is* given by the cortical "mapping" of the retinal image. Apparently, orientation with respect to the self is not as finely discriminable, and this is to be expected provided it is *not* based on anything given by neuro-anatomical projection from retina to visual cortex (for example, that the cortical projection of a retinally vertical image must appear egocentrically "vertical"). Thus the results are more in keeping with a theory that egocentric orientation is represented by memory traces of more or less vertical or horizontal orientations in the neural substrate. In daily life we do not obtain sufficiently precise infor-mation as to the orientation of an object with respect to the head to expect performance in this experimental task to be perfectly accurate and consistent.

If our supine observer were to view the rod with an optical device that tilted the image of the line by some fixed angle, he would misperceive the orientation of the line by that angle. Similarly, if he wore an inverting lens, he would misperceive which direction was egocentrically up, which down, etc. Our experiment did not formally concern itself with the polar-ity of "up" and "down" or "left" and "right" along the vertical and hori-zontal axes, but it was quite clear that the subjects knew which direction along the egocentric vertical was "up," which "down," etc. In a later vari-ation of this experiment in our laboratory, Arien Mack required observers to indicate when a luminous dot which rotated about another luminous dot appeared to be in the "12 o'clock" position. The room was otherwise dark. The observers were standing with head bent forward in a horizontal plane and the dot pattern was located on the floor below. Hence, the only basis for judging when the rotating dot was at the "12 o'clock" position was in terms of egocentric orientation. The observers were able to per-form this task with accuracy and with even greater consistency than in the case of the luminous-rod task. In this procedure the up-down polarity *is* tested, since "12 o'clock" is synonymous with egocentric "up."

The point I wish to stress is that the existence of egocentric orientation in adults, and its basis in retinal-cortical direction, suffices to allow us to predict that a subject wearing Stratton's device or a prism-device would misperceive orientation and would do so in the supine position, viewing objects in a horizontal plane, as well as in an upright position. It is very important to be clear that all the essential ingredients of the Stratton paradigm would exist for the supine (or otherwise horizontally oriented) observer and that in principle one could conduct the entire experiment in that position.

The Problem of Adaptation to a Disoriented Image

We can now return to the question of adaptation to an inverted or disoriented image. To review, the logic of Berkeley and Stratton led to the belief that the orientation of the scene could be veridically perceived regardless of the orientation of the entire image. The fact that in the human adult this is not the case led to the hypothesis of memory traces of specific orientations in the neural substrate which have become associated with specific egocentric orientations. If the specific orientation of these traces in the substrate is a product of learning, then in principle new traces can be acquired. Hence, I believe with Stratton that adaptation to an inverted image is possible. Adaptation would consist of supplanting the original traces with new ones having the orientation in the substrate yielded by the new orientation of the image—that are associated with or signify specific egocentric orientations. The problem now will be to consider how this could come about.

Obviously, if a stationary observer views an isolated line through a set of prisms and does not see his own body, there is no information that the line is oriented differently with respect to him than it appears to be on the basis of the orientation of its image. If, however, (1) he does see part or all of his own body, or (2) he moves, or (3) he looks at familiar things whose orientation is known, he will get information as to the line's true orientation with respect to himself. I will illustrate the process with a prismatically tilted field, not an inverted one. The adaptation process gets under way the moment information becomes available that a seemingly tilted orientation is actually parallel to the vertical axis of the head. Consider first information based on sight of the body. Some parts of the head and, of course, parts of the rest of the body are visible. Any part of the body seen through the prism will appear tilted. Consequently, any object in that tilted orientation is perceived to be parallel to the seen body. To illustrate, if the observer is seated and looks down at a line on the floor parallel to the vertical axis of his body, he will see it as aligned with his body as shown in Figure 2–3. In that case, although the line may at first appear tilted, the observer is nevertheless receiving information that a particular (tilted) retinal orientation is aligned with the egocentric vertical. That is, he is learning that he, too, is "tilted"; therefore nothing is tilted. Given awareness of how the head is felt to be oriented with respect to the rest of the body—for example, that it is aligned with it—the orientation of objects with respect to the *head* can be arrived at in this way by sight of the torso. A trace of the image of the line in the tilted retinal-cortical orientation is deposited and is associated with a trace representing the fact of alignment with the vertical axis of the body.[27] Ultimately, the line

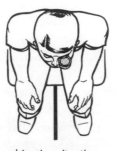

objective situation   phenomenal situation

Figure 2–3

alone in the tilted orientation will come to signify a direction aligned with the head because that phenomenal content—namely, "parallel to the head"—has been associated with that specific orientation in the substrate. The tilted image of the line can evoke imagery of the head and body as *aligned* with that direction.

The argument does not stand or fall on the presence of parts of the body in the visual field although this is certainly important. Information concerning the orientation of the self as an entity in the visual field becomes available in a more subtle manner—namely, via movement—the second source of information mentioned above. Suppose the observer is viewing

[27] The essential aspect of this hypothesis is that an association is formed between the physical properties of the proximal stimulus (orientation in the neural substrate in the present context) and information concerning the spatial properties of the distal stimulus (the orientation of objects with respect to the self). One way of understanding how a record of the physical properties of the stimulus can be carried in memory is to assume there are traces that represent these physical properties (the stimulus-copy trace referred to above), but an alternative possibility is discussed in the final chapter. For the sake of simplicity of exposition, however, I will continue to speak of the "stimulus-copy trace" throughout the book.

a vertical rod from a sitting position with the rod before him. If he were to get up, he should expect that the upper region of the rod will no longer appear straight ahead (see Figure 2–4a). In point of fact, however, when he does get up, he finds that the upper part of the rod, which is now at eye level, remains straight ahead, so that his head must have been gliding along a direction congruent with the rod (Figure 2–4b). This is so because the rod *is* parallel to the head. One might generalize and say that the displacement of the image based on movement of the observer is always in a direction congruent with the direction of displacement of the

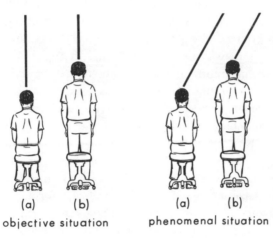

(a)   (b)   (a)   (b)

objective situation   phenomenal situation

Figure 2–4

head. Assuming, therefore, that information is centrally available as to the actual direction in which the head or entire body is moving (in the above example, along a path aligned with the long axis of the body), information is obtained that a tilted direction on the retina signifies an egocentrically vertical phenomenal direction. The same would be true for an animal looking down on the ground as it walked forward. A line on the ground parallel to the direction of its movement would at first appear diagonal to the path of movement. But because the line would continue to appear below the animal's head and the image of the line would flow in a direction congruent with that of the line, its orientation must be one of alignment with the head-body axis.

This last source of information is one dependent on bodily movement. In recent years Held and his associates have argued that not only is movement crucial for perceptual adaptation, but it must be of a kind actively initiated by, not passively imposed upon, the observer.[28] I will go into the logic and supporting evidence for this assumption in Chapter 4, since most of this work has been done on the problem of radial direction. It is sufficient to point out here that movement may be important for the reason discussed above, namely, that only through movement can certain kinds of information about the actual state of affairs concerning the perceived field be forthcoming. According to this view, movement is important only because it allows for certain kinds of information to be registered, not because movement per se is necessary. Furthermore, if movement is not self-initiated or self-directed, the information concerning the direction of displacement of the image might be ambiguous because the observer is not sure which way he is moving. If, in our last example, the animal were to be transported along a path oblique to the main axis of its body, that would "explain" why the line continued to appear directly under its head. Therefore, no information is registered that the directional significance of the various retinal orientations is in any way altered, and thus there is no reason to expect adaptation. In other words, movement can only provide unambiguous information if the actual direction of movement is veridically registered in the central nervous system. Whether that direction is given by proprioception or by a central record of neural impulses out to the muscles will be discussed in subsequent chapters. I hasten to emphasize, however, that the kind of information in which the altered significance of retinal orientation is given by direct perception of the body does not require movement. Consequently, movement may possibly be a sufficient condition for adaptation, but it should not be a necessary one.

It is at least logically possible that familiarity with the orientation of various objects in the environment can play a role in adaptation (this was the third possible source of information mentioned above). If certain objects (trees, houses, people, or the entire indoor or outdoor scene) viewed through a tilting prism are known from past experience to be upright in space, they may be perceived as upright despite the abnormal orientation of the retinal image. (This is related to the Wertheimer effect, the tendency for the coordinate directions of the visual frame of reference

[28] In addition to the references cited in the footnote on page 9, see: R. Held and J. Bossom, Neonatal deprivation and adult rearrangement: complementary techniques for analyzing plastic sensory-motor coordinations, *J. comp. physiol. Psychol.*, 1961, **54**, 33–37; R. Held and A. Hein, Movement-produced stimulation in the development of visually-guided behavior, *J. comp. physiol. Psychol.*, 1963, **56**, 872–876; H. Mikaelian and R. Held, Two types of adaptation to an optically rotated visual field, *Amer. J. Psychol.*, 1964, **77**, 257–263.

to define the vertical and horizontal of space, and is discussed in more detail in the Addendum.) If so, then given that the observer feels himself to be vertical in space via gravitational cues, he will perceive such objects as parallel, not tilted or inverted, with respect to himself. This possible source of information requires neither sight of the body nor movement. However, while it may prove to be a sufficient or supplementary source of information, it can hardly be a necessary one.

The Experimental Evidence

Adaptation to a Reinverted Image

Several reviews of the literature on the Stratton problem have been published, including an excellent one by Gordon Walls.[29] At the risk of repetition, however, the evidence will be considered again here in order to bring out certain points that others may have neglected. Considering first the experiments on a re-erected image, the evidence remains equivocal on the central question of whether or not adaptation occurs. Stratton viewed the world monocularly through a lens system that restricted his view to a field of 45° (Ewert and others who followed were unable to achieve even this wide a field, and it would seem probable that Stratton was incorrect in his measurements). The restricted field is conceivably an important factor. From the standpoint of one of the possible sources of information, adaptation would be hampered because very little of the body of the observer would be visible at any one time.

The procedure for the experiment was as follows: During his waking hours Stratton wore the lenses continuously in front of his right eye while the left eye remained covered. Upon retiring for the night, both eyes were immediately covered. Consequently, at no time during the experiment did light enter his eyes under pre-experimental or normal conditions. He either saw through the lenses or not at all. The lenses were worn for a total of 21½ hours (about three days) in the course of the preliminary experiment and for a total of 87 hours (about eight days) during the main experiment some months later. Stratton attempted to perform various routine activities such as walking, sitting, reading, writing, eating, etc., much as he would have done under normal conditions. He carefully recorded all experiences and observations from day to day, noting any changes that occurred.

[29] Walls, op. cit.

His findings can best be summarized under the following two categories:

MOTOR ADJUSTMENT   At first, all movements toward perceived objects were in the wrong direction. For example, things seen to the left were erroneously approached in that direction, so that the movement had to be reversed. Gradually, however, this initial difficulty was overcome, and by the end of the eighth day of the main experiment, his motor co-ordination was quite good.

PERCEPTION   The perceptual changes are not so clearly defined. By and large, Stratton's protocol gives the impression that he continued to experience the scene as upside down in relation to himself, but it must be added that there were many occasions when this was not the case, and they increased in frequency as the experiment progressed. At the beginning, things not only appeared inverted, but they also appeared strange and, in a sense, not real. Stratton felt that this effect was related to the fact that, during the early stages of the experiment, objects not at the moment visible through the lenses were mentally represented in their former pre-experimental positions and orientations. Consequently, things perceived were strange and unfamiliar not only because they were inverted (see Addendum for phenomenal changes of familiar objects), but also because they were at odds with the larger, surrounding field still represented in accordance with the pre-experimental conditions of retinal stimulation. He therefore anticipated that unseen objects would appear in their pre-experimental orientation as he moved his head about. This effect wore off, however, in the course of the experiment, so that toward the end things no longer looked strange, and objects beyond the range of immediate vision were represented in accordance with the visible scene.

As mentioned above, there were occasions when the field did not appear inverted. Thus, during the preliminary experiment, Stratton noted:

[If] full attention was given to *outer* objects, these frequently seemed to be in a normal position, and whatever there was of abnormality seemed to lie in myself, as if head and shoulders were inverted and I were viewing objects from that position, as boys sometimes do from between their legs. At other times the inversion seemed confined to the face or eyes alone.[30]

Subsequently, during the second day of the main experiment, Stratton reported that either when outdoors, or when indoors, in viewing a well-

[30] Stratton, op. cit., 1896, p. 616.

articulated scene, there was "no striking and obvious feeling that the scene was upside down"—but what he meant was that "an abnormal position of my body in viewing things might just as well account for the facts as would an inversion of the scene." [31]

During the fourth day, Stratton reported:

The feeling of the inversion or uprightness of things was found to vary considerably with the strength and character of the representation of my body. When I looked at my legs and arms or even when I reinforced by effort of attention their new visual representation, then what I saw seemed rather upright than inverted. But if I looked away from my body and gave exclusive force to its pre-experimental image, then, everything in sight seemed upside down. Especially was it noticeable that during active movements of the body, as in brisk walking or in coping with objects whose arrangement was relatively unfamiliar, the feeling of the uprightness of the scene was much more vivid than when the body was quiet.[32]

Finally on the eighth day, Stratton said:

As long as the new localization of my body was vivid, the general experience was harmonious, and *everything was right side up*. But when, for any of the reasons already given—an involuntary lapse into the older memory-materials, or a willful recall of these older forms—the pre-experimental localization of my body was prominently in mind, then as I looked out on the scene before me, the scene was *involuntarily taken as the standard* of right directions, and my body was felt to be in an inharmonious position with reference to the rest. I seemed *to be viewing the scene from an inverted body*.[33]

Stratton concluded that in time the experience of inversion would have permanently disappeared. Two other perceptual effects of the inverting lens system may be briefly mentioned here. One, referred to earlier, is the problem of intersensory disharmony. As the experiment progressed, this difficulty tended to disappear so that, ultimately, objects emitting sounds were seen and heard to be in the same place, and parts of the body were seen and felt to be in the same place. Another effect, occurring only during head movements, was that the visual scene as a whole seemed to swing in the direction of the head movement and at a greater apparent speed than that of the head. This "swinging of the scene," as Stratton called it, also gradually disappeared as the experiment progressed.

At the end of the eighth day, Stratton removed the lenses but continued

[31] Stratton, op. cit., 1897, p. 348.
[32] Ibid., p. 354.
[33] Ibid., p. 469.

to wear the empty tube on one eye (the other eye remaining closed) in order to keep conditions otherwise constant with those during adaptation proper. On opening his eye, he found that the scene had a "strange familiarity." He recognized the pre-experimental arrangement of things, but it nevertheless seemed surprising and bewildering for several hours—*although it did not appear that things were upside down.* In addition, for about the whole of the first day after removing the lenses, the "swinging of the scene" effect was experienced during head movements. Regarding motor coordination in this condition, Stratton found himself frequently making incorrect movements, as is evidenced by his constantly bumping into things. There were also distinct signs of vertigo while walking and moving about. Vertigo had occurred during the early stages of adaptation but gradually subsided as the experiment progressed.

Several features of Stratton's report are of special interest. The role of the perception of his own body is in keeping with the notion that this is one important source of information. That he frequently experienced *the scene* as upright, but not himself, calls for an explanation along the lines of the Wertheimer effect, which, of course, was not known in 1897 (see Addendum). That is to say, by virtue of known content, such as sky and ground, the up and down of space are given.[34] If, then, the sky is going to be seen as environmentally "up" and the ground as "down" wherever their images fall on the retina (because the visual field itself is such a strong determinant of the up and down of space), the fact remains the sky is also going to be located in an *egocentrically* "down" and the ground in an "up" direction because of the inverting optical device. Stratton apparently at times reconciled these two experiences—i.e., sky *environmentally* up and *egocentrically* down—by experiencing the world as upright and his body, or only his head and shoulders or eyes alone (!), as inverted. If he saw his body with his feet on the ground, then only the non-visible parts of his body could be inverted. In daily life we occasionally experience the world as spatially upright but egocentrically inverted when we view it with the head inverted. The effect he describes

[34] Actually, I am suggesting something about the Wertheimer effect that was not intended by the original notion. If a rectangular frame or a room is tilted 90° or 180°, it would end up with its sides horizontal and vertical once more. Structurally, therefore, there is no change in its orientation. Consequently, unless familiar content were to play a role, a Wertheimer effect could not be expected to occur. It is entirely possible, however, that familiar content is quite important—for example, it is known that a tilted room has a much greater effect than a tilted luminous rectangle, and this may not be due to a difference in degree of articulation, as Asch and Witkin suggest, but to past experience with rooms.

is similar to one obtained by Asch and Witkin, in which observers often report that a tilted room is upright but that they themselves are tilted.[35] In both cases, the non-alignment of scene and self is given by the altered orientation of the image and, prior to any adaptation, leads to veridical perception of that non-alignment. Hence, Stratton saw the world as egocentrically inverted, and some of Asch and Witkin's subjects saw the room as tilted with respect to themselves. But the Wertheimer effect or something like it may establish the up and down of environmental space and, in so doing, require a particular phenomenal orientation of the body in space if its fixed orientation to the scene is prescribed. In other words, if (1) the scene tends to appear upright, but (2) there is a sense of inversion between scene and self, then (3) the self must be upside down in space. This is what Stratton reported, and he certainly had no theoretical preconception for expecting a strange experience such as this to occur. In terms of the arguments I have presented that the Stratton experiment is properly to be considered as bearing on egocentric orientation, these experiences cannot be taken as evidence of perceptual adaptation, for the non-veridical perception of egocentric orientation remains, i.e., (2) above.

Stratton refers to the clash between the perceived orientation of objects seen through the lenses with the imagined orientation of objects in the area surrounding the lenses. I would explain this conflict as a function of the fact that the orientation of imagined objects is determined by directions within the neural substrate. Therefore, even if Stratton's inverted field had not been restricted, one would still have predicted a sense of inversion at the outset. But this conflict may well have been accentuated by the restricted field because Stratton was not directly confronted with information that objects in his peripheral field were oriented differently than he envisioned them.

It is worth underscoring Stratton's report that the scene did not appear inverted on removing the lenses. Had he reached the point where the scene appeared egocentrically upright continuously—which he did not claim to have achieved, but which some have mistakenly claimed he did— such adaptation would be reflected by a negative aftereffect, in this case the appearance of the scene as inverted on removal of the lenses. He *did* experience the scene as strange and he *did* experience motor difficulties with lenses removed, thus attesting to the reality of these aspects of adaptation. The "swinging of the scene" effect which Stratton and others since

[35] S. E. Asch and H. A. Witkin, Studies in space orientation I and II, *J. exp. Psychol.*, 1948, **38**, 325–337 and 455–477.

have reported is tangential to our present focus but deserves some comment here. With inverting lenses, which also reverse left and right, lateral head movements cause the image to displace in the direction opposite to the direction in which it customarily displaces. It is not surprising, therefore, that Stratton saw the scene move whenever he moved his head. But he adapted to this, and genuinely so. Proof of this lies in the fact that an aftereffect followed the removal of the lenses. Stratton reports that he once again experienced movement of the field with movement of his head.

In conclusion, then, concerning the central aspect of Stratton's findings, the following statements seem to me to be justified by his protocol: (1) At the end of the eight-day exposure period it was not the case that the egocentric location of objects was perceived veridically at all times or even most of the time, although (2) there were occasions when this was true, particularly when parts of the body were in view and/or in motion. (3) It does seem to be the case that by the end of the experiment the *scene* was perceived to be spatially upright much of the time, but not in relation to the self—the body or the head was then experienced as upside down.

The experiment of Ewert [36] is often cited as providing conclusive evidence that perceptual adaptation to an inverted image does not take place. He extended the duration of the exposure to fourteen days, used three observers instead of one, and replaced introspective observation with objective tests. These changes, of course, are in principle desirable, but it is questionable if the procedure Ewert followed was one that provided much opportunity for perceptual adaptation to occur. No information is given on the amount of time, if any, during which the observers could freely inspect their environment or move about unaided while wearing the apparatus. In fact, it seems clear that most of the time was taken up by the series of specific tasks. It is questionable whether these activities, by their very nature, would be such as to facilitate adaptation. These tasks focused on intersensory relationships or on motor learning. For example, in one task the subject was required to point to the region within a square grid painted on the dorsal surface of his hand which had just been touched by the experimenter. He saw the hand being touched. At first the subject tended to point to, say, the upper left region if the lower right region had been touched (because he visually located the touched spot in the upper left of his field). In time, errors declined, but the cause of the improvement is undoubtedly not a result of perceptual adaptation (i.e., seeing the touched spot as lower right). Because the subject was

[36] Ewert, op. cit.

allowed to see where his pencil pointed, he thereby obtained knowledge of his own errors. He knew he did not spontaneously point to the spot he had just seen touched and could not be expected to repeat his errors. The fact that pointing errors declined merely indicates that the subject learned to correct his movements in pointing. The same outcome would be predicted even if the experimenter did not touch the hand of the observer but merely pointed to a region of it or, in fact, if the hand were not used at all, and a grid on a chart were used as the stimulus pattern.

In a companion experiment, the hand was touched with the subject's eyes closed and the subject on opening his eyes indicated his response verbally, designating direction with reference to a small red star in the field. In this case there is no basis for change over time in terms of knowledge of results. Except for the area of the grid, the rest of the hand was covered by a cloth. This is a better experiment, because if perceptual adaptation had occurred, then tactual stimulation near the wrist would lead to a visual designation toward the bottom of the field for both the subject and the experimenter. In point of fact, it led to a designation toward the top of the field for the experimenter (which, for some strange reason, Ewert accepted as a correct answer), and there seems to have been no change in accuracy over time. Thus there were at least some tests included in the series that did provide a measure of perceptual adaptation, and the results of these tests must be interpreted to mean that adaptation had not occurred.[37] However, in tests such as those described above, the subject may have seen little more than the circumscribed region of his hand, which remained stationary throughout the hour-long period of the test. These conditions are hardly conducive to perceptual adaptation.

There have been several other studies of adaptation to a re-erected image. One was by Peterson, who wore Ewert's apparatus for about two weeks, under conditions similar to those of Stratton. The results were summarized by Peterson's son, following the father's death.[38] Although some of his experiences were similar to Stratton's, on the whole it would appear that he did not experience a righting of the field. Another study

[37] Unlike Stratton, Ewert utilized a binocular apparatus that necessarily was a pseudoscope, reversing depth based on retinal disparity. Walls correctly notes this fact and concludes that adaptation to the re-erected image would be extremely difficult owing to the conflict of depth cues, since perspective and other configurational cues are not reversed. As noted earlier, re-erecting the image in both eyes will necessitate divergence of the eyes wherever convergence would occur under normal vision and vice versa. Ewert's binocular device yielded double images at near distances and restricted the field of view to 34.5°.

[38] J. Peterson and J. K. Peterson, Does practice with inverting lenses make vision normal? *Psychol. Monogr.*, 1938, **50**, 12–37.

was by Snyder and Pronko, covering a period of a month.[39] In their experiment, the emphasis was on motor adaptation, which showed tremen-
dous improvement as the experiment progressed. As to the purely
perceptual aspect, the impression one obtains in reading the report is that
the field remained inverted although, as noted earlier, this fact is somewhat
obscured by the decreasing strangeness or, otherwise expressed, increasing naturalness of the inverted scene.

Thus it seems fair to say that of the four studies entailing a reinverted
image—Stratton, Ewert, Peterson, and Pronko and Snyder—each covering
a substantial period of time, the only evidence at all of a righting of the
optically inverted field is that of Stratton and that evidence is certainly
not sufficiently clear. In the face of these findings, and in keeping with
his views as to the anatomical basis for upright vision, Gordon Walls concluded that some factor peculiar to Stratton himself was the cause of his
occasional experience of the world as upright. He entertains two possi-
bilities. The first—which he eventually rejects—was that Stratton was able
to invert his proprioceptive body image, thus "feeling himself" in the
same orientation as the visually inverted scene. For the reasons discussed
earlier (pages 20–21), explanations of this sort do not stand up under
careful examination. The other, which Walls accepts as correct, is that
Stratton was capable of eidetic imagery, and he used this ability to
imagine the objects in the field outside of immediate view as in the same
orientation as those within the field of view. All this would do, however,
is to create a harmony between seen and unseen objects, while the entire,
now unified, field could nevertheless still be experienced as inverted. In
fact, Stratton reported that a harmony between seen and unseen objects
was achieved toward the end, whereas the orientation of the field was only
sporadically perceived as egocentrically upright. As for the occasions
when the scene did appear upright, I do not believe that all Stratton
meant was that the orientation of seen and unseen objects was consistent
(cf. the quotation on page 45). Rather, his descriptions seem to refer to
genuine instances of perceptual adaptation in which the field appeared
egocentrically uninverted.

Against these studies, there is only the most recent of all, that of Kohler
and Erismann at Innsbruck, in which it is claimed that complete adaptation did finally occur.[40] These investigators utilized a mirror rather than a
lens system. The subject viewed the scene through a mirror placed under

[39] Snyder and Pronko, op. cit.
[40] I. Kohler, The formation and transformation of the perceptual world (Trans. by
H. Fiss), *Psychol. Issues*, 1964, 3, No. 4, 1–173.

the visor of his cap with direct vision of the scene blocked. The mirrored image was therefore inverted, but not reversed with respect to left and right.[41] The mirror permitted a much wider field of view than any of the lens systems used by earlier investigators. Several subjects were tested for periods ranging from six days to two weeks. The reports are unfortunately not crystal clear in respect to the outcome, but one gathers that it is maintained that the subjects all achieved a righting at certain times. The investigators seem to believe that particular experiences led to righting, often suddenly and dramatically. For example, simultaneously touching and viewing the seen objects, holding a plumb line, or observing smoke rising from a cigarette, all had the effect of suddenly causing the inverted scene to appear upright. I find this difficult to believe because nowhere else does one find a genuine perceptual effect determined primarily by a piece of knowledge of this kind (i.e., smoke is known to rise upward, therefore the direction in which the smoke is moving is suddenly seen as upward, not downward). However, certain clever methods were employed to determine whether the observers actually experienced the world as upright or inverted. For example, the subject was presented with a form which represented one letter in one orientation (a W) and another in an inverted orientation (an M). The subject's spontaneous reactions to such tests suggested that righting had occurred. (Kottenhoff,

[41] Experiments were also performed in the Innsbruck laboratory with prismatically produced left-right reversals of the field (without up-down inversion). Although the report offers a great deal of qualitative data, it is not completely clear what the outcome was in terms of the basic question of perceptual righting. The impression one gets is that eventually the left became "left" again and the right became "right" again, but there are many contradictory experiences. Kohler believes that motor behavior and kinesthesis were particularly crucial for adaptation to this type of optical change. Charles Harris makes out a good case for the idea that the fundamental change in these experiments is proprioceptive. Due to the dominance of vision, a subject who continually sees his right hand in the left part of his visual field, because of reversing goggles, will come to *feel* his right hand to be in that location (i.e., closer to his left eye than to his right). If he answers questions about direction by referring to his hand, he will then say that an object that is physically on his right looks as if it is "on my right-hand side" through reversing goggles, because he sees it to be on the same side as he feels his right hand. But Harris maintains that the scene still "looks" the same as when the subject first put on reversing goggles; letters and numbers still look like mirror writing. C. S. Harris, Perceptual adaptation to inverted, reversed, and displaced vision, *Psychol. Rev.*, 1965, **72**, 419–444. Such responses would be understandable provided that decisions as to what is "left" and "right" are made on the basis of where the felt sides of the body are visualized to be. The problem of left-right reversal without up-down reversal is too complex to be treated adequately here. Suffice to say there is little immediately given purely visual information of such reversal in the stationary scene, the body being bilaterally symmetrical and the environment having no intrinsic left and right sides.

working at Innsbruck, presented his subjects with the ambiguous Schröder staircase figure. They were required to indicate whether they would approach it from the left or the right. If righting had occurred, the response to the question should shift from "right" to "left." Kottenhoff's subjects did not evidence complete righting until the last day of a two-week period.[42]) In Kohler's experiment, there were also reports of inversion experiences on removing the mirror. One subject reported complete righting of the inverted field after nine days and inversion experiences on removing the mirror.

There have been several studies with animals, in addition to the work of Sperry and his collaborators already mentioned, in which the orientation of the retinal image has been altered.[43] Pfister utilized left-right reversing prisms with adult hens who showed no adjustment after three months.[44] Von Holst and Mittelstaedt fitted inverting prisms on fish, and in another study rotated the head of the fly 180°.[45] The behavioral evidence in both cases was that no motor adaptation occurred. The question should be raised, however, as to whether the necessary conditions for motor adaptation exist in these experiments. It is difficult to see how a correct response, which would lead to reward, could be expected to occur in some of these lower organisms, given an innate linkage between locus of stimulation and direction of response. Perhaps some method of guiding the animal should be tried.

In contrast with these studies on lower species are the experiments by Foley and Bishop. Foley fit a binocular inverting lens system on a rhesus monkey and observed it for eight days.[46] The monkey was obviously profoundly disturbed by the device. There was a tendency for it to back away from objects at the outset and occasionally to view the world from

[42] H. Kottenhoff, Situational and personal influences on space perception with experimental spectacles, Part I: Prolonged experiments with inverting glasses, *Acta Psychol.*, 1957, **13**, 79–97.

[43] There have also been two interesting studies with animals on the Wertheimer effect, with contradictory results, which will not be discussed here. (B. F. Riess, The relationship between the tilt of a visual field and the deviation of body position from the vertical in the white rat, *J. exp. Psychol.*, 1951, **40**, 531–537; R. L. Fantz, Response to horizontality by bantam chickens in level and tilted rooms, *Psychol. Rec.*, 1959, **9**, 61–66.)

[44] H. Pfister, Über das Verhalten der Hühner beim Tragen von Prismen, doctoral dissertation, Univ. of Innsbruck, 1955.

[45] E. von Holst and H. Mittelstaedt, Das Reafferenz-prinzip, *Die Naturwissenschaften*, 1950, **20**, 464–467; E. von Holst, Relations between the central nervous system and the peripheral organs, *Brit. J. Animal Behav.*, 1954, **II**, 89–94.

[46] J. P. Foley, Jr., An experimental investigation of the effect of prolonged inversion of the visual field in the rhesus monkey, *J. genet. Psychol.*, 1940, **56**, 21–51.

between its legs with head inverted. However, during the last few days of the experiment the animal once more could successfully negotiate the environment and could localize objects correctly.

In what must be considered one of the best designed and carefully executed experiments in this area, Bishop has shown that kittens who first view the world through an up-down (but not left-right) inverting prism (having been reared in darkness until they are two months old) do not seem to have noticeably greater difficulty in getting about in the environment than control kittens treated in the same way except for the absence of the prism.[47] Although he did find that the control kittens improved *more* than the kittens wearing prisms over a period of four weeks on a series of locomotion tasks given each day, the fact is that the prism-wearing kittens did not seem to behave differently in their initial exposure to the visual world than the control kittens, and they did improve substantially on a day-to-day basis. An important feature of the procedure was the variation from day to day of the specific sequence of the obstacles in each spatial task, so that the kittens could not learn a particular path. Hence, improvement would presumably reflect the adequacy of perception or visual-motor coordination in general, rather than mastery of specific habits. When both groups were then transferred to the opposite condition (i.e., non-prism to prism, and prism to non-prism), the kittens of both groups experienced disruption in their performance by the change, although perhaps not as much as one might expect. However, the prism to non-prism transition was not as disruptive as the non-prism to prism transition. Again the kittens of both groups improved their performances substantially in subsequent days.

The study suggests that although there may be certain reasons why the normally inverted image leads to less difficulty in visual-motor coordination, it is not necessary for such coordination in mammals. (Bishop thinks that the reinverted image creates difficulties because of an innate connection between retinal location and fixating head movements, but another possibility is that it may have to do with an innate determination of direction of compensatory eye movements triggered by head movements.) The implication of this finding is that the inverted image is not necessary for the veridical *perception* of egocentric orientation, because it is difficult to imagine that a kitten could have non-veridical perception but nevertheless learn to *behave* appropriately (as a human being might be able to do).

[47] H. E. Bishop, Innateness and learning in the visual perception of direction, doctoral dissertation, Univ. of Chicago: Microfilm Thesis No. 4924, 1959.

Adaptation to a Tilted Image

It seems clear, in reviewing all the studies with human observers, that most suffer from the lack of an objective measure of adaptation. The Kohler and Kottenhoff techniques mentioned above are exceptions, but even here one might suspect that a subject who had grown accustomed to the mental set of making corrections for which direction appeared up and which down, would "see" or report a W as a W even if the M appeared egocentrically upright to him. The objective tests employed by Ewert, by and large, did not pertain to the question of experienced orientation, and those that did were not immune from the operation of sets and corrective cognitive operations. I believe that the difficulty lies with the selection of complete inversion of the image as the paradigmatic situation to study. It is clear historically why Stratton did select complete inversion, but on theoretical grounds there would seem to be no good reason why some other, lesser, degree of disorientation would not be as good a test of the issue. For those who believe an inverted image is necessary for upright vision, an image tilted by 30° should never yield anything but a field experienced as tilted by this amount.

There are several advantages in working with smaller degrees of tilt. For one thing, it is always good strategy to try to arrange conditions so that an effect can occur, and it seems reasonable to suppose there is a greater likelihood of obtaining an effect if the change required is small rather than large. Second, in many of the recent studies of perceptual adaptation, it has been possible to show continuous change over time—for example, a curved line will look less and less curved with increasing durations of inspection, and it is possible to measure this progressive transformation. Now, in the case of complete inversion, it does not seem plausible to expect a continuous transformation, because this implies that, after some given period, the field would appear only 150° tilted or only 90° tilted. Adaptation must be an all-or-none affair in the case of a reinverted image. If, however, adaptation to an image disoriented by some lesser magnitude, for example 30°, is studied, it does seem plausible that partial adaptation could occur after a given time period. The scene would continue to appear tilted, but not by 30°. There are varying degrees of possible tilt along a continuum, whereas inversion is a change of polarity. This leads to the third advantage of working with smaller tilts of the field, namely, the possibility of measuring adaptation objectively by requiring the observer to judge the tilt of a rod seen before and after exposure to the prisms.

Such a procedure conforms to the method that has evolved in recent years for testing adaptation effects of all kinds. Any change in perceived direction will be reflected by the difference in settings made by the subject before and after the exposure period proper. The post-exposure settings (without prisms) should tend toward the direction of the prismatically created tilt during adaptation. Conversely, a line parallel to the observer seen without prisms after exposure should appear tilted in the opposite direction (a negative aftereffect). The pre- and post-exposure measures should be taken in darkness, with a luminous test rod, since otherwise the presence of the visible lines of the scene would tend to determine the observer's judgments and thereby to block the appearance of an adaptation effect.

There have been two published studies of adaptation to a tilted (not inverted) field. G. G. Brown was interested in the effect of transforming retinal disparity by altering the orientation of the images. To this end he wore two Dove prisms in tandem in front of each eye at angles that produced a 75° tilted image and restricted the field of view to 10°. He wore this device for one week at home and around the campus. He found that "by the end of the second [day] one could scarcely conceive the perceived walls as inclining 75° from an imagined visual normal. . . . The new perceptual situation, however, never became quite 'natural' although during the last half of the week's experiment both the fact and the amount of inclination seemed to be very uncertain." [48] While some degree of adaptation seems to have occurred, it is impossible to assess its magnitude from Brown's comments. He did not employ objective measures such as those described above.

In a quite recent study, Mikaelian and Held also used two prisms in tandem to create a tilted image. Their device was monocular. It produced a tilt of 20°, and it provided for a field of 15° of visual angle.[49] In the first experiment, twelve subjects wore the prisms for one hour under active conditions, in which they walked up and down a hallway, and also under passive conditions, in which they were pushed in a wheelchair over the same path for an hour. Both before and after this exposure period, the subjects adjusted a luminous line to the apparent vertical using the same eye, but without the prisms. The mean difference between pre- and post-exposure settings of the line for the "active" condition was 6.8°. Three subjects who showed the most rapid rates of adaptation were then given

[48] G. G. Brown, Perception of depth with disoriented vision, *Brit. J. Psychol.*, 1928, 19, p. 135.
[49] Mikaelian and Held, op. cit.

an additional two hours of exposure. Under "active" exposure they each achieved full compensation, i.e., they set the line at approximately 20° from the true vertical in the direction the prisms had tilted the scene, a remarkable result for only a two-hour period and considering the very restricted size of the visual field. Under the passive condition, the mean effect for the twelve subjects was only 1.9°. For the three subjects given the longer-range exposure, the passive condition never yielded an effect beyond a few degrees.

There are two aspects of this experiment that are important. The first is that appreciable adaptation to a prismatically tilted retinal image was obtained; the second is that active movement was found to be a necessary condition (since the small effect obtained under conditions of passive movement can easily be accounted for on the basis of a normalization of the lines of the retinally tilted image [Gibson]). In our laboratory Arien Mack has confirmed the first finding, but not the second.[50] She performed an experiment similar to that of Mikaelian and Held utilizing an improved optical device that permitted a larger field of view, the image of which was tilted by 40°. To prevent movements of the head, the active subjects were required to walk while pushing a cart. The front end of the cart contained a vertical column at the top of which was a bite board. The passive subjects stood on a platform on the bottom of the cart, biting on the board, and were pushed. There were sixteen subjects, each of whom served under both active and passive conditions at different times. They were exposed to the tilted scene of a long corridor for a period of thirty minutes. Both conditions yielded an adaptation effect, although not as great as was obtained by Mikaelian and Held, but the effect was identical under passive and active movement, namely 3.7°.

Can we take these results as an answer to the experimental question posed by Stratton, namely, that adaptation to a modified orientation of the image does occur? In keeping with the analysis of the problem presented earlier, the crucial question is whether or not a change has occurred in egocentric orientation. Concretely, does a new (tilted) orientation on the retina now signify the egocentric vertical? Unfortunately, the method employed in these experiments does not provide an unambiguous answer to this question because the adaptation might have been to the direction that appears vertical in the environment. At the outset, all verti-

[50] A third experiment along this line has been completed, which also reveals an appreciable adaptation to a prismatically tilted scene. See S. M. Ebenholtz, Adaptation to a rotated visual field as a function of degree of tilt and exposure time, *J. exp. Psychol.*, 1966, in press.

cal lines in the scene appear tilted. With continued exposure to the prisms, the scene may appear less and less tilted with respect to the direction of the gravitational vertical. The tendency noted by Wertheimer for the vertical of space to be determined by the main lines of the field might facilitate this kind of change. Yet it does not necessarily follow that such a perceptual change entails any modification of the egocentric coordinates. While the true vertical of space might once more appear phenomenally vertical, it is not necessary that it must, ipso facto, appear egocentrically vertical. The observer may still have the impression that the field is tilted *with respect to himself,* tilted as much as it was at the outset. The perception of the scene as upright in space but tilted egocentrically would not be contradictory if the observer now felt that he himself was tilted.[51]

In addition to the measure of the orientation of the line, Mikaelian and Held also obtained a measure of the radial direction of two luminous points, one at a time—one slightly above eye level, the other slightly below eye level. The subject had to indicate when the point appeared straight ahead. Presumably, a change of the vertical in the direction of the prismatic tilt would affect the apparent "straight ahead" of the upper point in one direction and of the lower point in the opposite direction. This was determined by computing the tilt of the imaginary line connecting the average location of the two points for each subject before and after exposure to the prisms. The average shift of this imaginary line for the active condition was 7.0°, and for the passive condition −.8°. Since the judgment involved the radial direction of a point, one might think that this measure tapped a change of egocentric orientation and not merely a change of the perceived vertical of space. We cannot be certain of this conclusion, however, because a shift in the vertical of space could very well have an effect on the radial or egocentric localization of a point. It is known that the apparent "straight ahead" direction is affected by the structure of the visual field. This possibility could easily be checked by requiring *non-adapted* observers, i.e., observers who had not worn prisms, to judge the radial direction of points seen within a tilted field. If, in looking at a tilted room, the observer's judgments of the direction that appeared straight ahead were to be influenced by the tilt of the room, it would be clear that Mikaelian and Held's subjects might well have been revealing an aftereffect of such an influence.

[51] Sheldon Ebenholtz has suggested this explanation of the Mikaelian-Held findings. It follows from the general hypothesis propounded by Charles Harris that many types of perceptual adaptation are based upon the altered interpretation of proprioceptive stimulation. Also see J. Hochberg, On the importance of movement-produced stimulation in prism-induced aftereffects, *Percept. mot. Skills,* 1963, **16,** 544.

One further piece of evidence derives from the second experiment of Mikaelian and Held, in which the subjects viewed through the prisms a specially created environment consisting only of dimly luminous spheres. Such an environment does not contain line patterns which might generate a configurational adaptation to tilted lines. They performed this experiment as a control for the kind of effect Gibson had studied. There would also not be any tilted frame of reference generated by the prism system such as could be expected to yield a Wertheimer effect. Still the observers might obtain information about the prismatic tilt via movement, and hence adaptation could occur. The authors do not tell us precisely how movement yields information that could lead to adaptation, but one might explain it as follows. Suppose the stationary observer perceives the configuration of spheres as shown in Figure 2–5. Obviously, he has no way of

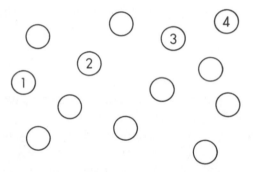

Figure 2–5

knowing his perception is not veridical. If, however, he now walks from left to right, he will find that spheres 1, 2, 3, and 4 successively appear at eye level. Thus he is getting information that that seemingly tilted direction is horizontal. Another way of putting it is to say that the direction of flow of stimulus elements is along the path 1, 2, 3, 4 depicted in Figure 2–5. Since the direction of flow along the retina always signifies the visual direction in the field parallel to the direction in which the head is moving, and since the head is moving horizontally during walking, the information is present that the direction 1, 2, 3, 4 is egocentrically horizontal.

Eight subjects exposed for ninety minutes under the active condition underwent a shift of about 2° (using the line as well as the point-location method of testing), whereas under the passive condition they showed no change at all. Two fast-adapting subjects given two-and-a-half hours of "active" exposure yielded shifts of around 5°. The authors speculate that the greater effect obtained in the earlier experiment was due to the presence of a greater density of contours in the normal hallway than in the "sphere room." I suspect that this is not the reason for the difference but rather that the subject receives much more immediate information about the nature of the new stimulus situation in the former case, information based on familiarity with the objects in the scene and their customary orientation. There is now evidence that a stationary observer will adapt to some extent if he views a room or corridor through prisms (see Addendum, page 70).

In any case, although Held's work clearly rules out an explanation in terms of normalization and the second experiment disposes of the Wertheimer effect as a *necessary* condition, it does not rule out the possibility that the adaptation obtained is essentially to the altered direction of the vertical and horizontal of environmental space. To eliminate this possibility, it would seem necessary to study adaptation to a prismatically tilted image under conditions in which the tilt does not in any way affect the vertical of space, but only the egocentric coordinates. This can be achieved by restricting the observer's view to a horizontal plane throughout the period of exposure to prisms. For example, he might be required to bend his head over and look down at the ground or, if supine, to look up at the ceiling. In this way the adaptation would entail only a change of egocentric orientation (i.e., a change in the retinal-cortical orientations that signify the egocentric "vertical" and "horizontal"), and not a change of the directions perceived as vertical and horizontal in the environment. Consistent with this methodology, it is also possible to test for an effect by determining apparent egocentric orientation in a horizontal plane. After the exposure period, adaptation would be revealed by the selection of a direction with respect to the head consonant with the direction of tilt produced by the prisms.

Work along this line is under way in our laboratory. In one experiment, done in collaboration with Arien Mack, the observer stood looking down at the floor with his head immobilized by a bite board. He saw his lower extremities through a right-angle prism which had the effect of twisting the image 50° clockwise or counter-clockwise about a vertical axis. In one variation of this procedure, on the floor was a large mirror through which the observer could also see his head and chest. Thus the entire front of the body was seen in a tilted orientation. Before and after the exposure period of approximately fifteen minutes, a test of egocentric orientation was conducted along the lines already described (see page 38). The observer could manipulate a handle which caused one luminous dot on the floor directly underneath his head to rotate about another. His task was to set the rotating dot so that it appeared to be in the "12 o'clock" position. To ensure that the observer was in the same position before and after the exposure period, a teeth mold was used. The results have varied depending upon the specific procedure used. In order to avoid delay between the end of exposure to the sight of the body and the final test and in order to avoid possible changes in head position, in one experiment the pre- and post-exposure tests were conducted *with* the prism in place. This led to a significant average change in the setting of the dot of several degrees in the predicted direction. Many observers show a very appreciable effect. When, however, the prism is removed for pre- and post-exposure tests, so that the observer must lift his head up before biting down again on the teeth mold, there does not seem to be a reliable change. We are investigating the effect of giving the observer a task which focuses his attention on egocentric orientation during the exposure phase, for example instructing him repeatedly to set a short line which rotates in a horizontal plane so that it appears either parallel or perpendicular to the long axis of the body. It is important to mention that many observers do not see themselves as tilted when they look through the prism, despite the very appreciable tilting of the image. Thus it is perhaps fair to say there is an immediate "adaptation." It is not clear why this "adaptation" does not then consistently carry over to the testing situation.

In a different experiment, sixteen observers were subjected to more active conditions of exposure. They wore two right-angle prisms in tandem, which tilted the field 23° clockwise or counter-clockwise. The subject was required to walk around the laboratory with his head always bent over so as to be parallel to the floor. For thirty minutes he had to walk a zigzag chalk path which was varied from time to time. Using the same egocentric "12 o'clock" measure as described above, an average change of about 6° in the predicted direction was obtained. Fifteen of the sixteen subjects showed an effect, and with many it was very appreciable.

Are these effects based on a proprioceptive change of some kind rather than a change of retinal local sign of egocentric orientation? One might think that either (1) the observer came to interpret his head as twisted with respect to his trunk since he saw his lower extremities and it could be said they appeared as if they were twisted to one side, or (2) he actually did twist his head into alignment with his seen feet since he was not constrained from doing so in some of the experiments in which the observer walked along the path. These arguments would only make sense if an altered interpretation of the "feel" of the head with respect to the trunk would have an effect on the "12 o'clock" measure used. Since it is believed that egocentric orientation is governed by the head axes, this is improbable, but to lay the argument to rest, a control experiment was performed in which the experimenter deliberately twisted the subject's trunk and head very considerably out of their customary alignment with one another to see if judgment of the "12 o'clock" position would be affected. It was not.

Thus these experiments provide evidence that adaptation to a tilted image occurs entailing a change in the coordinates of egocentric direction and in a fairly short period of time. As to the conditions necessary for producing it, the results suggest that sight of the body or information derived from movement alone can lead to adaptation. In one experiment, in which the observer walked along looking down at the floor, sight of the legs was blocked by means of a circular cardboard collar which he wore around his waist. A significant change was obtained. We interpret this effect of movement in terms of the information provided as to the new retinal coordinates of egocentric orientation.

SUMMARY

[N O T E : *Sentences in brackets refer to material presented in the Addendum which follows.*]

An analysis of the problem of the perception of orientation led to the conclusion that upright vision does not require an inverted image. The veridical perception of the orientation of objects with respect to the self should be based upon the orientation of their retinal images to that of the body of the observer. Since disorienting the image affects all objects alike (including the body), it should not matter whether the entire image is inverted, upright, or tilted. Yet optical systems that alter the orientation of the image do lead to an immediate impression of inversion or tilt. Various attempted solutions to the problem of why this is the case were considered and rejected. These theories stress the altered relationship between vision and other modalities, thereby failing to do justice to the fact of *visual* disorientation.

The hypothesis was advanced that, based upon past experience with an inverted retinal image, the specific (inverted) orientation of the image in the neural substrate is recorded in memory and is associated with phenomenal directions in relation to the self. Hence "upward" is associated with a downward retinal-cortical direction and "downward" with an upward retinal-cortical direction. An object aligned with the head is represented in the neural substrate in a vertical orientation, so that a memory trace faithful to that specific orientation in the substrate is deposited. The object is also experienced as aligned with the head. In time, therefore, that retinal-cortical orientation comes to signify the egocentric "vertical." Once that happens, a changed orientation of the entire image will lead to the impression of tilt. An experiment was described in which it was shown that, for adults, the orientation of the image of a line is correlated with an impression of the orientation of the line with respect to the head. [Another experiment is reported in which certain consequences of such egocentric directionalization are demonstrated in the perception of form.] In these experiments, perceived orientation with respect to the head was separated from the perceived vertical and horizontal directions of the environment.

If this hypothesis is correct, adaptation to a new orientation of the entire retinal image should be possible. It would be based upon the supplanting of old memory traces with new ones that represent the altered directional significance of specific orientations in the neural substrate. Adaptation, therefore, requires conditions that provide the information that the seemingly disoriented direction in the field is actually aligned with the head or that the seemingly "up" direction is actually in the direction forehead-to-chin and is, therefore, "down," and so forth. Three possible sources of such information were considered, namely, (1) sight of the body, (2) movements of the observer even when the body is not directly visible, and (3) the presence in the field of familiar objects whose actual orientation is known (or the presence of a visual frame of reference generating the Wertheimer effect).

Adaptation to a disoriented image is concerned with the perceived orientation of things to the self and should not be confused with the perceived direction of objects with respect to the vertical of environmental space. [For this reason, the effect of a tilted room on the perception of the upright, a problem studied by Wertheimer, Asch and Witkin, should not be confused with the effect of a tilted image on the perception of egocentric orientation as first studied by Stratton, even though the stimulus conditions in the two paradigms can at times be (superficially) quite similar and even though the two effects may not be completely independent of one another. To some extent configurational aftereffects initially studied by Gibson, and Köhler and Wallach may enter into experiments on adaptation to a tilted image, but these effects are not to be confused with prism adaptation.]

The evidence on adaptation to a reinverted image was reviewed, and it was concluded that—with the exception of certain occasions in Stratton's original study and possibly in the work of Erismann and Kohler—the results of experiments with a re-erected image are essentially negative (although an experiment with newborn kittens indicates that the reinverted image, if present from birth. does not lead to any obvious difficulties in the development of normal coordination). It was suggested that adaptation to a completely reinverted image may be difficult for various reasons, among which is that partial or less than complete adaptation cannot occur. If, instead, adaptation to an image tilted by some smaller magnitude is studied, objective measurement such as is now employed in other types of adaptation work becomes possible. Two such experiments have yielded significant adaptation in a fairly short time span, but the observers were upright; therefore, the prismatic tilt produced a change in the vertical and horizontal of environmental space. In order to distinguish adaptation to a directional change in the vertical of the environment from adaptation to new egocentric coordinates, experiments were undertaken in our laboratory in which, during exposure to prisms and test, the observer remained bent over so that the ground was perpendicular to his line of sight. The induced tilt was, therefore, an egocentric one. When the exposure consisted of viewing the stationary body, adaptation was obtained provided the observer viewed the test display through the prism. When the exposure consisted of walking along a zigzag line, an appreciable change took place even under conditions where the observer could not see his own feet. Thus it is concluded that a genuine alteration of the retinal coordinate axes that signify the egocentric coordinate axes can occur, as Stratton had believed.

ADDENDUM

The Role of Phenomenal Changes of Familiar Objects

Stratton and others have commented on the changed appearance and the difficulty in recognition of objects due to inversion. It is a fact that many figures look quite different when disoriented. A good illustration is shown in Figure 2–6. If it is turned counter-clockwise by about 45°, it will appear quite different, like a symmetrical arrowhead, balanced on a point. Other figures look quite different when *inverted* and familiar patterns such as words written in script and human faces are either unrecognizable or difficult to make out when seen upside down. How do these facts relate to the problem raised by Stratton's experiment? I believe they have only a coincidental or, at most, tangential bearing on it. The strangeness or unfamiliarity of objects or of the entire scene is not the issue. The issue is egocentric orientation. Suppose Stratton, while wearing the inverting lenses, viewed the scene with his own head inverted. Now the images of objects would return to their normal retinal orientations (because he would be reinverting the lens-inverted image) with the direct result that material such as text or script would immediately be recognizable again. He would perceive them as if they were upright in relation to himself (i.e., upside down in space as he now is) but, in doing so, his perception would not be veridical. The objects are upright in space and

Figure 2–6

not upright with respect to him, and true adaptation would require perceiving them accordingly. Therefore, the normal vs. strange appearance of shapes is not to be confused with their perceived egocentric orientation. With sufficient experience, familiar objects would undoubtedly cease appearing strange (because, I believe, new traces in the new orientation in the substrate are acquired), but this does not imply a righting of the scene. Furthermore, it is only true of objects actually seen during the experiment. Stratton and others did report a decreasing strangeness of objects while continuing to perceive the world as upside down. Conversely, one could imagine an experiment conducted without familiar objects, where adaptation is at least a plausible expectation. In that case, certain familiar objects introduced at the end of the exposure period but with lenses still on, while appearing right side up, might nevertheless appear strange or unrecognizable.

The one aspect in which the orientation of familiar objects may play some role in the adaptation process has already been mentioned, namely, as a source of information as to the true orientation of things in relation to the self. But this role of familiar objects has nothing to do with their appearing strange or phenomenally different as shapes. It is concerned with the fact that we know how familiar objects are oriented in the environment.

An Experiment on Form Recognition in a Horizontal Plane

The ability to orient objects with respect to the head when they remain in a horizontal plane (as described in the experiment with the observer in a supine position) attests to the independent existence of egocentric directionalization. The reality of the egocentric coordinates is further attested to by an experiment on the effect of orientation on form perception. Before it will be possible to appreciate the point of this experiment, it is necessary to supply the reader with background information. When a form is disoriented from its customary position in space, there are two possible factors operating to make it appear different: (1) its image on the retina is disoriented with respect to its normal position, (2) its position with respect to the up and down of space is altered. The two factors can easily be separated. Following a training exposure in which observer and figure are both upright, a test is given in which the observer is required to view a spatially upright figure with tilted head (yielding retinal change only) or conversely is required to view a figure tilted by the same magnitude his head is tilted (yielding change of perceived spatial orientation without retinal change). Various experiments have shown that, of the two factors, perceived spatial orientation is by far the more potent in producing phenomenal change.[52] When both observer and figure are tilted by the same magnitude in the test, the figure, which had previously been seen in an upright position by an upright observer, is now often unrecognizable. It looks quite different. Crucial to this effect is the misperception of the directions of the figure. For example, if Figure 2–6 were first seen in that orientation, and is now seen in the orientation shown in Figure 2–7, an observer whose head is tilted counter-clockwise 45°

Figure 2–7

[52] I. Rock, The orientation of forms on the retina and in the environment, *Amer. J. Psychol.*, 1956, 69, 513–528; I. Rock and W. Heimer, The effect of retinal and phenomenal orientation on the perception of form, *Amer. J. Psychol.*, 1957, 70, 493–511; I. Rock and R. Leaman, An experimental analysis of visual symmetry, *Acta Psychol.*, 1963, 21, 171–183.

may not recognize the figure. He will see as the top that region which is uppermost in the environment and that region is now the tip of the arrowhead. Since his head is tilted, there is no change in the orientation of the retinal image from previous to present exposure, indicating that what is crucial is the alteration of the figure's phenomenal top, bottom, and sides. In this case these directions are given by the environment and not the observer's egocentric "up," "down," and left-right directions. It would be egocentric indeed for an observer to define the tops and bottoms of external objects by their congruence with his own egocentric up and down when he is tilted.[53]

This brings us to the experiment in question. Suppose the observer views figures that lie in a horizontal plane. These could be presented above a supine observer or below an observer who bends his head over frontward. We chose the second alternative. The figures rested on the floor and were presented within a circular aperture so that the edges of the cards on which they appeared could not serve as a frame of reference. No other objects in the room were visible. The question to which we sought an answer was the effect of disorienting the figure in the horizontal plane. It might appear that in this situation a figure can only be disoriented retinally. As far as environmentally determined direction is concerned, there can be no top or bottom of a figure in a horizontal plane. But suppose the observer were to impose his egocentric up and down on the figure. Here it would no longer be inappropriate to do so. Whether or not this occurs can be easily determined by noting the effect of tilting figures by a specific angle. In the experiment, fragmented figures representing familiar objects were shown tilted 90° away from the egocentric vertical. They were correctly identified only 15% of the time. When these same figures were viewed by other observers under ideal conditions (i.e., observer upright, figures upright), they were identified 66% of the time.

Obviously, the experimental condition produces a very substantial decrement in recognition. Could this be due purely to the fact of disorientation of the retinal image by 90°? Apparently not, because when subjects are required to view these figures with their heads tilted sideways 90°, the figures remaining environmentally upright, correct identification is high, 51%. This then is a measure of the effect of disorientation of the retinal image without change of perceived direction, and it is clear the effect of this is small (51% compared to 66%). The score of 15% in the

[53] A disturbance based on the first factor (retinal disorientation) only seems to occur with certain types of forms that are visually quite complex (for example, script).

horizontal plane, therefore, indicates an effect entailing misperception of the directions which constitute the top, bottom and sides of the figures. That this conclusion is warranted is shown by the fact that the score for upright observers viewing figures tilted 90° in the environment is 12%, a value quite close to 15%. In other words, when a figure is tilted 90° in a horizontal plane, we misperceive the portion which is egocentrically uppermost as the top, precisely as we misperceive the top when a figure is tilted 90° from its environmentally upright position. Experiments with other material fully confirm this finding. The experiment further demonstrates the reality of the egocentric sense of up and down tied to the up-down axis of the head and indicates that such egocentric coordinates have certain consequences for perception.

The Wertheimer Effect

According to an experiment by Max Wertheimer, if a room is tilted with respect to the direction of gravity, it may nevertheless appear upright, or it may not appear tilted as much as it actually is.[54] The orientation of the room is itself a determinant of, or frame of reference for, the perceived vertical of space. In fact, Asch and Witkin have demonstrated that when gravity and the visual frame of reference are set in opposition to one another, the latter is the more potent determinant of the perceived verticality of an object. An observer will judge an upright rod seen within a tilted room as tilted; it will appear vertical to him only if it is actually quite tilted in the same direction as the room. On the surface, at least, this effect seems to suggest a "righting" of the field and, since it occurs immediately upon viewing the tilted scene (or at most after the few moments needed to allow the sense of contrast with the normally oriented scene to wear off), it appears to be a case of immediate adaptation. If so, it would seem to conflict with the immediate reaction of observers in a Stratton-type experiment in which they certainly do not immediately see the scene as upright.

However, the meaning of the Wertheimer effect is not yet clear. If a subject sets a rod parallel to the walls of a tilted room to indicate his perception of the vertical of space, does this mean the tilted room looks fully upright to him? Another explanation of such a response is that the subject is faced with a conflict to which there are three unsatisfactory solutions: aligning the rod with the direction of gravity (in which case

[54] M. Wertheimer, Experimentelle Studien über das Sehen von Bewegung, Z. *Psychol.*, 1912, **61**, 161–265.

it doesn't "look" right), aligning it with the vertical of the room (in which case it "looks" right, but the subject, aware of the fact that the room is tilted, also knows that the rod must be tilted), or setting it to some compromise position (which neither appears to be nor is right, so to speak). That the rod looks "vertical" when aligned with the tilted room, while the room itself may nevertheless appear tilted, can be explained as an instance of what Duncker, in discussing movement perception, has called "separation of system." [55] Certain perceived qualities of an object may be determined largely by its immediately surrounding frame of reference regardless of how that frame of reference itself is perceived. The rod's perceived direction may be primarily a function of its orientation with respect to the room, even though the room's orientation may be a function of its relation to the observer's sense of the vertical as given by the direction of gravity.

If this analysis is correct, then a tilted room may actually appear tilted to an observer despite the fact that, when asked to align a rod embedded in that room to the vertical, he sets the rod parallel to the tilted walls of the room. Given this analysis, certain seemingly contradictory reports in the literature may be explained in terms of whether an object such as a rod is used to judge the vertical, or whether the tilted room itself is judged. In order to determine whether the tilted room itself appears upright or less tilted than it is, the subject should be asked to judge its direction from immediate memory, by setting a rod to the direction the room had had, when the room itself is no longer visible. Assuming this technique yields results in line with the above analysis, namely, that observers remain aware of the tilt of the room—and preliminary results suggest that they do—then it is clear the Wertheimer effect is not a "righting" effect of the field as such, at least under the conditions thus far discussed. In that event, the fact that a *prismatically* tilted scene appears tilted at the outset is *not* a contradiction of the Wertheimer effect.

If an observer were to wear a prism that tilts the image of a room by some angle less than 180°, say 30°, then the orientation of the retinal image would be identical to that of an observer who views a room physically tilted by 30°. This realization has prompted certain authors to maintain that the Wertheimer and Stratton paradigms are essentially alike except for the magnitude of tilt in the original experiments of each. In my opinion, however, these are very different experiments which pose very different questions. The question involved in the Stratton experiment can be completely separated from any considerations having to do with

[55] K. Duncker, Über induzierte Bewegung, *Psychol. Forsch.*, 1929, **12**, 180–259.

the perceived vertical of space or from field effects such as those produced by a rectangular frame of reference. As noted earlier, the entire experiment could be conducted with a subject who, while wearing the prisms, views only a horizontal plane, such as the floor or ceiling and with no objects visible, which could produce field effects of any kind. The fundamental question here is whether, in time, the orientation of objects with reference to the self would be perceived veridically. The basis for such a change, as previously explained, would be information as to the orientation of objects with respect to that of the phenomenal self. However, even if the Stratton experiment is performed with an upright observer who views the scene through prisms that tilt the retinal image, the stimulus situation is still quite different from that of the Wertheimer paradigm. The room's image is *not* tilted with respect to that of the body, because the body's image is also tilted. Hence, over time, it is at least possible that adaptation to altered egocentric orientation would occur. That is, vertical lines in the scene would no longer appear tilted *with respect to the self*.

The tilted-room experiment (Wertheimer effect), on the other hand, is concerned with the question of the perception of the vertical of space. It is not concerned with what direction appears egocentrically aligned with the observer. Therefore, although the rod may appear upright in space only when it is parallel to the tilted room, it does not necessarily follow from this that it will appear aligned with the observer in that orientation, nor is it even relevant whether it does or does not. One could, in fact, study Wertheimer's question independently of Stratton's question by tilting observer and room by the same magnitude.[56] In this case there is no longer the question of adaptation to a changed orientation of room to self, because there is no change in orientation of room to self, but it is still meaningful to ask what direction would appear vertical in space. In the Wertheimer paradigm (subject upright, scene tilted) the information received concerning the orientation of the self to that of the the field is veridical. The field *is* tilted with respect to the observer. If he sees parts of his own body, they are tilted with respect to the room. If he moves, the information he receives is that he is not parallel to the upright direction of the room. Therefore, although it may be the case that, at first, a tilted room is a source of information that leads to perceptual adaptation, in the long run, given unrestricted conditions of exposure including sight of the body and movement, adaptation involving egocentric orientation is not to be expected.

Another major difference between the two experiments is that the

[56] A variation actually performed by Asch and Witkin, op. cit., 1948, II.

Wertheimer effect is an immediate one. At most, only a relatively minor additional "righting" occurs over time.[57] The question at issue here is how the visual field affects the phenomenal vertical of space, not whether exposure to a tilted room produces any enduring changes in the nervous system which would be manifest when the tilted room is removed. In the case of exposure to lenses or prisms, however, the question at issue *is* whether or not such change takes place.

I have taken pains to distinguish the meaning of the two paradigms because they seem to be quite similar. Nevertheless, when the Stratton type of experiment is conducted with an upright observer in the normal environment, the stimulus conditions for the Wertheimer effect are present. The prisms will tilt the image of the room. Here we are obviously faced with a complex situation in which interactions between determinants of perception of the vertical of space and of egocentric orientation will undoubtedly occur. Since the tilted room does very much influence the direction seen as vertical in space, it can be considered as information to the effect that a new orientation of the image represents the perceived vertical. Therefore, even though the tilt of the room is probably veridically perceived at the outset, it is possible that, over time, exposure to such a room may lead to an adaptive change.

The evidence as to whether exposure to a tilted luminous rectangle yields an aftereffect is, at the moment, contradictory.[58] No one has yet tested whether exposure to a tilted room containing the typical familiar cues as to which directions are vertical and horizontal yields an aftereffect, but there is presumptive evidence in studies using prisms that it does. Morant and Beller have shown that a subject who merely sits looking through a prism for fifteen minutes will subsequently show a shift in the direction which appears vertical providing he views a familiar room or corridor.[59] If instead he looks at luminous vertical lines through the prism, only a slight shift in judgments of the vertical occur, and these are predictable on the basis of the Gibson effect. If the subject walks around during the exposure period, an even greater adaptive shift occurs provided again he views the room and not the luminous lines. In our laboratory, Arien Mack and I have found that even a few minutes' exposure to a

---

[57] Ibid.

[58] W. Cohen and D. Tepas, Temporal factors in the perception of verticality, *Amer. J. Psychol.*, 1958, **71**, 760–763; R. B. Morant and J. Aronoff, Starting position, adaptation and visual framework as influencing the perception of verticality, *J. exp. Psychol.*, 1966, **71**, 684–686.

[59] R. B. Morant and H. K. Beller, Adaptation to prismatically rotated visual fields, *Science*, 1965, **148**, 530–531.

prismaticaly tilted view of a room will yield an aftereffect, despite the fact that the observer is stationary and does not see his own body. The large difference in magnitude of adaptation obtained by Mikaelian and Held with the corridor scene, in comparison with the scene containing only luminous spheres (6.8° vs. 1.9°), can perhaps also be best explained along the same lines.

Therefore it is probable that in studies of adaptation to a prismatically tilted image, at least one contributing determinant is the information provided by familiarity with the orientation of the scene. The data of the Morant and Beller study suggest that there may be a strong interaction effect between this information and that provided by movement of the observer.

It would be important to know whether there might be any effect on egocentric orientation of the disoriented scene, that is, a type of field effect in which the perceived orientation of objects to the *self* is affected. It is not possible to determine whether the effects described above entail a change of egocentric orientation. If, following exposure to a tilted room, the observer continues to feel that he himself is upright, then it is entirely reasonable to suppose that a tilted line which now appears vertical in space also appears parallel to himself.

However, it is possible that the effect of a frame of reference on egocentric orientation might be more direct and not even require any assumptions by the observer as to whether he himself is upright or not. Some years ago in collaboration with Sheila Hafter, I investigated the question whether egocentric orientation is subject to the influence of a frame of reference, much as is the vertical of space. As in the experiment described earlier, the observer, while supine, was required to indicate when a luminous rod appeared to be parallel to the vertical axis of his head. Surrounding the rod was a rectangular luminous frame which could be set at various angles with respect to the observer (see Figure 2–8). Since this frame lay in a horizontal plane, as did the rod, it could not be thought to bear on the observer's impression of the upright direction of space, and therefore any influence of the frame could not be considered to be the result of the Wertheimer effect.

In one experiment, ten observers were required to set the rod to the egocentric vertical when the frame was set either at 15° clockwise (cw) or counter-clockwise (ccw); 30° cw or ccw; 0°; or when the frame was not visible at all. The last condition was identical to the experiment previously reported and yielded comparable results. In the 15° or 30° conditions, however, the settings were clearly modified in the direction parallel

to the sides of the rectangular frame. At 15°, the mean of all subjects'
settings was 7.5° cw for frame cw and 10.3° ccw for frame ccw; at 30° the
mean values were 5.2° cw for frame cw and 9.8° ccw for frame ccw.
(It is interesting to note that the 30° orientation of the frame did not
exert a greater influence than the 15° orientation.) Of great interest also
is the fact that in the 0° frame condition, the accuracy and reliability of
settings increased. Four subjects made no error at all, always aligning the
rod parallel to the rectangle, which itself was perfectly aligned with the
subject's head.

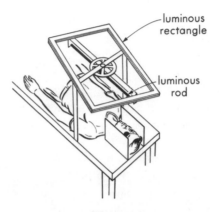

luminous
rectangle

luminous
rod

Figure 2–8

Thus it is clear that egocentric orientation, like the perception of
spatial direction, is affected by the visual frame of reference. It is
affected either adversely (in the direction of error) or positively (in the
direction of greater accuracy), depending upon the conditions. If the
frame of reference affects egocentric orientation, then an upright observer, on first wearing prisms that produce an angular tilt of the scene,
would not necessarily experience the vertical objects in the scene as
tilted with respect to himself by as much as they actually are. (The same
is true for an observer viewing an actually tilted room.) However, whether
or not this effect would operate over time to influence adaptation to an
altered egocentric orientation has not yet been determined.

The other side of the coin, namely, whether egocentric orientation
plays a role in the perception of the vertical of space, deserves a brief
comment. When it is said that gravity is a determinant of the visual upright of space, it is implied that the direction of gravity in some way
determines what particular orientation of the retinal image of a rod will
appear vertical. This orientation will vary depending upon the orientation

of the observer. One possible theory of how orientation of the image is
selected is as follows: The observer gauges the direction of the vertical
with respect to the vertical retinal orientation, since the latter direction
appears aligned with his head. Thus, if he feels himself to be upright,
the vertical of space must be parallel to his head; if he feels he is tilted
clockwise by, say, 30°, the vertical of space must be 30° counter-clockwise
from that orientation which would appear parallel to his head. Although
this is not the only possible explanation of the role of gravity in permitting
discrimination of the visual upright, it is one which gives a central place
to perceived egocentric orientation.[60]

According to this explanation, the reason the entire room may appear
tilted in the Wertheimer situation is that it is quite tilted from the observer's egocentric vertical. Since the observer feels that he himself is
upright, only a vertical line would appear upright. In later experiments
by Witkin,[61] the observer is himself *in* the tilted room. Separation of
system no longer applies because he—like the rod in the previous studies—
is now seen as inside the room. This leads him to experience himself and
hence to "feel" himself tilted, since he is aware that his own body is not
aligned with the room. Therefore, his own felt tilt will not result in
accurate judgment of the vertical. In fact, the observer's (incorrect)
felt tilt of his own body now fits in perfectly with the impression of the
walls of the room as vertical. As a result, the room often appears to be
upright. Hence, in this situation there seems to be a righting of the field
itself and not merely a righting effect on a rod within the field.

The Gibson Effect and Figural Aftereffects

Gibson has shown that tilted lines tend to normalize somewhat over
time—they seem less tilted than they actually are—and vertical lines seen
subsequently in the same region of the field appear tilted in the opposite
direction.[62] He and others had found that the effect requires localization
of the image on the retina during the exposure period and that the aftereffect is restricted to this locality. However, there is now some evidence

[60] There are difficulties with this hypothesis, however, chief among which is this
problem: Why is discrimination of the vertical space (subject upright, dark field)
so much more precise than discrimination of the egocentric vertical (subject supine),
if the former depends on the latter?

[61] H. A. Witkin, Perception of body position and the position of the visual field,
Psychol. Monogr., 1949, **63**, No. 7.

[62] J. J. Gibson and M. Radner, Adaptation, after-effect and contrast in the perception of tilted lines, I and II, *J. exp. Psychol.*, 1937, **20**, 453–467; 553–569.

that the effect is not a strictly localized one. The contradictory evidence is perhaps reconciled by a recent finding that there are two effects, one localized and one not.[63] Hence one might think an effect could be expected to occur under the conditions that obtain in experiments where subjects freely inspect their environment while wearing lens systems or prisms.

The Gibson effect is, therefore, similar in certain respects to the Wertheimer effect: In both cases, tilted lines appear less tilted from the vertical or horizontal of space than they ought to. They differ in that the Wertheimer effect is immediate and presumably quantitatively quite considerable, whereas the Gibson effect only develops over time and, from available evidence, is restricted to about 2°. The Gibson effect entails some change in the nervous system which, therefore, shows up as an aftereffect. The Wertheimer effect is based on the tendency of a frame of reference to define the vertical and horizontal of space, whereas the Gibson effect occurs for isolated tilted lines.

Köhler and Wallach have argued that Gibson's effect is a special case of a more general tendency of lines to be displaced away from the region where previously inspected lines had stimulated the retina.[64] Their theory, briefly stated, is that the pattern of excitation in the cortex corresponding to a perceived figure sets up a flow of direct current, which current "satiates" the cortical tissue through which it flows. As a result, the current generated by test lines subsequently appearing adjacent to the locus of the previously inspected figure is deflected toward less satiated regions, and the deflection results in the impression of displacement of those test lines. They showed that if a *vertical* line is fixated, a slightly tilted test line appears more tilted, not less tilted, if it is presented in the locus of the previously fixated vertical line. This explanation would cover the aftereffect of normalization (i.e., a vertical line appearing tilted after viewing a tilted line), but not the normalization itself (i.e., the tilted line appearing less tilted as it is inspected). However, it has been argued that the so-called normalization could be the result of the differential satiation between the line and the edges of the rectangular frame of reference within which the line is usually seen. This would be an alignment effect. An alternative is that the normalization is the non-localized component of the Gibson effect and is not based on satiation. Köhler and Wallach's theory is predicated on the assumption that Gibson's effect is localized

[63] R. B. Morant and J. R. Harris, Two different aftereffects of exposure to visual tilts, *Amer. J. Psychol.*, 1965, **78**, 218–226.

[64] W. Köhler and H. Wallach, Figural after-effects: An investigation of visual processes, *Proc. Amer. Phil. Soc.*, 1944, **88**, 269–357.

and depends upon a more or less stationary image, whereas, as noted above, that does not seem to be the case. But Held has also shown that certain figural aftereffects do not require a stationary image either.[65] Perhaps there are two types of figural aftereffect. In any case, Gibson's aftereffect could be a special case of figural aftereffect, but the theory of cortical satiation could not be the complete explanation of it.

That the negative aftereffect of tilt can be considered an instance of successive contrast is clear from Gibson's demonstration of a similar effect for simultaneous contrast. If a vertical line is embedded in a context of slightly tilted lines, it will appear tilted in the opposite direction by about the same magnitude as a vertical line seen after inspection of tilted lines, the negative aftereffect. A contrast effect becomes a plausible explanation of the negative aftereffect if one considers tilt as a relationship between lines. The embedded line or test line is "tilted" with respect to what surrounds it or what has preceded it. This general notion is taken up again in Chapter 6 in connection with Gibson's aftereffect of curvature.

What relevance do these effects have for the problem of adaptation to a disoriented image? All vertical lines in the environment become retinally tilted when the observer views the scene through a prism. Therefore, one might predict that the vertical lines of the scene would soon appear slightly less tilted with respect to the vertical of space provided Gibson's effect is one of genuine normalization. If, instead, it is an alignment effect, no change should occur in viewing the prismatically tilted scene, because here the entire scene is tilted. In any case, with prisms removed, the prior inspection of the prismatically tilted lines would result in a predictable aftereffect. Now in order for a line to appear vertical, it would have to be tilted in the same direction in which the prisms had tilted the field. For this reason, to the extent that the exposure field contains vertical and horizontal lines, it would seem reasonable to assume that a slight aftereffect will be generated which is independent of the process central to our interest here, namely, prism adaptation. As with the Wertheimer effect, however, it should be possible either to eliminate it or to allow for it. Mikaelian and Held did eliminate it in their luminous-sphere experiment described earlier. In our laboratory the method used as a control for a Gibson effect in prism adaptation is to require subjects without prisms to inspect a circumscribed field of tilted lines with eyes free to move within this area. Since such eye movement

[65] R. Held, Adaptation to rearrangement and visual-spatial aftereffects, *Psychol. Beitr.*, 1962, **6**, 439–450.

occurs in the prism procedure, this control would seem to be the correct one because we are only interested in finding out whether a Gibson type of effect is generated in the prism procedure. Whatever effect is obtained (and it is negligible) is then subtracted from the adaptation effect produced in the prism procedure.

Adaptation to
Movement of the Image
Produced by the
Observer's Movement

CHAPTER THREE

When we move our eyes, the image of the scene sweeps across the retina. The same is true when we move our head or entire body. Yet, despite this displacement of the image, the environment does not appear to move. This fact has been referred to as position constancy. As with the other perceptual constancies, a change of the proximal stimulus does *not* lead to a perceptual change, because the brain takes something else into account—in this case eye, head, or body motion. A corollary of the lawful relationship between movement of the self and displacement of the image yielding position constancy is the perception of movement resulting from images that are fixed on the retina (after-image; stopped image) with movements of the self. If displacement of the image by a certain magnitude in a certain direction due to body movement signifies no movement, then the non-displacement or altered rate or direction of displacement must signify movement. Therefore, it is not surprising that Stratton and others at first reported movement of the field with head movement, since the reversing lens system alters the customary direction of retinal displacement.

77

Re-afference and Efference Copy

It is clear then that when an observer moves his eyes or head or entire body through space the nervous system discounts the displacement of the retinal image. Yet the same displacement when brought about by actual movement of external objects does result in experienced movement. Apparently the nervous system is capable of distinguishing the two types of sensory change because the perceptual outcome is different in the two cases. The obvious explanation is that when the observer moves, kinesthetic feedback supplies the information that the retinal change is due to movement of the body, not external movement. However, Helmholtz long ago presented good reasons why this explanation is not adequate, at least in the case of movements of the eye.[1] If pressure is exerted against the eyeball with the finger, the eye moves and the image on the retina is, therefore, displaced. One would think that proprioceptive stimuli would signal this change of eye position just as when the eyes are moved normally. Yet, in this case, the displacement of the image is *not* discounted; the scene appears to move.

Therefore the nervous system reacts as if the eyes did not move although they did. The opposite case would be one in which the eyes do not move—so that there is no proprioceptive change possible—but the nervous system reacts as if they did. If an individual with a paralyzed eye muscle intends to turn his eyes to one side, he will experience the entire scene as jumping to that side. Since he actually does not move his eye, it is clear there is no proprioceptive change. The command to move the eyes is apparently registered centrally as it ordinarily would be when the eyes are free to execute the movement. A displacement of the image by an amount equal to the commanded eye movement would be the retinal change which in this case would *not* lead to any perception of movement. Hence the non-displacement of the image in the paralyzed patient must result in a perceptual change. A similar effect was noted in an experiment by Mach, in which he immobilized the eye by the use of putty.[2] He also found that an intention to turn the eye led to the experience of the scene moving.

By way of further confirmation of these facts, it has recently been demonstrated that the conscious appreciation of eye position is not based

---

[1] H. von Helmholtz, *Treatise on physiological optics* (Trans. from the 3rd German ed.; J. P. C. Southall, Ed.), Vol. III, New York: Dover, 1962, pp. 244–245.

[2] E. Mach, *The analysis of sensations*, New York: Dover, 1959, pp. 128–129.

on proprioception. Brindley and Merton have shown that when one or both eyes are moved passively by pulling the lateral or medial rectus muscle with forceps, there is no awareness of any change of eye position even if the change is as great as 40°.[3] (Vision is prevented during the tests.) Conversely, when the subject intentionally tries to move his eyes, he *does* experience eye movement, even if forceps prevent the eyes from moving. He has the same experience of the eyes moving whether the eyes are held stationary or not. From this it is clear that it is unlikely that the discounting of the displacement of the image when the eyes move is based on information derived from proprioception. This finding is all the more plausible in the light of accumulating evidence that the sense of the position of one part of the body with respect to another is based on receptors in the joints rather than on those responsive to stretching of muscles.[4] Therefore, the absence of a joint in the case of the eye would seem to rule out *afferent* information concerning its position.

Apparently then, in certain cases, the explanation of how the nervous system distinguishes visual afferent changes produced by the observer's own movements from those produced externally, would seem to be that there is a central record of movements commanded by the brain. This record is independent of the actual movements and exists even if for some reason the movements are never executed. It is this record that is compared by the brain to the retinal change. When the retinal change "matches" this record, it does not yield an impression of environmental change (but as Koffka points out, the individual does experience himself, or some part of himself, as moving [5]). When it does not "match," some change in the environment is perceived. The role of such a central record in perception was known to Helmholtz, Hering, Wundt and others and has been described as the "perceived effort of will," "feeling of innervation," or "innervation sense." Teuber has recently suggested an alternative term, "corollary discharge." [6] Von Holst proposed the term "efference copy." He also proposed that we call afferent changes brought about by the organism's self-initiated movements "re-afference" and those brought

[3] G. S. Brindley and P. A. Merton, The absence of position sense in the human eye. *J. Physiol.*, 1960, **153**, 127–130.
[4] V. B. Mountcastle and T. P. S. Powell, Central nervous mechanisms subserving position sense and kinesthesis, *Bull. Johns Hopkins Hosp.*, 1959, **105**, 173–200.
[5] K. Koffka, *Principles of gestalt psychology*, New York: Harcourt, Brace, 1935, pp. 384 ff.
[6] H.-L. Teuber, Perception, in J. Field, H. W. Magoun, and V. E. Hall, Eds., *Handbook of Physiology*, Section 1, *Neurophysiology*, Vol. 3, Chap. 65, Washington: Amer. Physiol. Soc., 1960.

about by external events "ex-afference." [7] Von Holst's terms have now gained currency among workers in the field of perceptual adaptation.

If displacement of the image in one direction is the re-afference which typically is discounted when the organism moves in a particular way, then a displacement in the opposite direction should lead to the perception of movement. An experiment by von Holst's colleague Mittelstaedt illustrates this point.[8] If a striped cylinder is rotated around an animal such as a fly, the fly turns itself around in the direction in which the stripes are moving. This is the well-known optokinetic reflex. If, however, the fly moves freely around within a stationary cylinder, the optokinetic reflex is not elicited, although here too the image of the striped pattern moves across its retina. The reason is that in this instance the movement of the retinal image is discounted; the stripes are not "seen" to move. Mittelstaedt was able to twist the head of the fly through 180°, thus interchanging the position of its eyes. Now when the fly moved freely within the cylinder, the optokinetic reflex was immediately triggered, with the result that it circled further in the direction it had just turned. This movement elicited further circling, the upshot being a paroxysm of forced circling to the point of exhaustion.

What happened to the fly would seem to be identical with Stratton's experience of the swinging of the scene. The left-right reversal of the customary direction of image displacement with body movement is created by head reversal in the fly rather than optical reversal. The result is the same: The field is seen to move in the direction of the organism's movement, only faster. The major difference is that we know about the outcome in one case by phenomenal report and in the other by behavior which typically is elicited by the perception of movement.[9]

Position Constancy Based on Passive Movement

According to the argument presented above, only movements initiated by the organism itself lead to the discounting of changes of the retinal image. It is obviously true that where there is no information that movement has taken place there can be no discounting of retinal change. If,

[7] E. von Holst, Relations between the central nervous system and the peripheral organs, *Brit. J. Animal Behav.*, 1954, 2, 89–94.

[8] H. Mittelstaedt, Telotaxis und Optomotorik von Eristalis bei Augeninversion, *Naturwissen*, 1944, 36, 90–91.

[9] It is possible that the relevant information in the case of head or total body movement of the observer is proprioceptive rather than efference copy, and this possibility cannot be ruled out in the case of Mittelstaedt's fly either.

for example, there is no afferent registration of eye position, as seems to be the case, then passive movement of the eye with a finger would have to result in the perception of movement. Or, to give another example, if an observer is moved in a vehicle, smoothly and at uniform velocity in a dark room, one would imagine that a stationary luminous target would appear to be moving because there is no adequate information that the observer is moving. Hence the displacement of the image must lead to the perception of external movement.

How then explain the fact that a passenger in a vehicle under normal circumstances does not experience the world as moving? Some people may contend that we do perceive movement under these conditions—i.e., we do see objects in the environment displacing rapidly in a direction opposite to that of the vehicle. I would maintain, however, that this is an experience of pseudo-movement, an awareness of objects disappearing from the field of view, and not one of genuine movement of the scene. In any case, a less debatable example may be given: If an observer is sitting in a swivel chair that is turned back and forth by another person, he will not perceive the room as moving despite the fact that its image is displacing. The explanation must be that information is available that the observer himself is moving, either through vestibular stimulation, as in the last example, or through the displacement of the entire visual surroundings, as in both examples. It is known that a sense of movement or rotation is induced in the observer when the entire visible field is either rotated around him or displaced laterally (induced movement of the self), and examples of this effect are well known in daily life. For instance, movement of an adjacent train creates the impression that one's own stationary train is moving. It does not seem to have occurred to anyone, however, that in many instances in daily life where the observer *is* actually moving through space (as in a vehicle, moving escalator, or conveyor belt) the stimulus conditions are not those which could be expected to lead to the perception of the world as stationary unless the principle of induced movement of the self is invoked. Whatever the cause, there are obviously cases of position constancy without active movement of the observer.

The Loss and Recovery of Position Constancy

An optical device that transforms the retinal image—be it a prism or lens system—will lead to a change in the direction or magnitude of displacement of the image with head or body movement, but not with eye movement. Ordinarily, every change in the position of the image (*a*) of a stationary point(*A*) is exactly compensated for by an equal angular change in the position of the eye, as is shown in Figure 3–1. Regardless of the kind of optical system placed in front of the eye, this same relationship would hold. For example, wearing an inverting lens system the subject would have to turn his eyes 30° to fixate a point 30° from the fovea. True, he would turn his eyes upward to fixate a point near the ground, but nevertheless in turning his eyes by a specific angle the image would displace in the opposite direction by that same angle just as it ordinarily

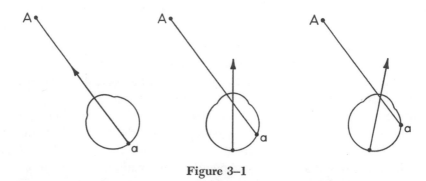

Figure 3–1

does.[10] Hence the point would not seem to move; position constancy would still operate. The same would be true in looking through a wedge prism. There are distortions in the optical image created by a wedge prism such that equal angles along the retinal image do not represent equal angles of visual space. Nevertheless movements of the eyes result in displacement of the image in the opposite direction by an amount equal to the excursion of the eyes. The principle that applies in these cases is quite simple, namely, that however many degrees a retinal image is from the fovea, the eye must turn by that many degrees in the customary direction to bring that image into the fovea, regardless of the actual position of the corresponding object in space. There is therefore no experience of movement due to eye movements alone.

The story is very different, however, for movements of the head. Under normal circumstances, when the head moves, the image displaces

---

[10] "Opposite" here refers to the direction in which the image displaces in relation to the direction in which the retina is turning in space. When the eyes turn upward, the image of a stationary point displaces upward on the retina because the retina is displacing downward.

in the direction of head movement.[11] To the extent that information about head movement is veridical, a given shift of the retinal image is accounted for by a corresponding shift in the experienced position of the head. The displacement of the image is discounted.[12] If the observer is wearing a lens system such as the one Stratton used, then whenever his head moves, the image will displace not in the same direction, as it normally does, but in the direction opposite to that of his head movements. The reason for this can best be understood by referring to Figure 3–2. In

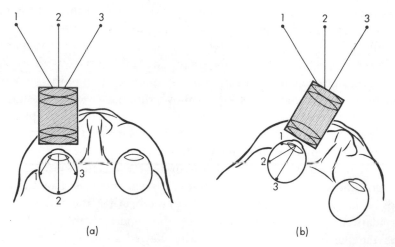

Figure 3–2

Figure 3–2*a*, the observer fixates point 2. He sees point 3 off to the left, although it actually is to the right. The image is not reversed as it normally is. Now if he moves his head to the right (Figure 3–2*b*), point 3 stimulates the fovea. Hence it traveled from the apparent left to straight ahead as the

[11] If the head turns to the right, an object that had stimulated the fovea will now stimulate the right periphery of the retina. Subjectively, however, one might say the point moves to the left edge of the visual field (or in the opposite direction).

[12] It is true that, up to a point, compensatory movements of the eye often tend to stabilize the image when the head moves. However, even if by continued fixation during head movement the retinal image were to remain stationary, the fact that the environment did not appear to move would still constitute a problem. Ordinarily, pursuit movements of the eyes are associated with a truly moving object—the object is perceived to move despite its retinally stationary image. Therefore, the possibility of compensatory eye movements eliminating displacement of the image during body movement will be ignored because the problem that concerns us would remain. In principle it is possible to arrange that the eyes remain stationary during head movements, and it will simplify matters if the reader imagines this to be the case in the various examples and experiments described in this chapter.

head moved to the right. A point changing its location in this manner when the head moves to the right would ordinarily be a moving point. It will be noted that point 1 is about to move out of the field entirely, but since it has been displacing along the retina to the left, it will shortly be seen moving out of the field to the right, in the direction the head is turning.

What the observer experiences, therefore, is a swinging of the entire scene in the direction the head moves, which, it will be recalled, is what Stratton and others reported. The rate of apparent movement of the scene is actually twice the angular rate at which the head is turning. This may be understood in the following way. If the image displaced normally, no movement would be experienced; if it were stationary, it would seem to move as fast as the head, i.e., to keep pace with it. Since it displaces in the opposite direction by an amount equal to the amount of head displacement, it must seem to move through twice the angle the head moves. Movement effects also occur with prisms or other optical devices because the normal relationship between head movement and magnitude of retinal displacement is altered.

Position constancy, therefore, is lost under these conditions. But Stratton and others have reported that the apparent movement of the scene tends to disappear after a few days. (As noted earlier, the genuineness of this adaptation effect is attested to by the report of an aftereffect, on removing the lens system; the normally viewed scene appears to move when the head moves.) Hence position constancy is re-established. Such an effect would be understandable if adaptation to reversal took place. Referring to Figure 3–2 again, the displacing image would be seen to go toward the apparent left as the head moves to the right if the leftward direction along the retina has, via adaptation, come to signify an egocentric leftward direction. If that were the case, the apparent displacement would be appropriate once more to the direction of head movement for stationary objects; that is, they would appear to displace in a (subjective) direction opposite to that of head movement. This would serve to explain why Stratton seemed to feel that the scene appeared stationary when he was able to imagine his body in its new visual orientation, that is, during those occasions when a visual righting occurred. But Stratton's adaptation to inversion and reversal was at best ephemeral, while his adaptation to the moving scene was apparently more or less complete and permanent. Therefore, it seems improbable that the latter can be fully explained in terms of adaptation to reversal of direction.

Taylor has made an important deduction about the direction of the aftereffect of adaptation to the apparent movement of the field, that is, the impression one gets on removing the prisms.[13] If such adaptation is *not* based on directional adaptation to reversal, then the aftereffect should be negative. The scene should appear to swing in a direction opposite to that of head movement. The reasoning in this case is fairly straightforward. If displacement of the field in the same direction as head movement has come to signify a stationary field, then displacement in the opposite direction must now signify a field moving in a direction opposite to that of the head. However, if the re-establishment of position constancy *is* based on directional adaptation to reversal and inversion, then the after-effect should be positive, that is, the scene should now appear to swing in the same direction as the head. The reason for this is as follows: Consider an object that is actually to the observer's right. With prisms removed, that object should now appear to be to his left if an egocentric left-right visual adaptation has been established. This much *would* be a negative aftereffect. Now when the observer moves his head to the right, toward the object, he will experience that object as displacing to the right, toward the center of the field, because in fact it is displacing further to the left. Therefore, the object must appear to move in the *same* direction as the head. Assuming this reasoning to be correct, the direction of the aftereffect can be considered to be a useful index of the nature of the perceptual adaptation achieved. Stratton's comment on this question was brief: "When I turned my body or my head, objects seemed to sweep before me as if they, themselves, were suddenly in motion." [14] It is possible that "before me" means in the direction he was moving and, if so, his aftereffect was positive, which then can be taken as an indication of directional adaptation. Yet he also states that the scene did not appear upside down on removing the lenses. In the work to be described later in this chapter, the aftereffect was always negative.

The Concomitance Principle

A more probable explanation is based on the notion that whatever retinal change occurs concomitant with movement is discounted. Von Holst implies that the relationship between movement and re-afferent change is innate and immutable, which may be true in many lower species.

[13] J. G. Taylor, *The behavioral basis of perception*, New Haven: Yale Univ. Press, 1962.

[14] G. M. Stratton, Vision without inversion of the retinal image, *Psychol. Rev.*, 1897, 4, 470.

But, at least on the human level, what matches what is apparently subject to modification. The re-establishment of position constancy in Stratton's experiment means that a displacement of the field in the *same* subjective direction as head movement ultimately is discounted. Such an outcome would be understandable if the nervous system has evolved to function in such a way that there is a discounting of afferent change when that change is causally linked with movements of the organism. That is to say, whatever change occurs concomitantly with movement of the observer is discounted or attributed to the organism's own movement rather than to movement of the environment. If no such tendency existed, it is difficult to see why any perceptual change should take place. Stratton could have continued to see the scene as moving every time he moved his head. If this principle operates innately, the discounting process would not have to be learned. However, in the mature organism, memory traces of magnitude and direction of retinal change associated with magnitude and direction of change of bodily position would exist in the nervous system. What matches what is now a function of the associations built up in the past, and departures from such matches will result in the perception of environmental change.[15] It is necessary to assume that the traces are faithful to the specific speed and direction of movement of the proximal stimulus across the retina for each speed and direction of head movement (perhaps generalized as a ratio of image displacement to head displacement) and, further, that these various trace combinations are each associated with information that the field is stationary.

Thus, at the beginning of Stratton's experiment, the scene seemed to move whenever the head moved. In time, however, new traces are deposited—i.e., traces that represent the new relationship between movements of the observer and concomitant movements of the retinal image. Since I am assuming that any re-afference can match any specific movement, and, further, that attribution of retinal change to movement of the self leads to the discounting process, as soon as the efficacy of the prior traces is eradicated, position constancy can be re-established. However, there is more to the process of adaptation than the operation of the concomitance principle and the acquisition of traces faithful to the altered nature of the flow of the image. I will, therefore, return to this question again in the last section of the chapter. What is being claimed here would

[15] Held has suggested a mechanism whereby the particular re-afferent change is stored in memory such that adaptation will occur. See R. Held, Exposure-history as a factor in maintaining stability of perception and coordination, *J. Nerv. Ment. Dis.,* 1961, *132,* 26–32. His work is discussed more fully in the next chapter.

suffice as explanation only if we abstract from the problem of perceived direction.

The explanation suggested above assumes that the simultaneity of displacement of the image and movements of the observer is all the "information" that is needed to establish that the scene is stationary. An alternative hypothesis is that some source of information (that objects are actually stationary) other than mere concomitance is necessary before the new re-afference will be discounted. For example, it might be supposed that information via touch perception or the like to the effect that the world is stationary plays a role in re-establishing constancy of position. The evidence presented below argues against this alternative.

The Experimental Evidence

Stratton's observations bearing on movement of the field and adaptation to such movement have already been mentioned. Others who repeated Stratton's experiment have reported more or less the same thing. Yet in all the years since Stratton's papers appeared, no experiments were performed with the specific purpose of exploring this problem.[16] Recently, however, two independent studies have been completed—one by Wallach and Kravitz [17] at Swarthmore and one by Robyn Posin in our laboratory.[18]

In order to be able to measure adaptation to altered rate or direction of displacement of the image, it is necessary to vary the rate at which the image shifts across the retina with movements of the head. If adaptation has taken place, a displacement of the image different from that which

[16] Taylor and Papert have focused their attention on the problem of stability of apparent orientation of objects in the field with tilting of the head. They noted that, with right-angle prisms, the apparent orientation of lines in the field at first changes when the observer tilts his head (in the same direction as that of head tilting), and they found that in time such changes cease to occur. In the case of one subject who wore the prism for 71 days, he reported stability with head tilting but continued to see the world as upside down. This finding again suggests that position constancy can be re-established without adaptation to altered direction, thus leading to the type of paradox discussed below. Upon removal of the prism, this same subject now saw the world tilting when he tilted his head, in a direction opposite to that of the head movement. See J. G. Taylor and S. Papert, A theory of perceptual constancy, *Brit. J. Psychol.*, 1956, **47**, 216–224.

[17] H. Wallach and J. H. Kravitz, The measurement of the constancy of visual direction and of its adaptation, *Psychon. Sci.*, 1965, **2**, 217–218.

[18] R. L. Posin, *Perceptual adaptation to contingent visual-field movement: an experimental investigation of position constancy*, Doctoral dissertation, Yeshiva University, 1966. A report of this work was made at the Conference on Adaptation, Massachusetts Institute of Technology, June 1965.

ordinarily occurs with head movement will yield the impression of a stationary field. That displacement which the observer experiences as stationary is, therefore, a measure of the magnitude of adaptation. In the Wallach and Kravitz study, head-contingent displacement is varied by means of a mirror mounted on a shaft, which in turn is mounted on headgear worn by the observer. The mirror reflects a small target from a stationary projector onto a curved screen. As the observer's head moves, therefore, it causes the target to move across the screen. By means of a variable transmission, the amount of rotation of the mirror per unit rotation of the head could be varied. The device used by Posin was very similar except that, instead of a mirror, a small projector was directly mounted on the shaft attached to the observer's helmet. Also, a slide of vertical stripes filling a large portion of the field was displaced rather than a small target. In both studies the targets were luminous in an otherwise dark field, since it was desired that the only basis for the detection of movement be a change in the location of the points in the field with respect to the observer, as is the case in daily life.

In the adaptation phase of the Wallach and Kravitz experiment, the observer wore a minification lens for a period of six hours, during which time he went about his daily routine. The lens had the effect of slowing down the displacement of the visual field by causing it to displace in the direction of head movement by one-third of the angle of head rotation. In the pre-exposure measures, they found that observers did indeed have position constancy (the average rate of target displacement which was seen as stationary during head movement hovered around 0). Following the exposure period, a displacement of the target of about one-sixth of the angle of head rotation was seen as stationary. For the lens system employed, this change represents about 50% of complete adaptation.

In Posin's study, the adaptation or exposure phase of the experiment was restricted to a brief period of five minutes, during which the observer remained in the chair used for testing and rotated his head or entire body back and forth through an arc of 40°. Originally the experiment had been designed so that the observer would look through a right-angle prism positioned to reverse left and right (mounted together with a minification lens to slow down the rate of displacement of the image), with the effect that objects in the field would at first appear to move in the direction of the head, similar to the effect produced by Stratton's lens system. Adaptation to such a prism was studied, but in the course of attempting to measure the perceptual change by varying the speed of the striped pattern (with prism off), it was discovered that there were certain aftereffects of the measurement procedure itself. That is to say, following exposure to several different head-contingent displacements of the pattern in the pretest, frequently it was found that subjects no longer perceived the stationary pattern as stationary, although they had done so at the outset.

This discovery led to two changes in the procedure finally used. One was the utilization of head-produced displacement of the pattern as the exposure condition proper (without prisms), in addition to using it for measuring the effects of such exposure. The other was the abandonment of attempts to obtain a precise measure of adaptation. If a brief exposure to a specific rate of displacement of the pattern during the test yields adaptive change, it would seem that the test procedure itself is contaminated by the very effect it is supposed to measure. Instead of precise measurement, therefore, a simple yes-no measure was obtained. Both before and after the exposure period, the observer, without the prisms, was shown a stationary pattern while moving his head. He merely indicated whether it appeared stationary or moving and, if moving, in which direction.

The results for active movement of the head were quite clear. The great majority of observers reported the stationary pattern as stationary before the exposure period and as moving in the predicted direction following the exposure period. The predicted direction depended on the exposure condition. Where the left-right reversing prism was used, since the pattern moved with the head during exposure, the predicted direction of the aftereffect was "opposite." Similarly, where the displacing pattern was itself used during exposure and made to displace slightly in the same direction as the head, the predicted direction of the aftereffect was also "opposite." Where, however, the displacing pattern was used, but in a direction opposite to head movement, the predicted direction of the aftereffect was "with." In addition to the predicted aftereffects, as a rule the observer also reported a slowing down or complete cessation of movement during the exposure phase proper.

On a different occasion, these same observers were run under a condition of passive movement of the head. The original intention was to turn the observer's head back and forth by means of a rod protruding from the back of the headgear. It was soon noted, however, that the observer was not sure whether in fact he remained passive or whether he was unintentionally cooperating with the experimenter by moving his head. Therefore, to make sure that the observer was not contributing to the movement, he was told to attempt deliberately to hold his head still while it was being turned by the experimenter. Since, however, it might still be questioned whether these instructions had the desired effect, a new group of subjects was added. The subjects in this group were exposed to an active and passive movement of the entire body. In the active condition the observer sat on a swivel chair and moved himself back and forth with his feet. In the passive condition his feet were raised off the floor and the experimenter rotated the chair back and forth.

The important result of both passive conditions is that adaptation was again achieved and was as great as adaptation under active movement. It is, of course, possible that the crude yes-no type of measure was insufficiently sensitive to pick up a difference in the efficacy of active and passive movement. For present purposes, however, what is important is the fact that adaptation was achieved by the majority of subjects under passive movement conditions. This outcome is not surprising in the light of the argument made in the previous section to the effect that discounting of movement of the image is possible under conditions of passive movement, provided some information is available that the observer is being moved. In the present case the information obviously derives from proprioceptive and vestibular cues during rotation of the entire body or of the head alone.[19]

Another very important implication of these findings is that this particular type of adaptation occurs in the absence of any information as to what is actually happening in the world. The observer does not have any physical contact with the objects he sees. For this reason, it is quite ambiguous whether the pattern he sees moving during the exposure period as he himself moves is moving or is stationary. The only information he does have, if "information" is the right word, is that the apparent movements of the field are concomitant with and in some way correlated with his own movement. Control experiments, in which the target did *not* move when the observer moved, or the target oscillated back and forth while the observer remained stationary, ruled out possible alternative explanations of the adaptation effects (for example, adaptation to movement per se as in the waterfall, or rotating spiral, illusion). One must conclude that the concomitance is the causal factor, that there is a powerful tendency

[19] After this chapter was completed, a second paper of Wallach and Kravitz appeared with essentially identical method and findings as in Posin's study—namely, adaptation obtained in ten minutes based on continuous movement of the observer viewing a target pattern that moved as a result of the observer's movements and with passive as well as active movement. H. Wallach and J. H. Kravitz, Rapid adaptation in the constancy of visual direction with active and passive rotation, *Psychon. Sci.,* 1965, **3,** 165–166.

to discount any displacement concurrent with movement of the self. Convincing proof of this tendency is that Posin obtained "adaptation" even under conditions where the pattern actually was moving during the exposure period, the effect thus being non-veridical. The proximal stimulus conditions are identical whether the retinal image displaces in a particular way when the head moves because of an optical device (with the world stationary), or whether the image displaces because a mechanical device yields an actual displacement of an external pattern when the head moves, the pattern being viewed with the naked eye.

For an animal to survive, it is obviously necessary that it be able to distinguish between cases where something is moving in the environment and cases where the identical proximal stimulus change is produced by its own movements. The same is true of various other kinds of change of the proximal stimulus, such as that of size, shape, and luminance. The principle of concomitance may, therefore, be one of wide significance.

The Paradox of Changing Direction

There is a problem I have skipped over which must now be faced. Consider a prismatically reversed scene which no longer appears to move with head movements. An object that had appeared on the left will appear on the right at the termination of a head displacement to the right. How is it possible for an object to change its location in this manner *without appearing to move?* True, under ordinary circumstances, objects change their apparent directions when we move while not appearing to move, but this is as it should be. Objects that were seen to the left will appear to be even more to the left when we move to the right. Hence the change of direction is fully accounted for by the change in the observer's position. The problem is all the more puzzling in the light of considerable evidence that change of phenomenal location is a sufficient condition (and possibly a necessary one) for the perception of movement.[20] As noted above, this problem would not arise if adaptation to altered egocentric orientation occurred first, that is, if objects on the left once more appeared on the left while those on the right appeared on the right. In that case, the phenomenal direction of displacement of all objects during head movement to the right would once more be to the left, a state of affairs compatible

[20] See I. Rock and S. Ebenholtz, Stroboscopic movement based on change of phenomenal location rather than retinal location, *Amer. J. Psychol.*, 1962, **75**, 193–207.

with constancy of position. However, I am assuming from the evidence at hand that position constancy is regained *before* adaptation of egocentric orientation develops.

The same problem comes up for optical transformations other than reversal. For example, in viewing through a minifying lens system, how can it be the case that an object which, before the head moves, appears straight ahead (in the sagittal plane of the head), at the end of a 30° head displacement appears 15° to the left of the head and yet appears to have remained stationary? In posing this question, I am again assuming that there is at this point no adaptation to the phenomenal length signified by a 15° visual angle. If there were—if a 15° visual angle appeared as a result of adaptation to be as great as a 30° visual angle had in the past— then the object now *will* appear 30° to the left at the end of the head movement. Although such a change in angular size perception may indeed eventually occur, there is reason for believing it has not done so at the point where adaptation to movement of the image has already occurred.[21] In short, then, the problem is how objects can appear stationary during movement of the observer if their directions change in a manner that indicates that they have changed their position in space.

I believe the answer to this question lies in the central interpretation of the direction or magnitude of the *observer's* displacement. In the minification example, a 30° lateral turning of the head may be interpreted as a 15° turning because the image displacement contingent on this head movement is 15°. It is possible that a very important determinant of perceived magnitude of body movement is the magnitude of the visual feedback. After all, if x and y are seen to be 15° apart, and if the head starts from a position in which x is straight ahead and moves until y is straight ahead, then it "follows" that the head has only moved from x to y, or 15°. If the head has only moved 15°, then it is no problem that x now appears 15° rather than 30° to the left, which distinguishes this situation from one in which the only available information is veridical and a 30° turning of the head must be interpreted as being just that.

When the lens is first put on, based on memory, a 30° head movement gives rise to the expectation that the image of the stationary environment will displace by that same angle. There is no doubt also a visualization that the head has moved by about this angle. This visualization may take the form of imagined sector of visual field traversed. It may be based

---

[21] In studies of adaptation to a minified image in our laboratory, we have not been able to obtain any change in the perception of size based on information derived solely from movement of the head, even after thirty minutes (see footnote 5, Chapter 5).

either on proprioception or efference copy.[22] But this visualization with the associated or anticipated rate of flow of the image is now at odds with the directly given information described above. In this conflict, the more immediately given visual information is dominant, with the result that there is a suppression of the visualization of magnitude of head turning derived from the actual amount of turning.

The same reasoning can be applied to the case of prismatic reversal. If an object on the left moves toward the straight-ahead position as the head goes to the right, there is information that the head is turning *toward* that object, not away from it. Based purely on the visual state of affairs, the head would be interpreted as moving opposite to the directional flow of objects in the field. Otherwise expressed, it would be interpreted as moving toward an object as the object comes into the straight-ahead direction from the periphery. This immediately given visual information is, of course, at odds with the visualized direction of head movement and the expected direction of flow of the retinal image. Again, the process of re-establishing constancy of position would depend upon the dominance of the immediately given information to the effect that the head was turning in the direction in which objects come into view from the periphery. The following statement from the sixth day of Stratton's experiment would seem to support this interpretation: "Movements of the head or of the body . . . seemed to be toward that side on which objects entered the visual field, and not toward the opposite side, as the pre-experimental representation of the movement would have required." [23]

Does this mean that the re-establishment of position constancy involves learning to *feel* the head moving in a direction opposite to the one in which it actually is moving? [24] Consider the case of up-and-down head movement for an observer wearing an inverting lens or right-angle prism with base up or down. With head in the normal position, the moon will appear in the lower part of the field. As the head moves upward, the moon will appear to move up toward the center of the field and eventually, as the head continues to be tilted upward, the moon will appear to go out

---

[22] At the outset, the neural command to turn the head is undoubtedly governed by the phenomenal angle the observer wishes to move it. If y appears 15° away from x, the command may be for a 15° movement. It will turn out that this is insufficient, and by a process of correction via continuous feedback, the head will end up being turned 30°.

[23] G. Stratton, Vision without inversion of the retinal image, *Psychol. Rev.*, 1897, **4**, 358.

[24] See C. S. Harris, Perceptual adaptation to inverted, reversed, and displaced vision, *Psychol. Rev.*, 1965, **72**, 419–444.

of the field in an upward direction. Hence, at the outset, the moon will appear to move in the direction of head movement. Position constancy—*in the absence of complete egocentric righting*—would seem to depend upon experiencing the head moving toward the moon as the head moves upward. As noted above, the directly given visual information does call for this perception. In time, the observer would begin to anticipate that if he moves his head upward it will be toward objects that appear in the lower part of the field, and hence he will anticipate that objects will displace upward toward the center of the field. Yet I doubt when this comes to pass that the observer *feels* an upward movement of the head is a downward one. A test of this question would be how the head was sensed to move if, at this time, the eyes were closed. Perhaps during this stage of the adaptation process—i.e., the re-establishment of position constancy without the re-establishment of veridical egocentric directionalization—the observer must tolerate a contradiction. He "sees" his head moving opposite to the direction of flow of objects in the field, and this fact eliminates the paradoxical change of apparent direction of objects which would otherwise make position constancy impossible. At the same time, via proprioception or efference copy, the information is at least potentially available (and probably could be elicited by questioning) as to the true direction of head movement, which, of course, is in the same direction as the flow of objects in the field.

This state of affairs should certainly lead, in the long run, to an egocentric righting of the field. If, say, the upward direction of displacement of objects in the field ultimately becomes associated with upward movement of the head, then that direction of movement in the field must be seen as egocentrically down. If the moon seen in the lower field is in the direction of an anticipated upward head movement, then it follows that it is in an egocentrically "up" direction. Yet until such an egocentric righting occurs, the pre-experimental state of affairs will still govern the interpretation of direction when the head is stationary. Hence the observer would report that the moon appears to be in a downward direction prior to moving his head.

If this analysis of the factors underlying the re-establishment of position constancy is correct, it forces a reconsideration of what was said earlier about the concomitance principle. It is no longer enough to say that whatever stimulus change is concomitant with movement of the observer will (in time) be discounted. Apparently it will only be discounted if it can be *accounted for* in terms of the nature of the observer's own movement. The principles governing whether or not this is the case would seem to be these: (1) Given a stimulus change concomitant with or contingent upon the observer's movement, there is a powerful tendency to interpret that change as one produced by the observer's own movement rather than as change in the environment. (2) There then follows a process of undoing the contradiction between the assumption that the stimulus change is self-produced (and that the scene is stationary) on the one hand and the tendency to see the scene as moving by virtue of the fact that such a change concomitant with this particular kind of movement has in the past always signified movement in the field. (3) This is achieved by the observer's interpreting his own movement in terms of the new stimulus change, by acquiring new memory traces of the manner in which the images displaces when he moves, and by suppressing a visualization of how he is moving based on the information arising from proprioception or efference copy. However, it does not follow that the true physical direction of movement of the observer is now no longer registered centrally or that with the eyes closed there would be any change in the manner in which the head is felt to move.

It is interesting to consider the aftereffect of such adaptation in the light of this discussion. The results of Posin's experiment indicate that the aftereffect is negative and this is true for the condition where reversing prisms were worn. (It is only in this condition that Taylor's deduction applies, namely, that the aftereffect should be positive if there has been adaptation to reversal of direction and negative if there has not.)[25] Just as this fact argues against the assumption that any visual adaptation to inversion or reversal of direction has taken place, so it also argues against the assumption that any change in the proprioceptive interpretation of direction of head movement has taken place. If, for example, a right turning of the head had come to be reinterpreted as a left turning, then with prisms removed an object to the right that would be seen as moving leftward as it approached the straight-ahead direction would have to be experienced as displacing in the *same* subjective direction as the head. In other words, a theory of adaptation to movement of the field based on a changed interpretation of proprioceptive information would have to predict a positive, not a negative, aftereffect, contrary to the findings in these studies.

If the explanation I have offered is correct, what must we predict about

[25] Therefore either of two things are possible concerning Stratton's comment referred to on page 85, about the aftereffect of adaptation to the "swinging of the scene." Either the statement "objects seemed to sweep before me . . ." was not intended to mean "in the direction in which I am moving" or he did achieve adaptation to the altered directions of the field.

the aftereffect? With the newly established traces to the effect that stationary objects displace in the *same* direction as the head, the proximal stimulus shift with prisms removed would now lead to the experience that the scene was moving in a direction opposite to that of head movement. The expectation acquired during adaptation that the head moved toward objects on the left as it moved (physically) to the right would now lead to the impression that objects were moving rapidly to the left, since they recede from rather than approach the straight-ahead direction.

Tentative Conclusions about the Role of Movement in Adaptation

It has already been noted that movement initiated by the observer himself is considered by some psychologists to be a necessary or at least major condition for obtaining prism adaptation. What can we say about this assumption in the case of the problem discussed in this chapter? Here, the phenomenon itself has to do with movement of the observer. Therefore, it is a fact, without any necessary implications for other types of adaptation, that any adaptive change to a new direction or magnitude of contingent image displacement will require movement of the observer. However, it is not essential that the observer actually achieve such movement by himself. Movement imposed on the observer can lead to the same outcome. One might conclude that if the retinal displacement can be attributed to the observer's own movement in space, it will be discounted. Otherwise the displacement of the image will be attributed to movement of the environment.

This discounting happens to be central to the type of adaptation being studied because what is being learned is that the environment is not moving. In other types of adaptation, however, such as adaptation to tilt, minification, etc., the question is not merely that of *discounting* the displacement or other visual changes, but of whether or not a particular aspect of the altered stimulus will undergo a change in what it signifies. Change of that aspect is determined by a test in which the observer is stationary. For example, in the case of adaptation to a tilted image, the central question is whether or not the scene will continue to appear tilted. In fact, the issue of discounting is not relevant at all in these cases when information as to how the optical device transforms the image can be obtained without movement.

When, on the other hand, information *is* derived from locomotion of the observer through space, then, of course, the question of perceived movement of the field and the ultimate discounting of it is relevant. However, the optical distortions that are employed in studying adaptation to tilt, displacement, minification, or change of curvature are less drastic in regard to the manner in which the image displaces with movement of the observer than is the case with inversion and reversal of the image. For example, in adaptation to a minified scene, the image moves more slowly than normally with movement of the observer; in adaptation to tilt, it moves in a somewhat different direction than it normally does. Therefore there will be some experience of movement within the field when the observer moves, but some component of the movement of the image will be discounted from the start. The important question is this: What is the relationship between the process of re-establishing complete constancy of position in these cases to the process of adapting to the altered spatial attribute such as size, orientation, or shape?

This is a complicated problem. The solution would be simple if the fundamental change is one of adaptation to the altered spatial attribute. Then, as explained above, position constancy would, ipso facto, be re-established as well. But the available evidence favors the opposite conclusion, namely, that the discounting process occurs first. If so, what effect does this have on adaptation to the altered spatial attribute? One might think it would be an important first step, since otherwise movement of objects in the scene would continue to be perceived and, if so, it can be argued that adaptation to size, tilt, or the like cannot get under way. Whatever seems to be moving in the environment when the observer moves could indeed be moving. If moving, the novel behavior of the image cannot be considered to be information concerning the effect of the prism on the spatial attribute in question. Whereas, once it is established that the objects in the scene are *not* moving, then the stage is set for adaptation to the altered spatial attribute. For example, a 30° movement of the head is correlated with a 15° extent in the field if objects do not appear to move. Therefore the observer can learn that what had appeared to be 15° actually represents a 30° extent. If, however, objects do seem to move when the head moves, it is possible to argue that no new information is registered concerning size signified by the minified image.

The difficulty with this argument is that in order to deal with the problem of paradoxical changes that would occur if discounting were achieved first, without adaptation to size, reversal, etc., it was necessary to assume that the observer reinterprets the nature of his own movement. If so, if he "sees" himself as moving left when he is moving right or as moving 15° when he is moving 30°, then this would *interfere* with adaptation to reversal or size. The information of the actual movement of the observer must "get through" if adaptation based on movement is to occur. Perhaps the answer to this is that, despite the suppression or dominance by the visual feedback, the information *is* registered.

As to the possible difference between active and passive movement of the observer in prism adaptation, it has already been shown that movement imposed on the observer (passive movement) will lead ultimately to discounting just as will active movement, but it is essential that the observer have information as to the direction or rate of his movement other than that supplied by induced movement of the self. If he does not, then the component of image displacement which is abnormal for any given movement of the observer through space, will, from the outset, not only be immediately discounted (because the nervous system cannot then react to the retinal change as *abnormal*), but there will be no basis via movement for adaptation to the altered spatial attribute. It is possible that in some of the experiments which have been reported, in which a condition of passive movement fails to lead to perceptual adaptation, the failure can be explained in terms of inadequate information concerning how the body is displacing through space.

SUMMARY

During movements of the eyes, head, or entire body, the retinal image shifts across the retina, but the world nevertheless appears stationary (position constancy). The nervous system discounts the retinal displacement if information is available that it was caused by the observer's own movement. In the case of eye movement (and possibly in other cases as well) that information is not afferent but rather is based upon a central record of intended (or commanded) movements. Another source of information derives from induced movement of the self, which may play a role when the observer is moved passively, as in a vehicle.

If, however, the displacement is not in a direction, or of the magnitude, typically caused by body movement (as is the case in looking through lenses or right-angle prisms), the observer will see the environment moving. This "swinging of the scene" was observed by Stratton and others. However, in time an adaptation occurs such that the scene once more appears stationary during movements of the observer. This adaptation does not appear to be the result of a directional righting of the scene. It was suggested instead that it is based on a tendency to discount whatever sensory change is concomitant with, and therefore caused by, movements of the observer. At the outset, however, the world will appear to move with each movement of the head, because head movements will evoke memory traces of speed or direction of image displacement (of stationary objects) different from that in which the image now displaces. Adaptation would require replacing these traces with those faithful to the new direction of image flow.

In addition to the incidental observations of Stratton and others that complete adaptation to the "swinging of the scene" occurs, two recent experiments were described in which the problem was directly studied and adaptation measured. In both studies measurement was achieved by means of a luminous target that was caused to move by movements of the observer's head. The rate and direction of its movement was variable. Following exposure to the device which altered the customary speed or direction of image flow during head movement, the test target no longer appeared stationary when it was stationary. The target had to move in the predicted direction in order to appear stationary. Adaptation was also obtained when the exposure condition consisted not of viewing through an optical device but rather of viewing a luminous target that was caused to move in a novel fashion by movements of the observer's head. It was also shown that adaptation occurred whether the observer moved actively or passively. In either case he clearly perceived himself as moving, so that the discounting process could be expected to occur.

If an optically reversed image eventually appears stationary during movements of the observer, we are left with the problem of explaining how this is possible in the light of the change of direction that occurs for all objects in the field. It was suggested that the observer tends to gauge the visual direction in which he seems to be moving on the basis of the directional flow of the image and to suppress the direction in which he visualizes himself to move (based on proprioception or efference copy). The re-establishment of constancy of position then only requires acquisition of memory traces that are faithful to the new direction of flow of the image associated with a stationary field. The relationship between the discounting of abnormal movement of the image during movement of the observer to adaptation to prismatically altered spatial attributes was discussed.

Adaptation to a
Displaced Image

CHAPTER FOUR

The Nature of Radial Direction

If an observer views the world through a wedge prism, the apparent direction of all objects is at first shifted to one side because the path of each ray of light is deflected by the prism (see Figure 4–1). There is mounting evidence that in a fairly short time adaptation to the prismatic shift occurs such that objects are either once again located veridically or they are not located as far to the side as at the outset. I will review the evidence later in this chapter, but first it will be necessary to lay a foundation for understanding precisely what is involved in the perception of the direction of an object and, hence, in adapting to a change.

One method employed in studying perception of direction is to ask the observer to indicate when a point appears "straight ahead," that is, when it appears to lie in the sagittal plane. Another method is to require the observer to point to a visual target. What is being studied is the experienced location of the point in space with reference to the observer as the origin; hence the term "radial direction" has sometimes been used to designate this meaning of perceived direction. All points in space in any frontal plane will have distinctive radial directions which can be specified by the angle that the line from origin to point makes within a three-dimensional coordinate system. If the observer uses only one eye, that eye would obviously be the origin, but since he typically uses both eyes and since, further, a point is experienced in only *one* direction, it has been suggested by Hering, Helmholtz, and others that the point *between* the two eyes (the "cyclopean eye") is the origin. Thus one axis of the co-ordinate system is a horizontal plane through the two eyes, and the other is formed by the sagittal plane of the head. Points in the horizontal plane are at "eye level," and those in the sagittal plane are "straight ahead." (See Figure 4–2.)

What are the stimulus conditions that determine radial direction? Obviously, retinal location alone is an inadequate determinant, because the eyes are constantly changing their position. Therefore, a given point in

Figure 4–1

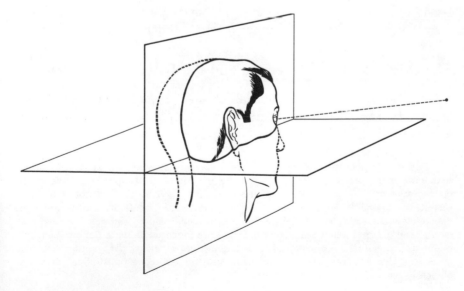

Figure 4–2

space will not always stimulate the same region of the retina—for example, a point straight ahead will not always fall on the fovea. Nevertheless, the radial direction of points in space remains constant regardless of the angle at which the eyes are turned (direction constancy).[1] Apparently, then, radial direction must be specified in terms of *both* retinal position *and* eye position—that is, the direction signified by all retinal points depends upon eye position. Thus, for example, "straight ahead" is given by foveal stimulation and eyes straight ahead, or by stimulation of the retina 30° to the left of the fovea and eyes 30° to the left, etc. Head position is also a relevant factor here, but it will simplify matters if we define radial direction as I have above, in terms of the head. In other words, if the head is turned to one side and the eyes remain straight ahead with respect to the head, a point falling on the fovea will be experienced as "straight ahead" *with respect to the head,* although it is off to the side with respect to the trunk. As long as the observer receives information that his head is turned to the side, he will be aware that the point, while straight ahead of his head, is off to the side with respect to his body. In defining radial direction with respect to the head, I do not wish to imply that the trunk is less important as an origin of self-referred direction. However, if the trunk were to be taken as the reference for radial direction, we would have to consider three variables in every instance (retinal position, eye position, and head position) rather than only two if we assume that the head is the reference (retinal position and eye position). Since any statement about radial direction with respect to the head can easily be translated into one with respect to the trunk (and vice versa), there is little danger of doing violence to the problem with this definition.

The Origin of Radial Direction and the Basis of Adaptation

How does a specific radial direction of, say, a point falling on the fovea come to be associated with a particular position of the eyes? If an object is actually straight ahead of the observer, i.e., in the sagittal plane, the

[1] This fact is generally referred to as position constancy. However, I have used that term in the previous chapter to describe the fact that the perceived world remains *stationary* when displacement of the image is caused by a movement of the observer. It is possible for an object to appear stationary while its radial direction nevertheless changes (for example, when the observer moves through the environment), and it is possible for an object to appear to move while its radial direction remains unchanged (for example, when a moving object keeps pace with a moving observer). Hence it seems desirable to distinguish the two concepts although they are obviously related.

visual axes of the eyes must point straight ahead for foveal vision of that object.[2] Even in an otherwise dark field, a target whose image falls on the fovea when the eyes are in this position will appear to be straight ahead. It is conceivable that this relationship between eye position, retinal position, and apparent direction is innate. There is evidence that in various lower species the perception of radial direction is innate, provided we substitute a behavioral measure of "straight ahead" for a phenomenal one.[3] But whether or not there is an innate basis for radial direction in man, we can still ask the following question: Is it necessary that the eyes point straight ahead in order for an object stimulating the fovea to be located phenomenally straight ahead?

For an object to appear "straight ahead," it must appear to lie in the sagittal plane of the *phenomenal* head. If the radial straight ahead is defined as that direction which appears to lie directly in front of the place at which the center of the head is experienced, then radial direction is a function of the position of a phenomenal object relative to that of the phenomenal self. Hence, the analysis set forth in the second chapter is applicable to radial direction just as it was to perceived orientation. From this it follows that an optical device which causes the image to be shifted to one side need not give rise to a phenomenal shift in radial direction, since all visual representation of the head and body will also be shifted to one side. An observer who wears prisms from birth, therefore, ought to learn in due time that objects which stimulate the fovea when the eyes are turned to one side are straight ahead.[4] This is so for the simple reason that the central axis of the trunk would stimulate the fovea only when the eyes were turned and, in general, all information as to the location of things would attest to the fact that only in that position of the eyes would fixated objects be straight ahead. The head and body seen in a mirror in the frontal plane would require a turning of the eyes to be seen foveally.

---

[2] In order to fixate an object which is straight ahead with both eyes, convergence is necessary, which means that strictly speaking neither eye is pointed straight ahead. Nevertheless, for the sake of simplicity I will call this the straight-ahead position of the eyes.

[3] However, in these species eye movement is either not present or minimal, so that each retinal point could invariantly signify a given radial direction with respect to the head.

[4] Although he would be unaware that his eyes were not physically straight ahead. Phenomenally he would experience himself as looking directly in front of his head. Only in observing other people's eyes or his own in a mirror could he find out that the pupil was off to one side when looking straight ahead, which were he sophisticated might strike him as a puzzling fact. This asymmetrical position of the pupil would no doubt also carry the "meaning" that someone was looking straight ahead.

As in the case of perceived orientation, information as to an object's actual direction with respect to the self might be provided by movement. Obviously if an observer looking through prisms did not see any part of his body and did not move, it would seem reasonable to conclude that he would have no information that things were not where they appeared to be.[5] If he moved, however, he might obtain such information, although the precise manner in which it is conveyed is not yet understood. Some investigators have pointed to the rubbery transformation of the field which occurs with lateral head or body movement as a source of this information. This rubbery impression derives from the fact that there is a differential refraction of light through the prism with varying angles of incidence, the angle changing for any object when the observer moves. But aside from alerting the observer to the fact that he must be viewing the world through some kind of distorting medium, it is hard to see how such "information" would lead to an awareness of the true direction of things. Others have pointed to the shift in the center of the expansion "flow pattern" which accompanies forward and backward movements as the source of information. This refers to the fact, originally emphasized by Gibson, that normally, during forward movement, the images of all points in the field shift outward about the image of the point which is straight ahead.[6] The image of the point straight ahead does not shift. In wearing a prism this is also true, but the center of the expansion pattern (corresponding to the point actually straight ahead) is off to the side of the fovea.

I believe that the change of direction of points with forward locomotion *is* a possible source of information as to their true direction, but simply to speak of the shift in the center of the expansion pattern does not make clear how the information is extracted and utilized. In Figure 4–3a, a point x that is straight ahead when seen through a wedge prism appears off to the side at x'. As the observer approaches x, it is true that its radial direction remains constant, and it is this constancy of direction that is implied in the expansion pattern analysis ($\angle \alpha$). But this means that the phenomenal distance of x' from that direction which appears straight ahead diminishes as the observer approaches (Figure 4–3b). That is, the phenomenal distance xx' shrinks as the observer approaches x. Finally, when he arrives at x it appears more or less straight ahead for the

    [5] However, there is information yielded by the structure of the scene, the nature of which is not yet clear. See page 108. Another exception is the case of moving an object toward a stationary observer. See page 130.

    [6] J. J. Gibson, *The perception of the visual world*, Boston: Houghton Mifflin, 1950.

simple reason that even an object that is substantially displaced by a prism will be only a few inches distant from the observer's sagittal plane when that object is immediately before him. That is, if *without* prisms a point which is off to the side appears increasingly farther to the side as we approach (because its angular separation from the sagittal plane increases), then an object seen through prisms which retains the same radial direction as we approach must be seen to be moving in toward the sagittal plane.

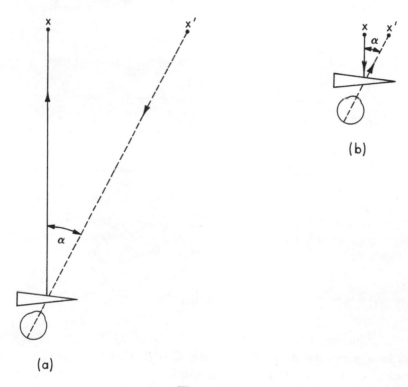

Figure 4–3

The converse of the above example is that of an object actually off to the side which, through the prisms, at first appears straight ahead (Figure 4–4a). As the observer moves forward, it no longer appears straight ahead, because it is now at such an extreme angle with respect to the observer's sagittal plane that the prismatic displacement is not sufficient to make it appear in that position (despite the increased displacement based on the extreme angle of incidence). Hence, as the observer draws nearer to the object, his perception of its direction approaches veridicality. Related to these changes that accompany locomotion is the fact that objects which appear to be in the line of march are, surprisingly, *not* physically encountered and those which appear well out of the way *are* encountered. Therefore, by moving forward an observer could be obtaining information as to the true direction of all objects with respect to himself.

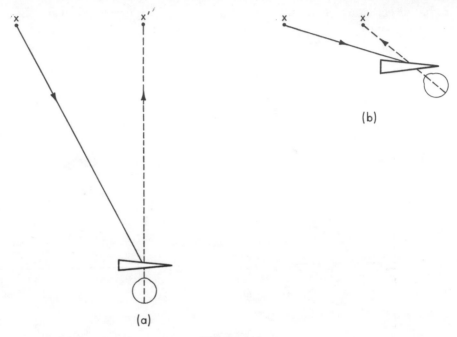

(b)

(a)

Figure 4–4

It is of interest to examine the situation in which the ground can be seen by the moving observer. Consider a path that is actually straight ahead (Figure 4–5*a*). It will appear displaced (and somewhat curved) but, in addition, it will also appear more displaced at the far end for the reasons given above (Figure 4–5*b*). Hence the situation in this respect is rather similar to that which results from viewing the ground through a tilting prism system, as discussed in Chapter 2. The observer will discover in moving forward that the seemingly displaced far end of the path is more or less straight ahead.

So much for an analysis of the probable sources of information as to the true direction of objects seen through a displacing prism. When the observer *first* views the world through prisms, things that are objectively straight ahead *do* appear off to the side. This is so because to be viewed foveally the eyes must now be turned to the side, and objects whose images fall in the fovea when the eyes are turned have, heretofore, not signified the radial direction "straight ahead." To make sense of this fact, it is only necessary to assume what we have previously assumed in discussing egocentric orientation and position constancy, that the previous state of affairs is carried in memory. In this case, what must be carried in memory is the association between the actual position of the eyes and the phenomenal direction of an image which falls in a particular locus. For example, a memory trace of the straight-ahead position of the eyes is associated with a trace of the experience "fixated object straight ahead." In time, however, new traces will be established in which eyes in the turned position are now associated with "fixated object straight ahead." When that comes to pass, and the old traces no longer have any influence, complete adaptation will have taken place.

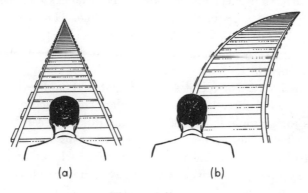

(a)   (b)

Figure 4–5

It is important to emphasize that the modifiability of radial direction has absolutely no implication concerning change in the neuro-anatomical basis of perceived direction in the visual projection area of the brain. What is given in the cortical map of the retinal image is the position of points relative to one another. There is no change in this respect when adaptation to a displaced image occurs. The fact is that, in species whose eyes move, radial direction could not logically be based solely on the retinal location of a stimulus. Therefore, radial direction is a joint function of where the eye is aimed and locus on the retina, and it is plausible to assume that it is a change in this *relationship* that takes place during adaptation. All retinal points collectively and systematically acquire differing radial directions with changes of eye position, but the perceived location of points relative to one another does not change with eye movements or during adaptation to a displaced image. A more detailed analysis of this problem is given in the Addendum.

If radial direction does derive from the location of visible objects with respect to the visible self (or to the self as an entity in the phenomenal field even if unseen), one might be led to wonder what would happen when the observer, in first looking through prisms, sees parts of his own body. An object directly in front of the body would appear to maintain this position with respect to the visible body. Yet the eyes would have to turn to the side to view that object, and memory dictates that such an object lies off to the side. I believe that here we are confronted with an interesting conflict between radial direction as immediately given in perception and that called for on the basis of memory. (An analogous conflict was discussed in connection with egocentric orientation.) In our laboratory we have been able to show that there is an immediate "adaptation" or correction effect under these circumstances—i.e., when only the target object and parts of the body are visible. The target immediately appears far less displaced than it ought to on the basis of the magnitude of prism displacement or on the basis of displacement obtained in the dark when only the target is visible.

If this analysis is correct, it suggests that, although eye position *alone* determines radial direction when no other contradictory information is given (as for example in a dark field), its influence can be considerably modified when other factors are operative. This conclusion is further attested to by the following observation. If one looks through a wedge prism at a normal scene, even if the body is not visible, there is also an immediate correction of the displacing effect of the prism. All objects appear much less displaced than they should on the basis of the prismatic displacement. The reader can easily observe this effect by looking through a prism with one eye and noting the apparent direction of any object. If he then opens his other eye, he will be able to assess the amount of prism displacement by noting where, in the normally viewed scene, the prismatic image of that object falls. It will be clear that objects which require quite deviant positions of the eyes for fixation may nevertheless appear straight ahead. The basis for this curious correction process is not yet known but, whatever the basis, it is clear that some information about direction derives from the structure of the array of visual objects in the scene.

From these observations one might conclude that under typical conditions in daily life radial direction is given with greater precision and stability than would be the case if it were determined solely on the basis of memory of eye position. Parts of the body *are* generally visible as are, of course, the objects in the field. If, therefore, the radial direction signified by all retinal points is a function of eye position alone when only the target is visible, it is perhaps not surprising that considerable error and fluctuation in perceived direction occurs under dark-field conditions. The autokinetic effect can be understood in these terms.[7] In an otherwise homogeneous field, perceived direction is a function of the precision with which eye position is represented in the brain, and the radial direction imparted by eye position is a function of memory. In full illumination, on the other hand, a point can be localized in relation to the visible body and in relation to objects in the field. Thus even when there is no contradictory information, eye position has certain limitations as a determinant of radial direction.

The specific direction of a point can be influenced by the contents of the visual field in a negative or non-veridical sense. If, for example, in an otherwise homogeneous field a rectangle is placed asymmetrically with respect to the observer, the apparent straight-ahead will be displaced toward the center of the rectangle. The actual straight-ahead direction, located as it is toward one side or at the edge of the rectangle, apparently

[7] The autokinetic effect can be described as a variability in the perceived radial direction of a stationary point when seen in an otherwise homogeneous field. It occurs even with continual fixation. If the *constancy* of eye position were not accurately represented as such in the brain, there would have to be uncertainty as to the point's radial location. That is, a point that continues to stimulate the fovea would be perceived as stationary only if the information is available that the eyes are perfectly stationary; it would be perceived as slowly drifting if the information is available that the eyes are slowly drifting. If the nervous system does not discriminate with great precision between these two conditions, then the perceptual situation would have to be ambiguous. If this reasoning is correct, autokinetic movement occurs under dark-field conditions because with only a single point visible there is no information available as to whether it is displacing relative to other points. Ordinarily the displacement of an object relative to others is an important determinant of perceived movement, and the absence of such displacement is a cue for non-movement. The outcome is, therefore, completely dependent on the subject-relative location or radial direction of the point which, in turn, is dependent on information concerning the constancy of the position of the eyes and this is probably not registered centrally with complete accuracy.

Another possible cause of autokinetic movement is actual movement of the eyes which is either not in awareness or is not registered centrally, so that the displacement of the image is not discounted. There is now some evidence for this interpretation. (L. Matin and E. G. MacKinnon, Autokinetic movement: selective manipulation of directional components by image stabilization, *Science*, 1964, **143**, 147–148.) However, the explanation I have offered—for which there is not yet any direct evidence—may also prove correct, since it would seem to follow from all that is now known about the perception of radial direction.

looks "wrong" in some way. This effect observed by Dietzel [8] and by Roelofs [9] belongs to the same class of effects as the influence of the visual frame of reference on the perceived vertical of space and on the ego-centric vertical (the effects described in the Addendum of the second chapter). Once again it is clear that eye position is not the only deter-minant of the radial direction signified by specific retinal positions.[10]

Nevertheless, information as to eye position is essential in determining radial direction when no other information is available and is at least a major contributing determinant under other conditions. All that matters for the argument here is that eye position *is* taken into account, but it is nevertheless of interest to inquire: How is information as to eye position given? Evidence was presented in the last chapter to the effect that *changes* in eye position are registered on the basis of a central copy of the neural command to the muscles of the eye, rather than on the basis of afferent feedback. It is not unreasonable to suppose that the same is true for fixed positions of the eye. In other words, the radial direction of all retinal points depends upon the efference copy of the command respon-sible for the eyes being maintained in any particular position. If this is true, there are many questions that remain to be answered. One is whether the feeling we have of the position of the eyes is simply the conscious correlate of the efference copy. Whether or not this is correct, for con-venience I shall continue to mean by the phrase "the felt position of the eyes" the sense of where the eyes are directed with respect to the axes of the head. Another question is this: How can a given neural command to the eye muscles come to impart a specific direction to an image that falls on the fovea? Consistent with the analysis in the preceding pages, I would assume that an object stimulating the fovea is often seen to have a particular phenomenal direction when the eyes are in a particular posi-tion (under normal illumination, with other information available as to where things are in relation to the self). As a result, memory traces of the

[8] H. Dietzel, Untersuchungen über die optische Lokalisation der Mediane, Z. f. Biol., 1924, 80, 289–316.

[9] C. O. Roelofs, Optische Lokalisation, Arch. Augenheilk, 1935, 109, 395–415.

[10] Werner and Wapner have demonstrated certain other factors that may have an influence on the apparent "straight ahead" or apparent "horizon," such as the nature of the stimulus whose position is judged (e.g., a bird or plane that has a certain direc-tion of flight) or the position of the head and eyes. (H. Werner and S. Wapner, Studies in physiognomic perception: I. Effect of configurational dynamics and mean-ing-induced sets on the position of the apparent median plane, J. Psychol., 1954, 38, 51–65; H. Werner, S. Wapner, and J. H. Bruell, Experiments on sensory-tonic field theory of perception: VI. Effect of position of head, eyes, and of object on position of the apparent median plane. J. exp. Psychol., 1953, 46, 293–299.)

efference copy of the muscular contraction required for that eye position have become associated with a specific phenomenal direction for an object that is fixated. Hence a command to position the eyes according to a particular muscular contraction would signal a particular radial direction for a foveal point (and, of course, for all other retinal points as well). Wherever the eyes happen to be pointed, whether during pursuit or random movements or whatever, the efference copy of the innervation which holds the eyes in that position would, by prior association, signify a specific radial direction for all retinal points. After adaptation to displacing prisms, the command yielding a turned position of the eyes, entailing an asymmetrical contraction of the eye muscles, would via memory produce the experience that an object falling in the fovea was straight ahead. The same command, if directly experienced, would also yield the impression that the eyes were pointing straight ahead. A further question is whether a given command can always achieve the intended position of the eyes despite such variable factors as muscular fatigue.

The Experimental Evidence

In a relatively short time-span a great number of experiments have been performed on adaptation to displacement, and hardly a week passes without reports of new work appearing. It would be difficult, therefore, to review all of this work and such a review would soon be outdated. Instead, I will try to outline the main developments, emphasizing those findings that seem to have important theoretical significance.

Adaptation Based on Arm Movement

Helmholtz was the first to observe that adaptation to a displaced image occurs.[11] He describes an experiment that incorporated all the essential features of the procedure recently employed by workers in this field.

Take two glass prisms with refracting angles of about 16° or 18°, and place them in a spectacle frame, with their edges both turned toward the left. As seen through these glasses, the objects in the field of view will all apparently be shifted to the left of their real positions. At first, without bringing the hand

[11] Czermak has been erroneously credited with this discovery, perhaps because he is cited in the Helmholtz volume. Czermak had merely commented on the error in localization produced by looking through a prism. J. Czermak, Physiologische Studien: III. Sitzungsberichte der kaiserlichen Akademie der Wissenschaften (mathematisch-naturwissen schaftliche Classe), Vienna, 1855, 17, 563–600.

into the field, look closely at some definite object within reach; and then close
the eyes, and try to touch the object with the forefinger. The usual result will
be to miss it by thrusting the hand too far to the left. But after trying for some
little while, or, more quickly still, by inserting the hand in the field and, under
the guidance of the eye, touching the objects with it for an instant, then on
trying the above experiment again, we shall discover that now we do not miss
the objects, but feel for them correctly. It is the same way when new objects
are substituted for those with which we have become familiar. Having learned
how to do this, suppose now we take off the prisms and remove the hand from
the field of view, and then after gazing steadily at some object, close our eyes
and try to take hold of it. We find then that the hand will miss the object by
being thrust too far to the right; until after several failures, our judgment of
the direction of the eyes is rectified again.

Here it is not the muscular feeling of the hand that is at fault or the judgment
of its position, but the judgment of the direction of the gaze, as is shown by the
fact that, if after having become used to looking through the prisms and finding
the visible objects with the right hand, then we close our eyes and try to touch
the same objects with the left hand, which has not been previously used, and
which was not in the field of view, we find that there will not be any difficulty
about touching them with perfect certainty and precision. Accordingly, in a
case of this kind the place is determined perfectly correctly, and thereafter it
can be found with certainty by another organ of touch.[12]

There are several aspects of this procedure that are worth noting. In
testing for the perceived displacement both prior to and at the end of
prism exposure, it is recommended that the eyes be closed before an
attempt is made to touch an object. The reason for this is that it eliminates
the possibility of continuous correcting or steering of the visible hand
to the visible target, which is something that can be done even though
objects appear displaced. This procedure also provides a measure of
adaptation based on the magnitude of the aftereffect. That is, it not only
shows that in time we cease mislocating objects seen through the prisms,
but also shows that by virtue of the same corrective mechanism we
erroneously locate objects to the opposite side on removing the prisms.

A third important aspect of this procedure is that it permits an answer
to the question of whether adaptation is visual—entailing a changed
"judgment of the direction of the gaze"—or is instead related to the way in
which the hand is proprioceptively experienced. Since the test is one of
pointing with the hand, the hand used during the adaptation period, it
could be argued that whatever change had occurred was in the hand
itself. Helmholtz, therefore, sought to exclude this latter interpretation

    [12] H. von Helmholtz, *Treatise on physiological optics* (trans. from the 3rd German
ed.; J. P. C. Southall, ed.), Vol. III, New York: Dover, 1962, 246–247.

by using a test involving transfer to the other, "unadapted," hand. Since this hand was as adept as the "adapted" hand in locating the prismatically displaced targets, he concluded that the effect must be visual. From evidence based on research conducted several years ago, it appeared for a while that Helmholtz was mistaken about this point. Several studies employing careful techniques and many subjects had failed to show transfer from the prismatically viewed hand to the unused hand.

Held and his collaborators used a technique quite like that of Helmholtz to study adaptation to a displaced image.[13] Instead of measuring the effect by requiring the subject to close his eyes and point at a target whose location was given by immediate memory, Held required his subjects to mark the apparent location of a visible target. He utilized a mirror that served the dual purpose of reflecting a target to the subject's

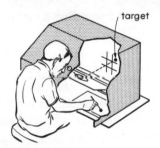

Figure 4–6

eyes and of blocking his view of his hand which was placed under the mirror (see Figure 4–6). In this way the subject's accuracy in locating a target could be permanently recorded by his markings on a paper placed under the mirror. The subject marked the target location before and after the exposure phase. During the exposure phase, the subject viewed his arm through the prism and the mirror was removed.

The central theme of Held's work concerns his hypothesis that a necessary condition for adaptation is self-produced movement.[14] To test that hypothesis in the case of displacement, the experimental design entails two groups of subjects, those who actively move their arm during the exposure period and those whose arm is passively moved by the experi-

[13] R. Held and N. Gottlieb, A technique for studying adaptation to disarranged hand-eye coordination, *Percept. mot. Skills,* 1958, 8, 83–86.
[14] However, Held recognizes that there are effects which are not dependent upon movement, such as configurational adaptation or adaptation based on "error information," about which see below, page 131.

menter. The extent and direction of actual displacement of the arm is equated in the two conditions. The active observer moves his arm back and forth from left to right for a given period of time, and the passive observer's arm is passively swung back and forth, pivoted at the elbow, through the same arc.[15]

The finding was that the target markings of the active observers, following the exposure phase, shifted in the predicted direction, whereas those of the passive observers did not. The magnitude of adaptation was considerable for the very brief three-minute exposure period during which the subject observed his hand moving back and forth through the prism. However, later studies using this same experimental procedure have shown that there is little or no transfer to the hand that is never seen through the prisms.[16] It is therefore, clear, that, regardless of what explanation may account for the adaptation effect demonstrated with the *seen* hand, this effect is *not* one entailing a visual change of radial direction. If it were, it would not matter which hand the subject used. Since we can point accurately to a perceived direction with either hand, if visual direction is altered it would lead to the same pointing with either hand.[17] Further evidence of the fact that there is no visual change produced by the type of exposure condition under discussion is given by the finding that the apparent "straight ahead" is not altered when the test is one of judging visual direction rather than pointing or marking targets with the hand.[18]

Several investigators have suggested that what did happen in these experiments was that the subject reinterpreted the felt position of his hand.[19] Harris has demonstrated that a displacement effect is obtained

[15] R. Held and A. Hein, Adaptation of disarranged hand-eye coordination contingent upon re-afferent stimulation, *Percept. mot. Skills*, 1958, 8, 87–90.

[16] See, for example, H. Mikaelian, Failure of bilateral transfer in modified eye-hand coordination, paper read at Eastern Psychological Assoc., New York, April 1963; C. R. Hamilton, Intermanual transfer of adaptation to prisms, *Amer. J. Psychol.*, 1964, 77, 457–462; C. S. Harris, Adaptation to displaced vision: visual, motor, or proprioceptive change? *Science*, 1963, 140, 812–813.

[17] The method of testing for adaptation to a displaced image used by Helmholtz and the method used by Held have one fault in common from the standpoint of revealing a possible change of *visual* direction, namely, the target is not an isolated visual object in an otherwise dark field. For reasons related to the discussion above (pp. 108–110), it is less likely that the entire visual field would appear displaced upon removal of the prisms, and the target object can hardly be expected to change its apparent location while the remaining objects in the field do not.

[18] A. Hein and R. Held, Transfer between visual-motor systems of adaptation to prismatic displacement of vision, paper read at Eastern Psychological Assoc., April 1960.

[19] C. S. Harris, 1963, op. cit.; Hamilton, op. cit.

when, following exposure to the wedge prisms, the subject points to an auditory target with the hand used during exposure, but that no effect is obtained when the other hand is used. The same effect is obtained when the subject points to the "straight ahead" (with eyes closed). These findings make perfect sense if it is the case that the subject has learned to reinterpret the directional significance of the proprioceptive pattern of stimulation accompanying a given hand position. During the exposure, when his hand points straight ahead, the subject sees it pointing somewhat off to the side. He might, therefore, learn that the "feel" of the hand in this physical position no longer means "straight ahead." Hence to point accurately at any target, in any modality, he would have to modify his hand position accordingly. Since only the felt position of the hand used during exposure has undergone a change, there would be no reason to expect an effect with the other hand. A further experiment by Harris makes this conclusion all the more plausible. In this experiment he demonstrated that blindfolded subjects judged their hands, placed at a given distance from each other, to be farther apart after exposure than before if the prism had caused the right hand to appear farther to the right than it actually was. Conversely, they judged their hands to be closer together if the prism had caused the right hand to appear farther to the left than it was.[20]

A later finding dovetails nicely with the proprioceptive-change hypothesis. Hay, Pick, and Ikeda have demonstrated that immediately upon viewing one's hand through a wedge prism, the hand *feels* as if it were where it is seen to be.[21] Thus, given conflicting visual and proprioceptive information as to location of the hand, vision is not only dominant, but it induces a non-veridical proprioceptive impression—one the authors refer to as "visual capture" following an earlier finding of Tastevin.[22] This being the case, it is plausible to suppose that, over time, an association would be formed between the proprioceptive stimulation for a given arm position and its new phenomenally felt location, thus leading to a change in the interpretation of the position of the arm even in the absence of vision. I believe that we can take this argument one step further: For sighted individuals, proprioception leads to a *visualization* of the location of various parts of the body with respect to one another. Thus what we really mean by a change in interpretation of the felt position of the arm

[20] C. S. Harris, Adaptation to displaced vision: a proprioceptive change (doctoral dissertation, Harvard Univ.), Ann Arbor, Mich.: Univ. Microfilms, 1963, No. 63-8162.

[21] J. C. Hay, H. L. Pick, Jr., and K. Ikeda, Visual capture produced by prism spectacles, *Psychon. Sci.*, 1965, 2, 215–216.

[22] J. Tastevin, En partant de l'expérience d'Aristote, *L'Encephale*, 1937, 1, 57–84; 140–158.

is a change in the visualization of its position. Data that will be presented in a subsequent chapter support the notion of visual capture and the further idea that touch perception tends to accommodate itself to altered visual stimulation over time.

The Role of Active Movement in Adaptation

The findings that exposure to the visually displaced hand results in a proprioceptive, not a visual, change must be considered in relation to Held's hypothesis that adaptation occurs only if the observer actively moves his arm. Although it is not obvious why active movement should be necessary for a proprioceptive change, it would be very strange indeed if it were necessary for *visual* adaptation. In fact, it is not evident why information based solely on arm movement of any kind should lead to *visual* adaptation any more than it is evident why sight of the stationary hand should do so. Such restricted information can hardly be considered an adequate basis for change of the apparent radial direction of the entire array.

Although Held has tended to avoid talking about perceptual changes in his experiments—preferring instead to talk about sensory-motor co-ordination—it is obvious from many of his statements and from some of the tests he uses, as well as from his references to von Holst's work, that he *is* concerned with visual perception. Von Holst himself stressed the difference between active and passive movement in order to explain certain phenomena of visual perception.[23] He spoke of re-afference in connection with the discounting process. A central record of a given body movement was thought to cancel out a given movement of the image on the retina (the re-afference), provided the movement was self-produced. Held sought to apply these notions to the problem of adaptation by pointing out that the re-afferent "match" of a given self-produced move-ment is not necessarily innately fixed, but rather can be determined by prior experience.

Held's theory of adaptation is based upon the notion that, although optical transformation alters the specific location of the proximal stimulus, *changes* of the stimulus are still correlated with changes of body position in a one-to-one fashion. Thus, for example, in moving the arm, although the location of its image is modified by a prism, the displacement of its image correlates perfectly with magnitude or direction of arm movement. Therefore, adaptation entails the substitution of new terms in the correla-

[23] E. von Holst, Relations between the central nervous system and the peripheral organs, *Brit. J. Animal Behav.*, 1954, **2**, 89–94.

tion between movement and change of the proximal stimulus. The aspect of movement that enters into the correlation, according to Held, is the efference copy of self-produced movement.

According to the theory, the basis for the re-establishment of visual-motor coordination is as follows. With an efferent signal to move in a particular way, the re-afferent change is compared with that re-afferent change which has been associated with that efferent signal during exposure to prisms and is now stored in memory. Thus, for example, if the observer points straight ahead, following adaptation, the re-afferent visual signal from the hand will be different from what it had been during the exposure to prisms. With the hand actually pointing straight ahead, the signal is: eyes straight ahead, image foveal. This re-afference is different from that which has been stored in recent memory based on the exposure to prisms, as associated with the efference signal: point straight ahead. That re-afferent signal had been: eyes to the side, image foveal. In my opinion, in order to explain the actual selection of the motor response appropriate to the new visual-motor coordination, Held would have to begin with the sensory object—that is, given the ex-afferent stimulation of a target in a particular location, the appropriate re-afferent visual memory of the hand in that position is selectively aroused and, by association, this arouses the appropriate, correlated, efference-copy memory, which in turn somehow evokes the appropriate efferent signal to the musculature. Without this addition, all that Held's theory explains is that the observer will be surprised by the apparent location of the hand on removal of the prism, once adaptation has occurred. He will not expect to see it where he does.

It seems clear that Held is concerned with a very different function of active movement in the arm adaptation situation than von Holst assigned it in its discounting function in visual perception. Held does not seem to be focusing on the question of the discounting of the movement of the retinal image with movement of the observer, because in viewing the moving hand through prisms, there is no discounting. The hand continues to be seen to move regardless of whether it is moved actively or passively. It would seem that the discounting process is relevant only when there is movement of the sense organ that receives the re-afference. By contrast, Held's extension of von Holst's analysis to the problem of adaptation *would* be quite plausible in cases where a new efference–re-afference relationship comes to signify "no afferent change"—i.e., where the discounting process now requires different feedback than it had previously. This is what one might assume takes place in adaptation to change in the rate or direction of displacement of the image produced by head movement as discussed in the previous chapter (although it was shown there that passive movement also led to adaptation). If, therefore, there is no obvious justification for extending von Holst's ideas to the problem of adaptation to altered radial direction, then there is no a priori reason to expect that active movement would have an effect different from passive movement.[24]

Whether or not Held's theory can account for the newly acquired visual-motor coordination, it does not adequately address itself to the perceptual aspect of adaptation. The theory does not focus on the problem of how things *look* or on information about the perceptual world in the sense I have been using the term. By contrast, in the explanation suggested earlier concerning how such a perceptual change might come about, it was argued that movement undoubtedly provides information as to the veridical location of prismatically viewed objects. Rather than attempting to handle the perceptual end of adaptation as an epiphenomenon of the central fact of visual-motor coordination, therefore, I would reverse this reasoning. The central problem is perceptual. Given a perceptual change, that behavior will be elicited which is appropriate to the new phenomenally perceived location of objects. If a target that is straight ahead is once more perceived to be straight ahead, it is no problem why movements appropriate to that location are elicited. A proprioceptive perceptual change will also lead to the elicitation of the appropriate behavorial response. The observer will position his hand on the basis of where he feels it to be.

In any event, because the change that occurs in viewing the moving hand through prisms is proprioceptive, it is no longer necessary to ponder the question of the differential effectiveness of passive and active movement of the arm for *visual* adaptation. But why should active movement be necessary for proprioceptive change? Immediate visual capture occurs even when the hand is absolutely stationary, and when the observer shuts his eyes he feels his hand to be somewhat displaced as a result of the prior visual capture. That mere exposure to the visually displaced hand is sufficient to yield a change in its felt location is further supported by the finding of Wertheimer and Arena that a one-second glimpse of the displaced hand produces an effect that is 40 per cent of complete adaptation.[25] Furthermore, there now appears to be some contradictory data on

---

[24] In Chapters 2 and 3, I noted that one reason why active movement might be important in adaptation is that it renders less equivocal the manner in which the observer is displacing through space. This does not appear to be Held's reason for stressing active movement.

[25] M. Wertheimer and A. J. Arena, Effect of exposure time on adaptation to disarranged hand-eye coordination, *Percept. mot. Skills*, 1959, 9, 159–164.

the question of active vs. passive movement. Singer and Day have repeated the experiment by Held and Hein with one slight change in the
method of testing, and they did not find any difference between the active
and passive conditions of arm movement.[26] Both conditions yielded significant adaptation. In other experiments Singer and Day have varied the
procedure in several important respects, the most interesting of which
was a change in the task imposed during the exposure phase of the
experiment.[27] The observer is required to make judgments concerning the
direction of objects or the visible hand, but no information is given as to
the correctness of these judgments. In some experiments it was found
that, whereas active movement of the hand does not affect adaptation
differently than passive movement, judgment activity during exposure
does increase adaptation. In one of their experiments, the sight of the
stationary hand through the prism yielded a significant effect when,
during the exposure period, the observer was required to make judgments as to the location of the hand with respect to arbitrary scale
markings seen adjacent to the prism. Pick and Hay have also recently
obtained evidence of adaptation during passive movement of the arm
when, during exposure, the subjects were required to indicate the position of the hand with respect to a numbered scale, although active movement did yield a greater effect.[28]

At the moment, therefore, the data do not support the conclusion that
active movement is a necessary condition for the proprioceptive displacement effect, although it may be correct to say that under certain conditions
active movement facilitates or increases the effect. The reason for the
superiority of active movement in the work of Held is not clear. It may
have to do with increased attention to where the hand is located at any
given moment when it is actively moved by the subject. The clarification of
this question remains for future research.[29]

[26] G. Singer and R. H. Day, Spatial adaptation and aftereffect with optically transformed vision: Effects of active and passive responding and the relationship between
test and exposure responses, *J. exp. Psychol.*, 1966, **71**, 725–731.

[27] Ibid. Also see G. Singer and R. H. Day, The effects of spatial judgments on the
perceptual aftereffects resulting from prismatically transformed vision, *Austral. J.
Psychol.*, in press.

[28] H. L. Pick, Jr., and J. C. Hay, A passive test of the Held re-afference hypothesis.
Percept. mot. Skills, 1965, **20**, 1070–1072.

[29] Held has recently revised his theory of adaptation to displacement in certain
important respects, but as of the date when this was written, the revised theory has
not been published. However, I believe the aspects of the theory which I have discussed here remain central to his way of thinking about adaptation.

Adaptation Based on Locomotion in the Environment

There have been other investigations which suggest that *visual* adaptation does occur under the right conditions. There is first of all the work of Erismann and Ivo Kohler, in which prisms were worn by subjects in the course of their daily activity.[30] Qualitative data suggest very clearly that, in time, the apparent visual direction of objects again became veridical. However, because their quantitative results are based on a pointing test, they cannot be considered relevant to the question of whether adaptation to displacement is proprioceptive or visual.

In a study by Held and Bossom in which the subject either walked around in the environment (active condition) or was pushed along the same path in a wheel chair (passive condition), adaptation was measured by requiring the subject to position his body so that a vertical line inside a cylindrical drum surrounding his head appeared straight ahead.[31] In one experiment, each subject was used as his own control and was exposed to the passive as well as the active condition, each for two one-hour sessions. The prisms displaced the image by 11°. The average shift in the localization of the straight-ahead position for the active condition was 1.29°, whereas for the passive condition it was −.22°. In a further experiment subjects were exposed to the prisms for periods ranging from 11 hours (distributed over two days) to 21 hours (distributed over four days). Eight of the fifteen subjects reached full adaptation (11°) in the active condition. Two of these eight subjects, given equivalent periods of passive exposure, showed no significant shift. In any case, a purely visual test of direction yielded a displacement effect in this study.

The question arises whether there is any reason why adaptation should *not* be expected to occur when an observer is wheeled passively. Undoubtedly he *does* veridically perceive himself as moving, rather than the environment, on the basis of induced movement of the self and possibly vestibular cues.[32] However, there might be a difference between active and passive movement as far as information about *direction* of movement

[30] I. Kohler, The formation and transformation of the perceptual world (trans. by H. Fiss), *Psychol. Issues*, 1964, 3, 1–173.

[31] R. Held and J. Bossom, Neonatal deprivation and adult rearrangement, *J. comp. Physiol. Psychol.*, 1961, 54, 33–37.

[32] In the case of active observers, the abnormal movement of the image with forward locomotion should lead at the outset to an impression of a certain amount of movement in the field. This would not necessarily be true for passive observers unless they had adequate information about the direction in which they were moving. See the discussion on pages 96–98, Chapter 3. With lateral movements, active and passive observers will experience rubbery transformations of the field as well.

is concerned, unless the passive observer is continuously made aware of the direction in which he is being pushed. In active movement the observer can relate changes in the apparent direction of objects to information concerning the direction of his movements. For example, if he walks directly toward x' in Figure 4–4a, then he will find out as he approaches it that it was not where it had appeared. If wheeled passively, it is conceivable he could interpret the apparent change in direction of x as a function of the peculiar path in which he is being wheeled. If, however, he directed his own passive movement, this ambiguity would be eliminated. Under such conditions, therefore, the informational aspect of passive movement should be equivalent to that of active movement.

Weinstein and his collaborators carried out an experiment designed to investigate this question.[33] They employed the same method of testing the apparent straight-ahead as Held and Bossom. During the exposure period, all subjects sat in wheel chairs and either propelled themselves or were pushed through a corridor for one hour. There were four conditions: passive, in which the subject was wheeled around by the experimenter; move-only, in which the subject moved the wheels but the experimenter steered the chair; direct-only, in which a blindfolded experimenter pushed the chair, but the subject directed the steering of the chair; and move-and-direct, in which the subject provided both locomotion and direction. The purpose of these conditions was to distinguish the decision-making or directional aspect of self-produced movement from the movement per se. The investigators believed that according to Held's hypothesis adaptation should occur only in the two conditions where the subject actively pushed himself; whereas they predicted adaptation only in the two conditions under which he directed his movement.

As a matter of fact, it is not clear whether turning wheels with the hands is the kind of self-produced movement that would be appropriate to locomotion of the body in space from the standpoint of a re-afference theory. If it were not appropriate, Held should predict no adaptation for any of the four conditions. In fact, he did perform an experiment in which the passive subjects were permitted to propel their own chairs by manipulating the wheels. The passive subjects showed no effect, whereas the actively walking subjects achieved appreciable adaptation.[34] However, Weinstein *et al.* found that all four of their conditions yielded signifi-

[33] S. Weinstein, E. A. Sersen, L. Fisher, and M. Weisinger, Is re-afference necessary for visual adaptation? *Percept. mot. Skills,* 1964, **18**, 641–648.

[34] R. Held and H. Mikaelian, Motor-sensory feedback versus need in adaptation to rearrangement, *Percept. mot. Skills,* 1964, **18**, 685–688.

cant adaptation, somewhat greater for the two conditions entailing direction by the subject.[35] These findings clearly conflict with those of Held and his collaborators, so that no definite conclusions can be drawn at this time about the role of active locomotion in the environment in bringing about adaptation to a displaced image. But both sets of data were based on a visual test of radial direction and, therefore, provide further support for the belief that genuine visual adaptation to a displaced image occurs.

Hay and Pick have conducted a thorough study of adaptation to a prismatic displacement of 11°, over a period of six weeks.[36] By including different types of tests they were able to distinguish between visual and proprioceptive effects. The eye-hand test they used was identical to the one developed by Held (shown in Figure 4–6), which required marking visual target locations without seeing the hand. This test revealed complete adaptation within several days. To determine whether the effect was entirely visual, the subjects were also required to mark the apparent location of a sound while blindfolded. This test did show a systematic error in localization on the first day, suggesting that some change in the felt location of the hand had also taken place, thus supporting the findings of Harris and others reported earlier. Since in the present experiment the subjects were not restricted to inspecting their moving arm during exposure to the prisms, one might wonder if such an effect is to be expected. I should think it is not an unreasonable expectation since, whenever the arm did come into view, a contradiction existed in its seen and felt location precisely as in the arm-movement experiments.

If during the first day of exposure no visual change had taken place, and if we legitimately assume the dominance of vision over touch, then one would predict some proprioceptive adaptation. Since, however, these unrestricted conditions of exposure lead us to expect visual adaptation as well, the picture becomes more complicated. If the arm no longer appeared displaced visually, one would no longer predict a proprioceptive change because the seen and felt location would once again be congruent. This is precisely what happened. From the second day on, the errors in marking the sound location disappeared (thereby reversing the trend of the first day). From these results we can conclude that the progressive im-

[35] It would have been desirable for Weinstein *et al.* to have included a condition in which the observer merely sits in his wheel chair in the corridor without it moving at all. Then any superiority of the other conditions could be unequivocally attributed to movement.

[36] J. C. Hay and H. L. Pick, Jr., Visual and proprioceptive adaptation to optical displacement of the visual stimulus, *J. exp. Psychol.*, 1966, 71, 150–158.

provement in the eye-hand test thereafter represents primarily visual adaptation.

In a second experiment involving certain additional tests, the authors present convincing evidence to corroborate this inference. Two of these tests were presumed to measure only visual changes. In one of these (eye-head) the subject was required to turn his head to face a visual target (similar to the type of test employed by Held and Bossom and Weinstein *et al.* to measure visual localization of the "straight ahead," except that here only the head is turned). In the other test the subject was required to report the apparent direction of an unseen sound source by calling out the number on a visual scale opposite the sound source. If there has been an apparent displacement of visual direction and if we assume that there has been no change in sound localization per se (a fact confirmed by a test of sound localization without vision), then a change is to be expected in the visual location of an unseen sound source. These two tests revealed a progressive change, reaching an asymptote by around the third day at about 40 per cent of complete adaptation, and furthermore the curves for the two tests are virtually identical.[37]

Two additional tests were designed to measure proprioceptive change, since both required indicating location with the hand. In one (head-hand) the subject pointed with eyes closed to that direction believed to be directly in front of his nose. In the other (ear-hand) he pushed a button with his hand directly under the unseen sound source. Both tests did reveal a change, but both show a reversal at around one day, leveling off after three days at about 15 per cent (using the 11° base line). Again the two curves are remarkably congruent. Thus it would appear that some slight residual proprioceptive change did remain, and this is borne out by the fact that a test of manual location of visual targets (eye-hand) reveals somewhat more adaptation than either of the two "pure" tests of vision described above. Presumably this test reflects both visual and proprioceptive change.

In all the studies described in which free locomotion is permitted, the observer has ample opportunity to gain information about the nature of the displaced direction in relation to the phenomenal self. One source of this information is derived from the fact that the subject can see his lower extremities. But even if he could not, information could be provided on the

---

[37] The value of 40 per cent is arrived at in relation to the prismatic shift of 11°. However, there is reason to believe the adaptation is greater, namely that the initial error is only about 7½°. In relation to this base line the visual adaptation achieved is 60 per cent.

124 of the stimulus

basis of the stimulus changes accompanying progression into the third dimension, outlined earlier. When the exposure phase is conducted indoors, information of this kind will also derive from the presence of the walls of corridors. A wall that is actually to the side, parallel to the direction in which the observer is moving, may appear to loom across his intended path. Yet it continues to flow by as the subject moves forward. Thus it cannot be directly ahead as it appeared to be at first. Or, conversely, the wall appears off to the side, but a moment later the subject almost collides with it and sees that it is directly before him.

Unfortunately there has as yet been little analytic work in the research on prism displacement concerning the question of what information is necessary for adaptation. One experiment conducted with this question in mind was done by Hay and Pick.[38] The subjects looked through wedge prisms for fifteen minutes. The investigators contrasted three conditions of exposure. In one condition, the subject sat and viewed his moving arm. This led to the expected effect, namely, proprioceptive change, but essentially no visual change. In a second condition the subject walked back and forth between two visual targets twenty feet apart, under instructions that tended to preclude sight of the body and, as a further precaution, the body was concealed by means of a cardboard box worn over the shoulders. This condition presumably tests the importance of information derived from movement into the third dimension in isolation from information given by sight of the body. No visual change occurred, but there was some change in the felt position of the hand (this change is hard to understand in terms of *any* theory!). It would be important to extend the time of exposure for this condition and to alter the content of the visual field before final conclusions about the role of movement are drawn. In the third condition the subject was forced to pay attention to his own body by being required to walk a particular path and repeatedly to drop and catch a small ball on an elastic cord while walking. This condition yielded visual change as well as proprioceptive change. Obviously a good deal of information of various kinds is supplied in this condition. Changes in the apparent direction of the path were probably of great importance (see p. 106 above), so that it is by no means certain that the sight of the body was crucial here.

In contrast to all the evidence cited above that visual adaptation to displacement does take place is the work of Hess with newly hatched chicks fitted with head masks that contained wedge prisms.[39] In one

[38] Hay and Pick, op. cit.
[39] E. Hess, Space perception in the chick, *Sci. Amer.*, 1956, **195**, 71–80.

experiment the prism in front of each eye was mounted with the base to
the same side. An adult human viewing the world through these prisms
would, prior to adaptation, misjudge the radial direction of an object
with respect to himself. The point of the experiment is that the chicks also
misjudged the radial direction of objects with respect to themselves.
They consistently pecked to the side of the grain of food offered them, and
moreover there was no indication of any change over time. One might
also include here the work of Sperry and Stone cited in the chapter on
orientation, because the behavior studied there involved the radial direction of a point (the lure), even though the entire image is re-inverted in
these experiments. As noted, the amphibia failed to adapt.

If we add to this the evidence of the Schlodtmann study on the apparent direction of a pressure phosphene, which also seems to be concerned with radial direction, then all three experiments (Hess, Stone, and
Schlodtmann) suggest that radial direction is given innately (and the Hess
and Sperry studies further indicate that no adaptation occurs).[40] This
conclusion is difficult to apply to the Schlodtmann study in view of the
dependency of radial direction on eye position in man. It would imply
that even without any opportunity for learning, eye position can impart
definite radial direction to retinal points. For if this were not the case, how
could Schlodtmann's subjects have experienced a definite radial location
of the phosphenes? A phosphene on the temporal side of the retina of,
say, the left eye should yield a sensation located off to the right only
if the eyes are straight ahead. If turned to the left, that same phosphene
should be located straight ahead. The precise nature of the questions and
answers in Schlodtmann's study is not given in the report, again suggesting the desirability of repeating the experiment. Eye position, however, is not a factor in the Hess and Sperry experiments because neither
chickens nor salamanders have any eye movements to speak of.

In any case, as far as radial direction is concerned, we can now say
with reasonable certainty that it is subject to learning or relearning in
humans (a fact not quite as well established in the case of egocentric
orientation). Hence a possible innate basis for it in some or all species must
be viewed in this light. Once again it should be pointed out that radial
direction in animals may be more a matter of an immediate linkage in
the nervous system between place of stimulation and response than of
subjective experience of location (and this is all the easier to understand

---

[40] However, the Hess findings may only mean that the chick turns its head until the
food object is fixated and that that turned position of the head governs the direction
of the pecking response.

in species whose eyes don't vary their position in the head). Thus we may be dealing with a different phenomenon, and this may account for the fact that it may not be subject to learning in *lower* animals. (Evidence for adaptation in monkeys is described in the next section.) However, as I have indicated earlier, it is also possible that these animal experiments have not been performed in a manner that would permit adaptation to occur.

Adaptation Based on Head Movement

I have skipped over the first major study on adaptation to displacement, that of Margaret Wooster published in 1923, in order first to consider the work based on sight of the moving arm and on locomotion in space.[41] Wooster's subjects viewed targets through a prism to which they then had to point. They could not see any part of their bodies, not even their arms, because the pointing was done underneath a partition in front of which they sat. There were several conditions, including one in which the target made a noise, thus presumably giving them information as to its actual location. This did not seem to have very much of an effect. When, however, they were permitted to find and touch the target with their finger after each response, most subjects made great progress. The same was true when they could see their own finger through a narrow slit as it reached the pointing area or when the target was the finger of their other hand seen through the narrow slit.

The kind of information available to Wooster's subjects in any of the conditions is quite limited. At best it consists of finding out where the target actually is via touch or vision, but this information comes in a form not too different from that gained by being told where the target is. Hence one might be entitled to suspect that the adaptation obtained reflects a conscious effort at "being right," more than it does a genuine sensory change, were it not for various facts that Wooster musters against this interpretation (for example, instructions to subjects *not* to do this, the gradual nature of the improvement, and negative aftereffects on removing the prisms). But in any case it is a major weakness in the Wooster experiment that there is no separate exposure phase in which the task used in the test phase is not practiced. Exposure phase and test phase are here fused into one. Adaptation, if it occurs, does so as a result of the information obtained in the act of pointing. Hence the observer can learn

[41] M. Wooster, Certain factors in the development of new spatial coordinations, *Psychol. Monogr.*, 1923, 32.

via trial and error how to point correctly. This possibility is avoided in the procedure now adopted by most investigators.

There was one condition in Wooster's study where no information at all was supplied, or at least so it seemed. The subject at no time received any feedback as to where he was pointing. Yet this condition produced a clear adaptation effect. Recently, however, Bossom obtained an adaptation effect with monkeys under conditions where they did not see any part of their body.[42] They were restrained in a chair, looking through displacing prisms at a horizontal shelf below the head. The monkeys overcame 44 per cent of their initial reaching errors in a seven-hour exposure period. However, Bossom did not obtain a significant effect when the monkeys were not permitted to move their heads. Wooster did allow her subjects to move their heads, and in one condition where they merely sat still, she did not obtain an effect. Hence it is a fair guess that the mysterious effect in the condition under discussion was based on head movements and that at least some of the effect obtained in the previously described conditions is also attributable to head movement.[43] The importance of head movement is further indicated by the results of several recent investigations employing the arm-movement procedure during the exposure phase, in which partial transfer from the practiced arm to the other arm *does* occur provided the head is not prevented from moving during the exposure period.[44] In other words, head movement leads to some degree of *visual* adaptation and, therefore, is revealed by tests with either arm. This finding may also explain why Helmholtz obtained evidence of such transfer, while investigators who restricted head movement did not. (Partial transfer implies that much of the effect is still in the felt location of the moving arm and this, of course, does not transfer.)

The question, therefore, arises as to why head movement leads to visual adaptation. Although it is true that there is a rubbery transformation of objects in the field due to changes in the angle of incidence as the head moves, this does not provide information about the actual location of

[42] J. Bossom, Mechanisms of prism adaptation in normal monkeys, *Psychon. Sci.*, 1964, **1**, 377–378.

[43] Harris draws this conclusion but believes that head movement leads to a change in the felt position of the head relative to the body. This interpretation is discussed in the last section of this chapter. See C. S. Harris, Perceptual adaptation to inverted, reversed, and displaced vision, *Psychol. Rev.*, 1965, **72**, 419–444.

[44] J. Bossom and R. Held, Transfer of error-correction in adaptation to prisms, *Amer. Psychologist*, 1959, **14**, 436 (abstract); Hamilton, op. cit.; H. B. Cohen, Transfer and dissipation of aftereffects due to displacement of the visual field, *Amer. Psychologist*, 1963, **18**, 411 (abstract).

objects. These changes may lead to a realization that an optical device of some kind is producing distortions, but not that the main distortion is a lateral displacement. Furthermore, Hamilton has shown that an equal effect occurs when the head moves but the prism, through which the subject looks, is held stationary.[45] Since in this case there are no rubbery effects, these changes are clearly not necessary for prism adaptation.

The most plausible assumption, therefore, is that some information of the kind described earlier, based on approaching and withdrawing from objects, is playing a role here even though such movements of the observer are necessarily slight when only the head moves. Unfortunately, although this may be a sufficient factor, it could not explain the equally large effect obtained in the experiment just referred to by Hamilton, where he used a large prism *not* attached to the head. Information based on changes of distance does not occur under these circumstances. Nevertheless, Hamilton did obtain transfer to the other arm, so it can be assumed that some visual adaptation occurs when the subject looks at his arm and the head is free to move. We are left, therefore, with the following set of facts concerning adaptation based on head movement: (1) It occurs without the subject seeing any part of his body (Bossom, Wooster), thus suggesting that a sufficient source of information derives from changes of distance between subject and objects in the field. (2) It occurs without such information and without rubbery transformations (Hamilton's detached prism experiment), provided the observer sees his arm (whether or not the arm has to move is not known). A possible basis for this second type of effect will be considered later in this chapter.

Adaptation in a Stationary Observer

There is some evidence that adaptation to displacement can occur without any movement on the part of the observer, provided he does get information as to the altered visual location of his body or of things with respect to his body. One method is to permit the observer to view his body. Wallach, Kravitz, and Lindauer used two methods of testing for adaptation, judging when a target appeared straight ahead and a pointing test.[46] In the testing, the observer's head was held stationary. During the exposure period, the observer stood relaxed with his head bent forward looking down at his legs for a period of ten minutes. The choice of the procedure of looking down at the legs was based upon the idea that a con-

[45] Hamilton, op. cit.
[46] H. Wallach, J. H. Kravitz, and J. Lindauer, A passive condition for rapid adaptation to displaced visual direction, *Amer. J. Psychol.*, 1963, 76, 568–578.

flict would exist between the gravitationally given information to the effect that the legs were vertical in space and the immediate visual impression produced by the prism that they were off to the side, and hence tilted with respect to the vertical of space. Wallach had earlier employed a different conflict situation to achieve perceptual modification.[47]

The results of the pointing test showed a marked adaptation (in the vicinity of 35 per cent of full adaptation to the 11° shift produced by the prism). The straight-ahead test also showed marked adaptation that was of about the same order of magnitude as the pointing test. While the observer was *not* told to keep his head stationary, only very slow (and presumably slight) head movements occurred, and these were recorded. The records indicated that the magnitude of such movement was not correlated with the magnitude of adaptation.

In another experiment the observer was required to lie horizontally in a supine position with his head raised to permit him to see his legs through the prism. It is not stated whether head movement could occur, but it is obvious that, even if permitted, it would have been minimal. Using this procedure, there is no longer a conflict between the prismatically displaced visual direction and the vertical direction of the body relative to gravity. Hence the authors did not expect adaptation to occur. However, not only did it occur, but the effect as measured by the visual straight-ahead test was much greater than that obtained in the previous experiments with standing observers (about 65 per cent of complete adaptation). The pointing test, however, yielded a non-significant effect. (It is difficult to understand how a change in visual direction can fail to lead to a change in the direction of pointing.)

The adaptation obtained in these experiments is certainly not surprising from the standpoint of the hypothesis put forth in this chapter, namely, that "straight ahead" is that radial direction which is directly in front of the *phenomenal* head and body. Normally this direction is one in which the eyes are actually straight ahead while fixating an object. But when wearing a prism this direction is one that requires turning the eyes to the side. The subjects in this last experiment are learning that "straight ahead" is the direction in which the eyes are turned—or, to state it more carefully, the centrally registered information to the effect that the eyes are turned to the side by so and so many degrees is associated with the subjective impression that a fixated object is straight ahead. They are learning this because they quite literally see that an object fixated with

[47] H. Wallach and E. B. Karsh, The modification of stereoscopic depth-perception and the kinetic depth effect, *Amer. J. Psychol.*, 1963, 76, 429–435.

that (turned) position of the eyes is "straight ahead"—that is, it is the direction aligned with the central axis of the body. This interpretation can apply as well to the first situation in which the subjects look down at their feet. Here again the subjects are given direct information that the prismatically shifted direction in which the feet appear is, by definition, straight ahead. Gravity is a superfluous cue.

It has been maintained that Wallach's findings are an artifact based upon the uncontrolled position of the head. Hein has argued that observers tend to turn their heads in order to view their prismatically displaced legs.[48] In other words, Hein argues that the prism brings about an atypical posture of the head, and nonvisual adaptation to this posture is responsible for the effect. To prove this point, Hein repeated the experiment of Wallach *et al.* and included a condition where the eyes were closed, but the head was set in the position it had been in for that particular subject in the eyes-open condition. In still another condition in which the eyes were closed, head and trunk were so positioned. The results indicate that in the eyes-closed conditions there is a change in marking the location of targets, and when both head and trunk position were manipulated, the change is not significantly less than that obtained with eyes open.

Hein does not make clear why he expects that maintaining an atypical posture would lead to the effects that Wallach *et al.* obtained. Is there a normalization of the new posture such that the observer now interprets his twisted head as straight? If so, it could be argued that the observer would misperceive the location of objects with respect to his trunk, thus possibly leading to the effects obtained. In the test in which the head is actually straight, it would now be experienced as twisted, so that an object in the sagittal plane of the head might be interpreted as displaced with respect to the trunk.

There is another way of providing a stationary observer with information about the prismatically altered direction of objects with respect to the self that does not involve sight of one's own body: that is to move objects toward and away from the observer. This technique was used by Howard, Craske, and Templeton.[49] They moved a long rod oriented in the sagittal plane of the head back and forth so as to touch the observer centrally on the mouth. The observer viewed the rod through mirrors

[48] A. Hein, Postural aftereffects and visual-motor adaptation to prisms. Paper read at Eastern Psychological Assoc., Atlantic City, April 1965.

[49] I. P. Howard, B. Craske, and W. B. Templeton, Visuomotor adaptation to discordant exafferent stimulation, *J. exp. Psychol.*, 1965, **70**, 189–191.

which caused it to appear off to the side. Hence contact with the mouth informed him that the rod was not where it had appeared to be. A significant adaptation effect was obtained. A control group given similar exposure, but which was deprived of actual physical contact with the rod, did not adapt.

In a second experiment reported in the paper referred to earlier, Weinstein *et al.* sought to demonstrate that what is crucial for adaptation is informational feedback about the prismatic displacement.[50] In the exposure condition the subject sat immobilized in a chair and made judgments about the straight-ahead position of the target (as he did in the pre- and post-exposure conditions). However, in the exposure period, following each judgment, the experimenter rotated the chair to the correct or zero position, thus providing the subject with knowledge of his error and of the correct position. Significant adaptation following a half hour of exposure trials was obtained. A criticism that can be lodged against this experiment is that the effect obtained could have been the result of a purely intellectual exercise—that is, the subject may have consciously learned the principle that "the true straight ahead is so and so many inches to the left (right) of what appears straight ahead" (see the comments concerning Wooster's experiment and those in Chapter 2, page 48, on certain of Ewert's experiments).

The term "error information" is often used to refer to the kind of information available to the observer in experiments such as this one by Weinstein *et al.* It is often implied that such information does not lead to a genuine adaptation effect or at least that whatever effect it does lead to is quite different from the effect that develops when such information is not available. I believe there is some confusion here. I would agree that when, as in the above experiment, the information is such as to make it possible for the subject to correct his test performance by feedback that provides information about his error and if, further, this correction is cognitive and can be made even if there has been no change in perception, then it is proper to consider such experiments irrelevant to the question of perceptual adaptation. The Weinstein experiment just described may be an instance of this kind. The confusion arises when other experiments such as the one by Howard *et al.* are also disposed of in terms of this criticism. To be sure, when the rod touches the mouth, the observer is receiving information about his error in localization, but this experience is not directly tied to his test performance, and there is no reason to think that it will lead to a conscious effort at correction at the time of

[50] Weinstein *et al.*, op. cit.

the test. Of course, it is desirable to rule out the possibility of conscious correction, but then many experiments on adaptation are vulnerable to this same objection. Isn't the perception of the hand as displaced from where it ought to be during exposure to prisms also "error information"?

Brief mention may be made of an experiment now in progress in our laboratory in which adaptation to a displaced image is obtained without any movement on the part of the observer and without sight of his body. On page 108 reference was made to an immediate correction effect when a stationary observer views a room through displacing prisms. If the region of the room which is straight ahead continues to appear straight ahead (or almost so) when seen through prisms (the correction effect), then conditions exist for adaptation to take place. A turned position of the eyes is required to view the region which appears straight ahead, so that this new association can become established. In brief periods of five- or ten-minute exposure to prisms which displace about 11°, we have obtained changes of approximately 2° to 3° in the direction which appears straight ahead. The measurements are made in the dark without prisms before and after the exposure period. The observer himself adjusts a small luminous spot of light until it appears straight ahead. The magnitude of the effect obtained is quite appreciable in comparison to many of the experiments described in this chapter. It is entirely possible that the necessary conditions for such a correction effect are also present in many of the experiments performed to date, whether the observer is moving about or is stationary. For example, the greater adaptation effect obtained by supine observers in comparison with upright observers in the experiment by Wallach *et al.* cited above, may be based upon the fact that, in the supine position, the observer is looking across the room.

Is All Adaptation to Visual Displacement Proprioceptive?

Several different investigations have revealed an adaptation effect to a displaced image which, by virtue of the tests used or the presence of intermanual transfer, would seem to be visual. Yet there are those who would argue that even in these studies the change is proprioceptive (that is, in the position sense) and not visual. Harris has claimed that in those experiments where the observer adapts by walking around while wearing prisms, what undergoes change is the felt orientation of his eyes relative to his head, or his head relative to his body.[51] Ivo Kohler reported

[51] C. S. Harris, 1965, op. cit. Harris notes that "felt position," especially of the eyes, may not be based on proprioceptive afference but rather on efference copy.

that his subjects tended to turn their heads in looking at objects that were actually straight ahead of the trunk, and that after a while they were completely unaware of this head turning. Evidence of a reinterpretation of eye position was particularly clear-cut in an experiment in which prisms were worn only in the upper half of the field. The subject would often move his eyes diagonally in viewing a long vertical object without any awareness of doing so. Furthermore, tests without the prisms indicated that diagonal eye movements signified a direction that was felt to be straight up and down by the subject. (This experiment is discussed in more detail in Chapter 6, pages 205–207, which the reader may wish to consult at this point.)

In considering the problem of precisely what has taken place in adaptation, the first question to settle is whether the change is visual, proprioceptive, or whatever. It is visual if there is a change in the way things look; it is proprioceptive if there is a change in the felt position of a part of the body. When a target in the sagittal plane of the head appears off to the side when prisms are removed, we have a visual change; when it appears straight ahead but, when touched, feels off to the side, we have a proprioceptive change. There is, therefore, no question about the fact that in many of the experiments entailing free locomotion in space or head movement, visual adaptation occurred.

Once it has been established what kind of change has taken place, then because there may be several ways of accounting for such a change, it becomes necessary to ask a second question, namely, what is the mechanism or underlying basis of the change? For example, if visual adaptation to a displacing prism were to occur in an animal which did not have the capacity for eye or head movement, it would seem necessary to conclude that a change in local sign had taken place. The central region of the retina would no longer signify the straight-ahead direction. In man, however, no retinal locus signifies an invariant radial direction; rather, eye position must be taken into account. Therefore adaptation must entail a change in the direction signified by every retinal locus for any given eye position. With the eyes straight ahead, a *peripheral* retinal locus now signifies the radial direction "straight ahead"; a turned position of the eyes now imparts a straight-ahead radial direction to an image falling on the fovea. Radial direction happens to be a visual phenomenon which by its nature is partly a function of non-visual information. There are other such examples in perception: for example, size perception, which depends in part on accommodation and convergence, or perception of the vertical of space, which depends on proprioceptive and vestibular information as to the direction of gravity. Thus one cannot claim that visual direction remains unchanged while the felt position of the eyes comes to be reinterpreted. Definite visual direction depends upon eye position so that any change in one, ipso facto, entails change in the other.

Apart from the question of the kind of change and the underlying basis of this change, a third question to consider is the cause of the change or the conditions necessary to achieve it. In the case of viewing the moving arm through a prism, it is probable that the cause of the adaptive change is the dominance of vision in the conflict created by the prism between vision and proprioception, which leads to certain enduring changes in the interpretation of proprioceptive stimuli. Besides, in viewing the moving arm, information that could lead to a visual change is inadequate. In the case of true visual adaptation to a prism, I have argued that the cause is the assimilation of information that objects stimulating the periphery of the retina with eyes straight ahead or objects seen foveally with the eyes turned are directly in front of the body, thus leading to the formation of memory traces that represent these new associations.

For a complete understanding of adaptation, however, it is necessary to consider these different questions together. For example, keeping in mind that we have been dealing with exposure to *visual* distortion, a proprioceptive change makes sense only on the basis of a conflict created between vision and touch. Why else should a transformation of visual stimulation have a non-visual outcome? Hence the nature of the outcome is bound up with the cause of change. Where there is every reason to think that the change is a function of visual information, there is no reason to think the change that occurs would be anything but visual. In the case of viewing an external object through prisms, there is no conflict between where it appears and the felt position of the eyes or head in viewing it. From the outset, objects are seen precisely where the eyes are felt to be fixating or where the head is felt to be directed. The hypothesis of a conflict between seen and felt position is not applicable to eye position, because the reinterpretation of the felt position of the eyes can hardly be based on a conflict between the seen and felt location of the head with respect to the eye. Hence there must be some other source of information to the effect that the object is not where it seems to be at the outset. Whereas the proprioceptive-change hypothesis says that visual perception changes *because* the sensed position of the eyes changes, I would say that because visual adaptation to displacement occurs, so that an object seen foveally with eyes turned to the side appears straight ahead, it follows that the observer "feels" his eyes to be straight ahead when in fact they are turned. If he experiences himself looking straight ahead then he could scarcely "feel" his eyes to be turned.[52]

An illustration from a different area of perceptual adaptation may serve to clarify some of the points made above. In looking through a base-left or -right wedge prism, straight vertical lines appear curved, but there is evidence that in time they appear less curved or straight (see Chapter 6). Harris has suggested that this effect may be based upon a reinterpretation of the path of eye movement in scanning the line—the curved path of eye movement coming to feel "straight." In terms of the three questions distinguished above, I would say: (1) The effect is visual because the line *appears* less curved or straight. (2) The mechanism could conceivably be the one Harris suggests, although the belief that appreciation of visual shape is based on eye movement has long been discarded on the basis of evidence such as that entailing tachistoscopic exposure. (3) The cause of the change could not be an immediate conflict between vision and eye-movement-proprioception created by the prism, because the image of the line is curved and is therefore in agreement with the curved path of eye movement required to scan the line.[53]

Why therefore should there be any adaptation in this situation? Clearly, adaptation would have to be based on visual information as to the

[52] There is an implicit premise here, namely, that we feel we are looking at whatever object stimulates the fovea. In other words, the difference between foveal and peripheral stimulation of the retina is not merely one of acuity. There is also the definite phenomenal experience that one's gaze is directed at the point falling on the fovea. That being the case, perhaps what we mean by the felt position of the eyes is essentially the experienced direction of gaze.

[53] Harris has suggested that a possible basis for the existence of a conflict between visual and proprioceptive stimulation, other than that of directly seeing a part of the body through prisms, is visual information derived from movement of the observer. For example, where proprioception informs that the head and eyes are facing along the path of movement, the pattern of flow of elements within the retinal image indicates that they cannot be facing along that path. (See C. S. Harris, 1965, p. 440, op. cit.) He would argue that a conflict of this kind exists in other cases as well, as for example in prismatically created changes of curvature, where visual information based on movement of the observer indicates that a line is straight, but proprioceptive information based on fixating different parts of the line indicates it is curved. Stated in this way, there is considerable agreement between the position of Harris and the one I have developed here. In these examples it is agreed that the outcome is visual change (that is, things *look* different following adaptation) and it is agreed that visual information is responsible for the change. The main area of disagreement is that Harris believes the mechanism underlying the adaptation is a proprioceptive change of some kind (for example, a changed interpretation of the position of the eyes or the path of movement of the eyes), whereas I believe the mechanism need not necessarily entail such proprioceptive change but that in many cases such a change is a consequence of the visual change.

actual shape of the line and not on eye movements. That being the case, it is reasonable to suppose the basis or mechanism for the adaptation concerns a change in the visual shape signified by a curved retinal image. Once it came to pass that a curved image yielded an impression of a straight line, no doubt the eye movement required to scan the curved image would then be interpreted as "straight." If one is scanning a line which appears straight, it "follows" that the eyes are moving along a straight path. Again Harris may be putting the cart before the horse.

The proprioceptive-change hypothesis becomes tenable in those instances in which the emphasis is placed on what happens to the relationship between head and body, where the body, or part of it, is visible. In the following discussion it will be helpful to imagine that the eyes do not, or cannot, move in relation to the head—that they remain in the straight-ahead position. If the observer looks through a prism, one might say there will be a conflict between the felt and seen positions of parts of the body. For example, the trunk and legs are felt to be directly below the head, but their visual location off to the side is such as to suggest that the head is twisted to the opposite side. Thus it is possible that, because of the dominance of vision, the observer might come to interpret the straight-ahead position of his head as tilted away from his trunk or, conversely, he might interpret the twisted position of the head necessary to look at the feet as "straight ahead." If that were to happen, some of the tests of adaptation typically used would reflect the kind of change that has been reported. For if a subject felt his head to be twisted when it was not, in the test when he viewed a target that was actually in front of his head, he would have to point to the side of his trunk. Or if he localized the straight-ahead in terms of his trunk, a target straight ahead of his nose would not be judged as straight ahead. This argument could also be applied to the experiments described earlier in which the observer remains stationary. It is similar to the hypothesis tested by Hein. Hein was apparently assuming that an atypical posture of the head will, in time, no longer be experienced as atypical. But the same result should be expected if normal posture of the head comes to be experienced as atypical. It is possible that the observer ends up by interpreting his head as twisted to the side when, in fact, it is perfectly straight. Harris and Hamilton believe that the adaptation obtained when an observer views his moving arm, but is permitted to move his head freely, is based upon such a changed interpretation of the position of the head with respect to the trunk. This explanation may be correct because, as we have seen, Hamilton's detached-prism experiment leads to an apparent visual effect although there does not seem to be any useful visual information available for the kind of change of radial direction I have been considering. However, it is not clear why head movement should be necessary for such a process to occur.

If, therefore, the conflict between seen and felt location of parts of the body with respect to the head were the cause of adaptation, the change in the felt position of the head plays a rather different role than if adaptation is caused by the registration of visual information as to where objects actually are located. In the first case this proprioceptive change is the central fact, and it would directly lead to the effects that have been obtained. Visual information concerning where objects actually are is irrelevant. In the second case, where adaptation is visual, the proprioceptive change is a mere by-product of the principal change, for if one turns the head to look directly at an optically displaced object, and if that object is now seen as straight ahead of the trunk, then it would be contradictory to experience the head as turned. (Or if the head is not turned, but peripherally located objects come to be perceived as straight ahead of the trunk, then it would be contradictory not to experience the head [or eyes] as turned to the opposite side.) The effects reported by Kohler concerning the way his subjects experienced their head position may, therefore, be a result of the underlying *visual* adaptation.

There are, however, good reasons for rejecting the hypothesis that a *necessary* factor in adaptation to a displaced image is the conflict between the seen position of the trunk and the position it is felt to have with respect to the head (indeed Harris does not claim it is a necessary factor). One is that adaptation has been obtained where the body is not visible. Another is that it is by no means clear, and in fact it is doubtful, that judgments which have been used in visual tests of radial direction (the straight-ahead) are based on the perceived relationship between target and trunk rather than between target and head. If the observer is asked to indicate when a target appears straight ahead of his head (or nose) and a change in his judgments occurs, then it cannot be reasonably argued that the change is the result of a reinterpretation of the felt position of the head. It would be irrelevant where the head is felt to be with respect to the torso. In the experiment by Hay and Pick, such a test (the eye-head test) revealed appreciable adaptation. A change also occurred in a test of visual localization of an unseen sound source. If adaptation were based on a change in the felt location of the head, then an unseen sound straight ahead would be interpreted as off to the side of the trunk just as would a visual target straight ahead. Hence no change between vision and sound localization is to be expected; yet it occurred. This evidence attests to the fact that in many cases adaptation entails a change in the perceived direction of objects with respect to the head, which means that a change has taken place in the radial direction signified by all retinal points for a given eye position. If this does occur, then to the extent that it occurs adaptation cannot be based on a reinterpretation of head position.

SUMMARY

[NOTE: *Sentences in brackets refer to material presented in the Addendum which follows.*]

Radial direction refers to the apparent direction of a point with respect to the self. Since the phenomenal direction of an object does not change when the location of its retinal image changes with eye movements, it must be the case that the position of the eyes is taken into account. Ordinarily when the eyes point straight ahead, an object whose image falls on the fovea will be located straight ahead. It was contended that since "straight ahead" refers to direction with respect to the *phenomenal* head and body, it is probable that the perception of radial direction is based on past experience. When the eyes are straight ahead, the visible body falls in the center of the field. Hence that position of the eyes has come to signify that a foveally viewed object is straight ahead. In viewing the world through wedge prisms, it is necessary to turn the eyes to the side to view the body or objects directly in front of the body. Hence that new position of the eye will eventually come to signify that a foveally viewed object is straight ahead. The association between eye position and phenomenal direction is carried in memory in the form of traces of specific eye positions and specific directions. These traces must be supplanted by those that represent the new associations in order for adaptation to occur. Eye position may be represented centrally, not via afferent feedback, but rather by a copy of the neural command to the eye muscles. Hence the traces of eye position would have to be based on such efference copies. During exposure to prisms, information as to the veridical direction of objects can be obtained either by seeing the body or by moving about in the environment. Changes in the apparent location of objects, as observer and objects approach one another, was suggested as the major source of information in the case of movement.

[Any given eye position establishes a definite radial direction for *all* retinal points. It is generally assumed that the position of retinal points relative to one another is given. That being the case, once eye position establishes a specific radial direction for any retinal point such as the fovea, it will ipso facto establish it for all other points on the retina.] Hence the modifiability of radial direction has nothing to do with change of local sign of retinal loci. The position of points relative to one another—which is what is given by retinal location—is not altered. When contradictory information is given—as, for example, in viewing the body through prisms or in viewing the arrangement of objects in the visual scene—such information will immediately compete with eye position as a determinant of radial direction. Thus, in daily life, radial direction is in part a function of information derived from objects in the field and in part a joint function of eye position and retinal locus. This would explain the fact that although radial direction can be judged in a dark field, it cannot be judged with perfect accuracy or consistency (autokinetic effect).

Adaptation to a prismatically displaced image has been obtained in situations where an observer merely watches his hand move back and forth. However, if measured by manual tests of target location, this adaptation does not transfer to the unseen hand. Considerable evidence has been presented to support the view that what happens in this situation is that there is no change in visual direction, but rather there is a change in the felt location of the hand relative to the trunk, based on the dominance of vision. This interpretation bears on the finding that only active movement, and not passive movement, of the arm yields an adaptation effect, although there is some evidence which contradicts that finding. From the standpoint of an information type of theory of perceptual change, there would not seem to be any additional visual information in seeing one's arm move that is not given in seeing it stationary; neither condition seems adequate for a change of visual perception. Held believes that movement-produced visual feedback is necessary for prism adaptation, but apparently not because of the discounting process emphasized by von Holst. Rather he believes that sensorimotor coordination depends upon a correlation between a central copy of motor signals and the resulting visual re-afference, and that the optical transformation yielded by prisms merely leads to a new correlation. This theory was questioned in several respects, but chiefly on these grounds: (1) the basis for maintaining that the notion of re-afference is relevant to problems of adaptation other than that of discounting of the changes of the proximal stimulus during movement; and (2) its failure to explain perceptual phenomena or changes of perception.

When the observer moves around in the environment, *visual* adaptation does occur, as is evidenced by tests of the apparent radial direction of a target and other measures. The finding that here again active movement is essential has been empirically challenged. It was contended that passive movement should result in adaptation provided the observer has information as to the direction of his own physical displacement through space. Knowledge of the precise nature of the information provided by movement is still quite meager. Evidence was considered and evaluated that radial direction is innate in lower species and is not susceptible to adaptation.

Experiments have also shown that mere head movement yields visual adaptation, thus explaining why Helmholtz did achieve transfer to his unseen hand and why Wooster obtained an effect under conditions that seemed to provide no information at all. The nature of the information given by head movement is, at present, unknown, but it appears to be of two different kinds: (1) based on changes of distance between observer and objects in the field and (2) based on sight of part of the body.

Although still controversial, there is now some evidence that a completely stationary observer will adapt to displacement provided he sees his own body or otherwise obtains information as to the veridical direction of objects. When this evidence is based on providing the observer with error information as feedback of his test judgments, it may well be spurious. However, if information is provided during an exposure phase that does not entail the response later to be tested and does not lead to a deliberate cognitive effort at correction during the subsequent testing, it cannot be lightly dismissed.

The claim was considered that even when adaptation to a displaced image seems to be visual, it is proprioceptive, entailing a change in the felt position of eyes with respect to head or head with respect to torso. Inasmuch as some adaptation to displacement affects the direction in which objects are *seen*, this claim is clearly incomplete. Since radial direction depends upon taking eye position into account, it is true that adaptation to displacement necessarily entails a change in the perceived direction of every retinal point as a function of each specific position of the eye. Thus the nature of the change is visual; the basis of the change concerns a transformation of the radial direction that is imparted by each position of the eye; and the cause of the change is visual information as to where objects are actually located in relation to the self.

ADDENDUM

Radial Direction of All Points in the Field

Throughout the chapter, for purposes of simplicity, I have confined the discussion primarily to the direction signified by the foveal region of the retina. In this section I will extend the analysis to include all locations on the retina. Because every location on the retina will signify a specific direction as a function of the position of the eye, is it necessary to assume that the brain must be capable of responding differentially and simultaneously to all possible combinations of retinal position and eye position? Taken separately, there are an infinite number of such combinations. If, however, the location of points relative to one another can be considered as given (by the relative location of the corresponding cortical points of excitation), then this problem is eliminated.[54] It is only necessary to deal with the coordination of eye position and any one retinal location, such as the fovea. To illustrate, suppose we confine our analysis to three points, A, B, and C, which are located as shown in the figure below. Point B is located in the observer's sagittal plane. If we can assume that the relative position of the three points is given, then just on this basis we can assume that the observer will perceive three points

. . .

A B C

in space with the middle point, B, closer to A than to C. Change of eye position will have no effect on the phenomenal location of the points *relative to one another*. Point B will continue to appear closer to A than to C. I wish to stress the fact that if now the radial direction of any of these points were to be established, for any position of the eyes, the radial direction of the other points consistent with their positions relative to one another would also be established. Thus, if B is fixated and its radial direction is straight ahead, A will appear to the observer's left, C to his right; furthermore, A will appear less to the left than C does to the right (see Figure 4–7a).

[54] One has the impression that most workers in the field of perception today do assume that the position of retinal points relative to one another does not have to be learned, based upon the facts of the cortical "map" of the retina. With this assumption, a plausible explanation of the learning of radial direction can be developed. Without it, a rather unwieldy, not very plausible, total empiricism is required, such as Helmholtz tried to develop.

Hence, it follows that, given relative position, all that is necessary to establish the radial direction of *all* points in the field is an association of each position of the eye with the radial direction of any single retinal point, such as the fovea. By analogy, if we know the distance of several objects from one another, then as soon as we give the distance of any one of them from an origin, we automatically know the distance of all of them from that origin. In our example, if the array of points *A, B, C* moves 30° to the right, then if the radial direction of *B* is veridically given as 30° to one side of the straight ahead direction, *A* will ipso facto appear 10° to the right of the straight ahead, and *C* will appear 70° to the right of straight

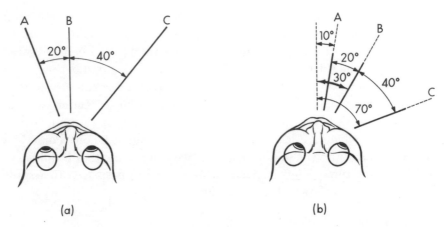

(a)   (b)

Figure 4–7

ahead, because in our example *A* and *C* are 20° left and 40° right of *B* respectively (see Figure 4–7*b*). In other words, with the central reinterpretation of the direction of *B* with change of eye position, the reinterpretation of the direction of all other points necessarily follows.[55] (The reader should keep in mind that in the above example, the array *A, B, C* changes position in the environment. If, however, *A, B, C* remained stationary when the eyes moved, then the radial direction of these points in the environment would *not* be seen to change.)

There is one further assumption. It was suggested in the second chapter that there is no reason to believe egocentric orientation is innately

[55] The analysis presented here is similar to that of Gordon Walls (The problem of visual direction, *Amer. J. Optom.*, 1951, **28**, 115–146; see the discussion in Chapter 2). What I have called perceived relative position in a frontal plane, he calls oculocentric directionalization, and what I have called radial direction, he calls egocentric directionalization. However, Walls assumes that oculocentric directionalization includes up-down and left-right localization and that this is innate and immutable.

determined by the locus of excitation in the visual cortex. Yet without ego-centric orientation the radial direction of all points would be essentially indeterminate. If, as shown in Figure 4–8, B is fixated, unless we can assume that the orientation of the horizontal retinal direction along which A, B, C fall is egocentrically "horizontal," why should A and C appear to the *left* and *right* of straight ahead? A and C could just as well signify "above" and "below" straight ahead if this were not the case (A', B, C' in Figure 4–8). A might appear, radially, 20° to the "side" of B, but that could be anywhere on the circular path shown in Figure 4–8. Similarly, C might appear 40° to the opposite "side" of B anywhere on the circular path shown in Figure 4–8.

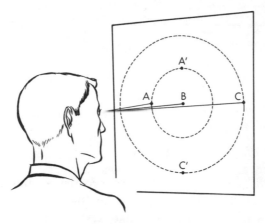

Figure 4–8

The dependency of specific radial direction on egocentric orientation can be illustrated by one of the measures used in the experiment of Mikaelian and Held described in Chapter 2 (page 57). It will be recalled that, following exposure to a prism system which tilted the retinal image, subjects had to judge when each of two points appeared straight ahead. One was above eye level, the other below it. The finding was that the upper point had to be displaced in one direction and the lower in the opposite direction before they appeared straight ahead. In order to make the illustration clear, I am going to assume the subject was required to fixate a point at eye level, midway between the upper and lower points. As can be seen in Figure 4–9b, if the egocentric vertical is now given by a tilted retinal meridian, then the radial direction of all retinal points would be systematically altered. In the normal situation (a), with eyes straight ahead, a retinal point x would give rise to an impression of a point located straight ahead and somewhat below eye level, y to a point located straight ahead and somewhat above eye level. Following adaptation to a disoriented image, retinal points x' and y' (see b) would give rise to these perceived radial directions. The lines V and H represent the retinal directions that signify the egocentric vertical and horizontal before (a) and after (b) adaptation.

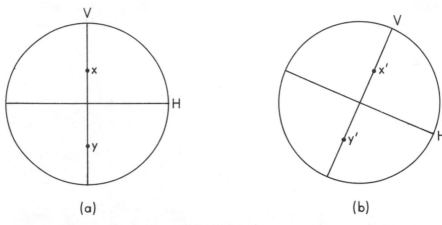

(a)   (b)

Figure 4–9

To summarize, assuming the observer experiences the position of all points in a frontal plane, relative to one another, and with respect to a left-right, up-down, egocentric coordinate system, then all that is needed to impart a radial direction to every retinal point is an association between each eye position and the radial direction signified by one particular retinal point, such as the fovea. Hence, as the eyes move, the radial direction signified by every retinal point systematically changes. If, for example, the eyes move up, every retinal point signifies a radial direction of an increasingly upward value, but the *change* of value is the same for all points.[56]

[56] This is reminiscent of Hering's theory that, with the eyes in the straight-ahead position, all retinal points have fixed height and breadth radial values (presumably innate and immutable) and that these values change with each (intended) change of eye position. However, I am suggesting that what is innate and possibly immutable is the location of points relative to one another. Radial direction as a function of eye position is learned, is far from precisely determined, and is certainly changeable.

Adaptation to
Altered Image Size

CHAPTER FIVE

A question which, to the writer's knowledge, has never before been raised is that of the nature of the relationship between the absolute size of the retinal image and the specific phenomenal size of the corresponding object. To be sure, a great deal of attention has been devoted to the fact that the size of the image changes with changes of the object's distance, while the phenomenal size of the object may remain more or less constant. But the focus of interest here is the constancy or non-constancy of size yielded by the varying image of the object. The question I am posing, however, is this: At any fixed distance a particular object yields an image of a certain size. An apple, for example, at arm's length might subtend a visual angle of 7° or 8°, thus yielding an image of about 2 or 3 mm. If we were to restrict ourselves to a world at arm's length, we could, therefore, state that a 2- to 3-mm. image signifies an object of about 60 mm. (the size of an apple).[1] The question is: Why is this the case? Is this innately determined, or is it learned?

Is it a problem that such a small image can signify such a large phenomenal size? It is, only if one starts with the premise that there should be

---

[1] Of course, for some other distance, the relationship would be quite different. Since, for any given distance there would be fixed visual angles for particular objective sizes, it will simplify the problem under discussion to abstract from the fact of changes of distance and imagine we are dealing with a world in which all things are at one particular distance.

a direct correspondence between the physical size of the image (or, more to the point, the size of the cortical "image") and the phenomenal size of the corresponding object, a premise that is obviously absurd given the size of the brain and the size of objects in the world. Rather one can only say that there is a correlation between image size and phenomenal size.

But what does it mean to say we experience the apple to be about 60 mm. in diameter? Is there anything else we can say that will provide a more complete description of the phenomenal size? Yes: we can indicate how the size of this object compares with that of other objects. For example, an apple is larger than a grape but smaller than a grapefruit. One such comparison is between the size of the object and the size of the phenomenal body—the apple is of a size that fits in the hand. Standard units such as centimeters, inches, etc., are convenient scales for specifying size and carrying it in memory, but their phenomenal meaning rests on comparisons with all other objects, including the body (as witness the origin of a unit such as the foot).

If, therefore, the phenomenal meaning of "apple size" or "60 mm." is in terms of comparisons with other objects, then the absolute size of the retinal image ought not to be of any consequence. If the entire image were suddenly to be magnified or minified, the images of all objects would undergo the same transformation. The image of an apple would remain larger than the image of a grape, smaller than the image of a grapefruit, and about equal to the width of the image of the hand. The correlation between visual angle and phenomenal extent would remain unchanged. In other words, the image signifies size by relationships which, for any fixed distance, are given quite veridically.

Yet, as everyone knows, we do experience a sense of enlargement on looking through binoculars or of diminution on reversing the binoculars. At this point, the parallels between the problem under discussion and the problem of the inverted image become quite striking. In the second chapter it was argued that uprightness was a relationship between orientation of an object and orientation of the phenomenal body of the observer —that is, between two phenomenal objects given by two retinal images. Hence, unless some further factors are at work, no disruption of phenomenal orientation is to be expected as a result of disorienting the entire image, as in Stratton's experiment. The same fate will befall all images, including that of the self. Yet it is a fact that re-erecting the image does lead to perception that is egocentrically inverted. This fact posed a problem, and the solution suggested was in terms of traces having specific orientations. In the case of size, we now see that phenomenal impressions of size rest on the relationship of the size of images to one another and that this relationship is not disrupted by altering the size of all images. That perceived size is affected is, therefore, also a problem, and the solution I would suggest is again in terms of the nature of memory traces representing size.

Insofar as size is carried in memory, the important fact is the phenomenal impression of size at the time of the original experience. Thus we see an object and remember that it was such and such a length. This fact, the phenomenal length, is represented in some way by the memory trace. Ordinarily, the specific visual angle of the stimulus is of little consequence in this regard. We do not consciously remember visual angle. If the object is seen a second time at an entirely different distance, it is immediately recognized as the same object and as the same size despite the great change in visual angle. (This is not a case of recognition of the same shape despite transformation of size, but is rather recognition of the *same* size.) In an experiment that I conducted in collaboration with Ethel Weiss, memory for size was tested under conditions in which distance from observer to object was either changed or held constant from training exposure to test.[2] Change of distance had little effect on the size of object selected as matching the previously seen standard.

But granting the saliency of the phenomenal impression of size, it is still entirely possible that the specific size of the cortical "image" is recorded in memory. In fact, there is evidence that this must be the case. When familiar size is said to be a cue to the distance of an object, what is meant is that for any distance a familiar object yields a specific visual angle which, if such a cue is to be effective, must be recorded in memory. There has been considerable controversy in recent years as to whether familiar size is a genuine cue to distance in the absence of all other cues. The point I wish to make, however, is that whether or not it does operate spontaneously, observers are capable of utilizing the memory of visual angle. For example, if we present a half-size playing card to a monocular observer in a dark room and inquire as to its distance, there is no question that observers can at least *judge* or *reason* that it is a normal-size card at a greater distance. They can only do this if they have information stored in memory that an object the size of a playing card yields a retinal image of that size when it is quite far away.[3]

[2] Ethel Weiss, *Memory for size* (thesis research paper), New School for Social Research, 1961.

[3] I believe that the visual angle subtended by an object is available to experience during the *perception proper* and is not completely swallowed up by the central organizational process in which distance is taken into account in yielding an objective

In any case, I will state as a hypothesis that in addition to the aspect of the memory trace that represents phenomenal size there is also an aspect that is faithful to the specific size of the original retinal-cortical image, the stimulus-copy aspect. Thus, to pursue the parallel with the orientation problem, in this case we assume the specific size of the cortical image is a factor, whereas in the Stratton paradigm we assumed that the specific orientation of the cortical image was a factor. If this assumption is correct, it is no longer surprising that macropsia and micropsia occur in viewing the world through size-distorting optical devices. Although the size relationships are not changed by these devices, the absolute size of all images is changed, and this can be appreciated by the observer because images of specific sizes have become associated with specific phenomenal sizes. It would also follow—as in the orientation problem—that such an absolute change would have consequences only for an experienced observer. For a newborn child or newborn animal, wearing an optical device that enlarges or diminishes the retinal image should have no effect.[4] The existence of the stimulus-copy aspect of the trace would also explain how it is possible to judge size fairly accurately when only an isolated object is visible.

It also follows that an adult who wears such a device for a sufficient period of time should adapt. The necessary information as to size is conveyed by the unchanged size relations given by the optical device. Familiar objects optically minified might at first appear small, but when seen in relation to all other objects and to the observer's own body, the information is provided that they are, in fact, normal in size. New traces would be established that are now faithful to the actual size of the minified retinal image. It should be made clear that if genuine adaptation to a magnifying or minifying optical device occurs, it will affect the apparent size of all objects seen, whether familiar or not. For example, a line of a certain length will once more appear to be equal to its true length and, if seen without the optical device, will appear larger or smaller than its true length. Familiar objects may be used to facilitate adaptation, but transfer to any and all objects is assumed.

_____

size experience. For a full discussion of this issue and evidence supporting this claim, see I. Rock and W. McDermott, The perception of visual angle, *Acta Psychol.*, 1964, **22**, 119–134.

[4] Nevertheless, it is possible that in animals the absolute size of the retinal image does matter prior to any learning. One property of a stimulus that is adequate to trigger an instinctual response may be its size. For example, not all sized particles will elicit a pecking response in a newly hatched chick. It seems doubtful that the chick would respond to a particle of grain if it were seen through a magnifying lens device.

There would seem to be two necessary aspects of the adaptation process. (1) The information must be given that the new visual angle yielded by a particular object (at any particular distance) stands for a certain phenomenal size, namely, the size the object would have if it were seen without the optical device. This information is given by the relationship of the sizes of all objects present to one another, including that of the body to external objects. To repeat what was said above, information is given by the fact that the object can be seen to retain its proper size in relation to all other things. (2) Memory traces that carry the association of these sizes with the *new* visual angles must be deposited in sufficient strength so that these new traces rather than earlier, pre-experimental traces begin to be tapped. The mere acquisition of traces of objects that are altered in size would not suffice for adaptation. That is to say, acquisition of traces of, let us say, diminutive familiar objects ought not to yield adaptation if these objects were to continue to be perceived as diminutive; adaptation would occur only if the necessary information were supplied that these objects were, in fact, of normal size. However, as will be made clear in connection with experiments to be described, the problem of the effect of exposure to familiar objects of abnormal size is a complicated one.

As suggested above, the size of objects relative to the phenomenal self is of great importance. For one thing, the body is an object that is for all intents and purposes always present. More important, however, is the fact that the concrete, operational meaning of size is given only in relation to the body. That an apple is larger than a grape but smaller than a grapefruit is, of course, an essential part of the meaning of its phenomenal size. But if this were the only information we had about the size of an apple, it would lack the concrete meaning it normally has, namely, that it is an object which can be grasped, held in the hand, etc. For a mouse, an apple obviously would yield an entirely different impression of size, despite the fact that its size relative to all other external objects is the same for a mouse as for a human. Even for a child this aspect of size would be quite different, and there is anecdotal evidence that this is the case. It seems to be a fairly universal experience that objects such as rooms, beds, etc., appear rather surprisingly small when the site of a childhood dwelling place is revisited. For the child, in relation to itself, a room would, of course, seem large, and so it will be remembered if it is not seen for many years. On seeing it again as an adult, it is no longer so large in relation to himself, and hence its size is at odds with the earlier memory.

The role of the relative size of familiar objects in creating impressions of phenomenal size is, of course, well known in daily life and is often made use of by artists and others. I observed a particularly striking example in connection with a puppet show. At the end of the performance, the puppeteer came on stage among the puppets to acknowledge the applause. He appeared to be gigantic. Figure 5–1 illustrates the same fact. If the reader first covers the man on the right, the fish has the appearance of a minnow. If he then covers the hand on the left while at the same time uncovering the man on the right, the fish takes on the proportions of a very large catch.

Figure 5–1

As was suggested in connection with other types of adaptation, information about the size of the body in the field may be available to the observer even when he does not see his own body. For example, the observer is aware of which region of the field is at eye level. Hence the height of that point from the ground must, ipso facto, be equivalent to his own height. If that distance at first appears small (in a minified image)—much less than his own height—he is nevertheless receiving the information that it is in fact equal to his own height.

Movement of the observer could conceivably be another source of information as to the altered size signified by specific visual angles. If a stationary observer views an unfamiliar object through a minification lens, there is, of course, no reason for him to be aware that it is larger than it appears to be. If, however, he moves his head, all points on the image of the object will displace across the retina, but the rate of displacement will be altered by the optical device. The amount by which the image displaces indicates the arc within the visual field through which the head has moved. To illustrate, assuming the observer is aware of the points along the object which successively appear straight ahead, then he will be receiving information that when he moves his head, let us say 30°, it corresponds to an angle that formerly had appeared to be 15°. As shown in Figure 5–2, object *xy* in (*a*) at first appears half its true size (*b*). The observer's head is facing *x*, and *x* is seen as straight ahead. Now he moves his head until *y* is straight ahead (*c*). Thus it is clear to the observer that he has moved his head from *x* to *y*. Still, information in the form of efference copy or proprioception is available that the head moved 30° which, in my opinion, ordinarily is translated into a visualization of extent of head movement. If so, in principle at least, information is centrally available that the head has

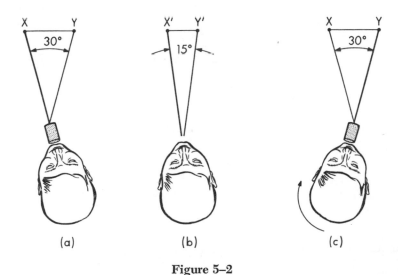

(a) (b) (c)

Figure 5–2

traversed a 30° angle, but this is now correlated with an extent in the field that appears to be 15°. Hence object *xy* must be of greater extent than it had at first seemed to be. Similar information would be conveyed by locomotion of the entire body through space. If the observer walked along a path parallel to *xy*, he would find out that the distance from *x* to *y* is greater than it had appeared to be.

It is true that if such information is to have an effect, the abnormal rate of displacement of the image must not continue to lead to an impression of movement in the field. At the same time, the specific quantitative values of head or body displacement must be veridically represented in the brain, and there is some reason to think this might not be the case. If the head is *seen* to turn from *x* to *y* and that angle is misperceived, then so may the magnitude of the head rotation be misperceived (based on the dominance of vision over proprioception). This was the argument advanced to deal with what would otherwise be a paradox of changing phenomenal direction in the re-establishment of position constancy (see p. 92). It is probable that this does happen at an early stage in the adaptation process and it is likely that the tendency to visualize the magnitude of head movement based on its actual movement is suppressed. Nevertheless the information may be registered centrally. At a later stage, therefore, it is possible that movement may play a role in bringing about a change in the phenomenal significance of visual angle.

It is conceivable that, via movement, a generalized adaptation to the altered significance of visual angle might occur rather than adaptation

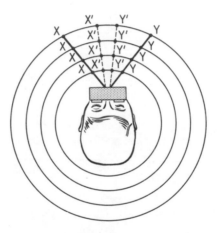

Figure 5–3

merely to a visual angle at a specific distance. That is, the observer might learn that a sector of the field, considered as visual angle rather than linear extent, signifies a visual angle different from the angle formerly signified. As illustrated in Figure 5–3, the observer may learn that the apparent angular extent of XY (regardless of the linear extent XY may have as a function of its distance) is greater than it first had appeared to be ($X'Y'$). He thus comes to anticipate that a turn of the head from X to Y will require, say, a 30° rather than 15° rotation. The anticipation of the magnitude of head rotation necessary to traverse a given extent may be one aspect of the phenomenal meaning of visual angle.[5]

[5] Preliminary attempts in our laboratory to obtain adaptation to altered image size based purely on head movement have thus far failed. Observers moved their heads back and forth for a period of 30 minutes while viewing an array of irregular, novel geometrical shapes through a negative lens. There was no information available as to

Experiments on Transposition of Line Patterns

If phenomenal size derives from the relationship of the images of objects to one another, the situation in viewing a magnified or minified scene is actually one of conflict. Because of the perfect transposition of all size relations, we should predict no change in the phenomenal size of objects. However, because of memory for the absolute size of images associated with specific phenomenal sizes, there is an impression of change. Each familiar object in the optically transformed scene would yield a retinal image whose size, via memory, suggests a phenomenal size different from the familiar one. I believe that the existence of such a conflict is borne out by the variability and ambiguity of impressions yielded by the optically altered images. Some observers comment on the diminutive character of the scene created by a minified image; others seem not to be spontaneously aware of it.

If the reasoning outlined above is correct, what would be the outcome of transpositions where familiar objects were not present? Even unfamiliar objects (or simple geometrical shapes which can have any size) would be characterized phenomenally in terms of how they compared to the stimulus-copy aspect of memory traces. Hence a line whose image was optically reduced in size would presumably convey an impression more or less in keeping with the size that (reduced) image (at that distance) had conveyed in the past. But if the line were seen in a context that was transposed in its entirety, how would its length compare with a line of that length seen in the same context without minification? This question could be answered by looking at an array of unfamiliar objects with and without an optical reduction system and comparing the apparent size of one object in the two views. If the object were a variable-length line in the non-reduction view, the observer could match its length with his impression of the line seen in the reduction view (or vice versa). If the relationship of the size of images to one another is as important as I have claimed, the line ought to appear to be the same size in each view, despite the optical reduction, because all such relationships will remain un-

---

the optical minification other than that provided by movement. A possible reason for the failure is that objects seen through minifying lens systems appear to be farther away than they actually are (see the discussion of this problem on page 164 of the Addendum). Another possible reason is that objects will, at the outset, be seen to move because of the abnormal rate of displacement of the image. If so, strictly speaking, head movement does not provide information about the minification created by the lens.

changed. However, based on memory, the line in the reduction view should appear smaller. Therefore, the outcome may be a compromise between absolutely equal image sizes and relatively equal image sizes.

It should be made clear that in this suggested experiment I am talking about the immediate impression of size on being first confronted with the optically reduced scene and not with the question of adaptation over time. Sheldon Ebenholtz and I have conducted experiments along this line. Instead of optically reducing or expanding the image, however, line patterns of transposed sizes were used. One important implication of not using optical transformations is that the phenomenal body is not transposed. Thus the experimental situation in which transposed line patterns are viewed is quite different from that in which a subject wears an optical device and is given the opportunity to see his own body or otherwise to obtain information about its size relative to the size of other objects in the field. Therefore, in order to provide no visual information at all concerning the body, the patterns were made luminous and displayed in the dark to a stationary observer.

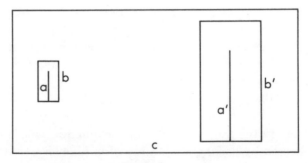

Figure 5–4

This leads to another implication of working with transposed line patterns. Optical transpositions are complete, i.e., everything is transposed. Constructed line patterns, on the other hand, if displayed in a room, would not be completely transposed because ultimately the same room serves as a frame of reference for the two objects being compared as shown in Figure 5–4: *a* represents one line which is to be judged and *b* its context—*a'* and *b'* represent the other line and context, *c* represents the room. Then the relation *a–b* is transposed (because *a'–b'* is in the same proportion), but not *a–c* or *b–c* (because *a'–c* or *b'–c* are not in the same proportion). Only by presenting *a–b* and *a'–b'* luminously in the dark can the problem be avoided. To avoid relations such as *a–b'* or *a'–b* from confounding the situation, *a–b* should be presented spatially apart from *a′–b′*. We placed *a–b* 180° away from *a′–b′*, the subject being in the center and equidistant from both.

Only the outlines of the procedure and results will be given here because the work is reported in detail elsewhere.[6] The two rectangles were transposed in the ratio of 3 : 1, *b′* being 12 inches high, *b* 4 inches high; *a* was the standard, set at 3 inches; *a′* was the variable whose length the subject equated with *a*. Pains were taken to instruct the subject that what was called for was a match based on the equality of apparent length of the two lines (*a* and *a′*) *to each other*. Several experiments were performed, in some of which the equidistance of *a–b* and *a′–b′* from the subject was quite evident to him since full binocular vision was permitted; in others, distance cues were eliminated. This proved to make little difference.

The results of a typical experiment were as follows. On the average, the variable line *a′* was set at 6 to 7 inches. An absolute size match would have been 3 inches (which is about what the subjects averaged when they compared *a′* with *a* in a control procedure with rectangles removed). A match based completely on the relationship or proportional size of *a′* to *b′* would have been 9 inches. Thus the average setting is a bit more than halfway between the two positions. Almost 40 per cent of the subjects made judgments reflecting total transposition or close to it. What is remarkable about the result, in my opinion, is that in conditions where distance cues are permitted the subjects can quite clearly see the specific length of the two lines. They are equidistant and nearby. Hence, on the average, they are equating a 3-inch line with a 6- to 7-inch line, so strong is the effect of the context of the surrounding rectangle.[7]

The transposition effect obtained is quite substantial, but it is not complete.[8] An explanation for why it is not complete may be that there are

[6] I. Rock and S. Ebenholtz, The relational determination of perceived size, *Psychol. Rev.*, 1959, **66**, 387–401.

[7] Although not relevant to the present discussion, the experiments on transposition have a bearing on the problem of size constancy. If the determinant of size is the proportionate size of images to one another rather than the absolute size of the image, then there should be no change in perceived size with variations in distance. The *relationship* of size within the image, for example, of a man next to a building, does not change with distance even though the size of the image of man and building does change. In the paper referred to, this implication is developed and concrete evidence for it is offered. It is concluded that this factor plays an important contributing role in yielding size constancy, but that it is not the only factor operating. Constancy is also a function of taking distance into account.

[8] Nevertheless, the line's apparent length is very much a function of its relationship to its context—but this is not true of the rectangle. We tested this by keeping *a′–b′*

two factors determining size. One is the size relationship of images to one another; the other is the memory factor. Based upon our subject's past experience, the line *a* appears to be about 3 inches long and *a'* when matched for complete transposition would appear to be about 9 inches long. If the subjects had had no prior visual experience, it still would be the case that in the experiment *a* or *a'* would deposit a trace which would be faithful to the objective length of its visual image. As a result the observers could match the two lines in the absence of the rectangles, as did our subjects. That the comparison of the two lines on this basis undoubtedly occurs for our subjects is borne out by their ability to make such a match when all cues to distance are eliminated. In this case, comparison based on specific phenomenal size is not possible because the lines presumably do not yield such specific phenomenal size impressions under these circumstances. Hence the memory factor would oppose the proportionality factor quite apart from memory for specific phenomenal size.

The type of effect studied in the experiments described is an immediate effect of context on size. It tells us nothing about the impression of size yielded by an isolated object. To return to the question posed at the beginning of this chapter, if the observer views an object in isolation (at some definite distance), it does have a specific phenomenal size. I have argued that this size derives from an association between the impression given by the relationships of objects to one another in the observer's past experience *and* that particular visual angle. Hence it should be possible to modify the apparent size of even an isolated object by undoing that association and substituting a new one.

Adaptation to a Minified Image

Based upon the reasoning outlined above, I set out to establish that adaptation to optically altered size will occur and to explore the relevant factors in such adaptation. There was a choice of either magnification or minification, but the latter seemed preferable since any optical system necessarily reduces the size of field. With magnification this difficulty is compounded because a small region of the environment will fill that reduced field; minification tends to offset the difficulty because a fairly

---

and *a* constant and varying *b*. The subjects matched on the basis of absolute size. We believe the reason for this is that *a* and *a'* are relatively insulated from direct comparison with each other, whereas *b* and *b'* are not. There is a "separation of system" operating for the lines. (See page 68.)

substantial region of the enviroment can be seen in the reduced field. For reasons presented in the Addendum, a convex mirror was used in lieu of a lens system to create the optical minification. Other details of the procedure and apparatus are also given in the Addendum, as are descriptions of experiments not discussed in the body of this chapter.[9] For the exposure or adaptation phase of the experiment, the subject sat at a table looking through a tube at a mirrored scene of himself and objects on the table. (See Figure 5–5.) The images of objects thus seen were reduced by a factor of about two. During this exposure phase, the subject engaged in three activities successively, each for one third of the total time: card playing (solitaire), drawing pictures, and playing checkers.

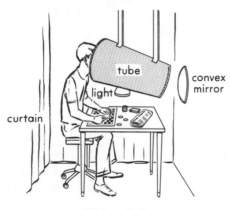

Figure 5–5

The method of measuring adaptation was first to present a standard object (a line) to the subject, which he then judged from memory. The line used was 12 inches long but was not identified as having any particular length. If adaptation occurred, the subject would select a shorter line, following the exposure period, as representing the remembered length of the line than he had prior to the exposure period. In other words, assuming the subject accurately remembered the length of the standard line at the time of the post-exposure test (a fact substantiated by a control experiment), in seeking to communicate this remembered length, he would have to select a shorter line if adaptation had occurred. This is so because shorter images of lines would now signify phenomenal extents previously associated with longer images. The standard line was presented on the wall for a brief period with room lights on. The lights were then turned

[9] A brief account of the work to be reported has been published. See I. Rock, Adaptation to a minified image, *Psychon. Sci.*, 1965, **2**, 105–106.

off, and the subject indicated when a variable-length luminous line appeared equal to the just-seen standard. This process was repeated several times to provide ample experience with the standard and a base line against which to measure adaptation. Following the period of exposure to the mirrored scene (which lasted one half hour in the first series of experiments), the subject was brought back to the same position near the wall. He now made two settings of the luminous line based on his memory of the length of the standard line seen previously.

The usefulness of the method just described depends upon the ability of subjects to remember the size of the standard after the exposure period and hence to judge its size fairly accurately and consistently. To ascertain how accurately this can be done, a control experiment was performed in which subjects were *not* exposed to the convex-mirrored scene between pre- and post-exposure testing. Instead they were exposed to the same scene, reflected by a plane mirror, and viewed through the tube. Here no adaptation is expected to occur. The results confirmed this expectation. The mean difference between the pre-exposure judgments of the length of the standard and the post-exposure judgments was negligible, namely, +.11 inches.[10]

The procedure for the main experiment was essentially identical to that of the control experiment, except that the convex minifying mirror was employed in place of the plane mirror. Here a substantial decrement in the post-exposure judgments of the length of the standard was obtained. The mean difference between pre- and post-exposure settings of the line was −1.35 inches, a statistically significant change. Hence adaptation to a minified image was attained in a fairly short period of time. Total adaptation would require a post-exposure setting of about half of the pre-exposure setting. Against this base line, a reduction of 1.35 inches is 23 per cent of full adaptation.[11]

[10] This value is one of the two possible measures of adaptation employed. Detailed results are given in the Addendum.

[11] After some of our earlier experiments were completed, a doctoral dissertation from Clark University by Duilio Giannitrapani came to my attention: Changes in adaptation to prolonged perceptual distortion, Doctoral dissertation, Clark University, 1958. Giannitrapani used a magnifying lens system with children, a 10-minute exposure period, and a measurement procedure which entailed matching a visual extent to a rod held but not seen. Although he reports a substantial effect comparing the pre- and post-exposure measures with lenses on (a comparison open to question), the same comparison with lenses off yielded only a negligible change. Hence it is not clear that he actually did obtain an adaptation effect. There are various reasons for doubting that his procedure would yield such an effect.

Subsequent to the appearance of the preliminary report of our work, Joan E. Foley

Adaptation to a "Miniature World"

The experiment reported above employed an optical method of reducing the size of images of objects in the environment. Since the entire visible world is thereby consistently transposed downward so to speak, adaptation to the minified image is to be expected. All information that the observer obtains attests to the true sizes of things seen. What would be the effect of creating the same reduction of retinal image size not by optical distortion, but by actually constructing a "miniature world"? In the case of familiar objects such as we employed, this is a relevant question because the impression one gets in viewing such a world should at first be indistinguishable from that of viewing the optically minified world. In saying this I am assuming for the moment that the observer does not view his own body or parts of it in either scene and also that he does not move. In other words, the retinal image of a half-sized playing card is indistinguishable from that of a normal-sized card viewed through an optical device that halves the apparent size of objects at a certain distance.

Ought adaptation to occur to such a miniature world? The answer, I believe, depends very much on what other information is supplied to the observer. If no other information is given, it is possible that the subject would react to this new image as veridically representing the various objects contained therein. We have seen that the transposition of geometrical line patterns has a powerful effect on size. That is to say, from the work cited above, we should predict that there would be a tendency for an object within the miniature scene to look very much the same size as one seen normally in the same context of other objects. Furthermore, the relationship of the size of *familiar* objects to one another is preserved

---

undertook research on adaptation to size and distance, in which her subjects wore magnifying or minifying binoculars over a period of three weeks. The effects obtained are slight, difficult to interpret, and primarily represent changes in the judgment of distance. The binoculars created false impressions of distance similar to those we encountered when using a lens system. J. E. Foley, Adaptation to magnifying and minifying spectacles, unpublished paper.

The effect of magnification and minification on motor performance has been explored in an experiment by K. U. Smith and W. M. Smith. Chapter 11 in *Perception and motion*, Philadelphia: Saunders, 1962. Subjects were required to perform manual tasks guided only by the televised scene of their hand and target objects. The scene was either magnified or reduced. Performance was not noticeably affected despite the fact that a conflict existed between vision and proprioception.

here so that this defining aspect of the phenomenal size of objects calls for acceptance of things as normal in size. But in addition to these reasons, based on familiarity with the normal size of objects, there may be a tendency to interpret these half-sized replicas of familiar objects as larger than they actually are. In that event, the "information" would be incorrect, but it may nevertheless produce an adaptation effect. The smaller visual angle produced by the half-sized object may become associated with the normal phenomenal size of the object rather than with the actual diminutive size of the object.

Thus there are reasons for believing the process of adaptation would be set in motion under the conditions described. On the other hand, the observer is not given information that these half-sized objects are normal in size in relation to the phenomenal self because, under the conditions being considered, he does not see his body. In fact, if he did see his body, the small size of the objects present would be confirmed. If the observer remains stationary, no information is available via movement concerning the actual size of the objects. It is, therefore, difficult to predict the outcome of such an experiment. The best guess would be that some adaptation will be achieved, but not as much as when the entire scene of objects and self are optically minified.

To test this question, the observer viewed a scene essentially identical to the one employed in the previous experiments. The major difference was that the objects were half their customary size and the mirror through which they were seen was a normal or plane one. Checkers and checkerboard were made half size, playing cards and several pages of a familiar newspaper were photostatically reduced to half size. These objects were distributed around the surface of the table. This experiment was performed with two different groups of subjects under slightly different conditions. For both groups no part of the body was visible. For Group A the head was placed on a chin rest inside the tube, minimizing but perhaps not completely eliminating head movement. The exposure period was 30 minutes. For Group B a bite board was used, completely preventing head movements, and a 10-minute exposure period was used. The subjects in Group B served in five different conditions, but an interval of several days separated these conditions. Thus these subjects served as their own controls in the comparison of different conditions. For both groups the testing before and after exposure was identical to that employed in the previously described experiments.

The mean difference between pre- and post-exposure settings obtained for Group A was −.80 inches, and this is significantly greater than 0. Although this value is not significantly different from the average difference score in the experiment described earlier entailing minification, namely, −1.35 inches, it is nevertheless probable that exposure to minification does yield a greater effect than exposure to half-sized objects. This conclusion is strongly supported by the results for Group B. The average difference score for these subjects was −.27 inches, which is not quite significantly greater than 0, but it is significantly different from an average difference score of −.71 inches achieved by these same subjects under conditions of minification. This condition entailed a 10-minute exposure to the optically minified scene of familiar objects. The subject's head was held stationary by a bite board, but his hands were free to move within the scene. Here the subject saw a good bit of his own body through the convex mirror. The smaller adaptation effect achieved in this condition (−.71 inches) in comparison with the effect obtained in the main experiment reported earlier, is possibly attributable to the shorter time of exposure, but may also be a function of the population tested. In any event, the use of the same subjects in both conditions (minification and half-sized objects), with the resulting clear-cut difference in outcome, allows us to conclude with confidence that there is a factor in minification that leads to greater adaptation than merely the presence of familiar objects half their normal size. Concerning the failure to achieve a significant effect to exposure to half-sized objects for Group B, the fact that the result approached significance, that it *was* significant for Group A, and that, in many repetitions of this condition with slight variations, an effect was obtained, allows us to feel quite certain that there is an effect of such exposure on subsequent impressions of size.

That the effect obtained with half-sized objects may be based purely on the information provided by familiarity with identical objects of normal size, rather than on information based on the relationships between object sizes, is shown by the results of an experiment in which only one familiar object at a time was exposed. For one third of the exposure period the observer viewed only the half-sized newspaper, with no other objects visible and similarly the other objects were presented in isolation. This procedure yielded a modest but nonetheless significant effect. The fact that in this and the preceding experiments the test object (a line) was different from any of the objects seen during exposure indicates that the effect that occurs is one that pertains to size in general and is not merely specific to the familiar objects employed. One must conclude that mere exposure to a diminutive replica of a familiar object can have the effect of altering the entire system of calibration in the neural substrate according to which specific image extents signify specific phenomenal extents.

Is the effect obtained with half-sized familiar objects one which could be considered to be of the same kind as prism adaptation? Of course, an optical device is not employed, but we have seen in the work on adaptation to altered displacement of the image contingent on head movement that effects indistinguishable from those yielded by prisms can be obtained without prisms, provided the relevant changes in the proximal stimulus are created in some other way. The answer, I believe, rests on the question of whether the effect obtained is based on information about the environment or whether it is based on configurational interactions. The effect is clearly not merely configurational, because it depends upon the content of the objects seen. Exposure to a rectangle the size of a half-sized newspaper will not yield any effect.[12] The miniature replica of a familiar object *is* a source of information concerning the environment. Hence I would consider the effect to be of the same kind as prism adaptation.

Given prolonged exposure of a less restricted kind to a world of miniature objects, I should imagine the kind of effect we have obtained would tend to disappear. If the observer sees his own body it will be evident that, in relation to the self, these objects are actually smaller than their normal size.[13] If the observer has information that all visible objects are half size with respect to himself and if, in addition, he has information based on his own movements that all objects are half size, and if, further, this information is present during longer periods of exposure than used in our experiments, then I would predict the effect of familiarity would soon be eradicated. Conversely, given the same prolonged and unrestricted conditions of exposure to optical minification, adaptation should increase over time and, in this case, familiar size would be a cooperating determinant. The argument here parallels the one advanced earlier concerning the probable long-term differential effect of exposure to true prismatic tilting of the entire field vs. exposure to an actually tilted room.

[12] Relevant to this question is the fact that we did not obtain any effect when exposure to the minified scene was only of 10 seconds' duration. This seems to argue against an interpretation in terms of successive contrast.

[13] We did obtain a slight effect in experiments in which the observer could see his hands among the half-sized objects, but the period of exposure was as brief as in the experiments described above and the exposure was also confined to what could be seen on the table through the tube.

SUMMARY

[N O T E : *Sentences in brackets refer to material presented in the Adden-dum which follows.*]

The question was raised as to the nature of the relationship between the absolute size of the retinal image and the specific phenomenal size of the corresponding object. It was argued that the phenomenal impression of size is based on the size of an object relative to all other objects, including the body of the observer. This information is conveyed by the size of the retinal images of objects, including the body, relative to one another (assuming for the sake of simplicity that all objects are located in a plane at one distance from the observer). That being the case, the absolute size of the entire retinal image is not directly relevant—the correlation between retinal size and phenomenal size is not vitiated if the image is optically magnified or minified. Evidence attesting to the importance of relative image size in size perception was described. The apparent size of a line is to a considerable extent a function of the size of the frame of reference within which it is viewed.

However, it is the case that for an adult observer all objects in an optically minified scene initially appear somewhat diminutive and that an object seen in isolation from other objects does appear to be a specific size. To explain these facts it is necessary to assume that the absolute size of the retinal image has come to signify a specific phenomenal size. From prior experience, an association is established between a given size of image and information concerning the phenomenal size of the corresponding object. Adaptation to a magnified or minified image would therefore consist of replacing the memory traces representing this association with new ones faithful to the altered size of the retinal images of objects. Information as to the true size of objects could be based upon the perceived size of objects relative to one another and to the self, upon familiarity with objects known to have specific sizes, or upon movement of the observer through space. In the case of movement, the information would be based upon information that the head traverses a different angular extent in scanning an object than the apparent angular extent of that object.

Evidence was presented that exposure to an optically minified scene (yielded by a convex mirror) of durations of 10 to 30 minutes results in adaptation to the altered size. [It is sufficient for the observer to view the scene of familiar objects including portions of his own body while remaining stationary.] A somewhat smaller adaptation effect was obtained when the observer was exposed not to an optically reduced field but to an actual "miniature world" of familiar objects. However, it was predicted that over a sufficient period of free and active exposure, in which information as to the diminutive size of these objects in relation to the self would be continuously available, this adaptation effect would tend to disappear.

ADDENDUM

Methodology and Details of Procedure in Experiments on Minification

The optical system first employed to study adaptation to a minified image was essentially a reverse Galilean telescope. It consisted of a negative lens which had the effect of reducing the image of objects at a distance of 18 inches or more by about half. To alleviate the strained accommodation that would be required in order to view the nearby virtual image formed by the negative lens, a positive eyepiece lens was placed in front of the negative lens. Rays coming through the positive lens to the eye were more or less parallel. The lenses were set in a tube that allowed a field of about 40°.

This device proved to be a failure, but it was not immediately clear that this was the case. As a matter of fact, several years of research were conducted before it became evident that adaptation was not consistently produced with this lens system. Although it still is not certain why this device failed in its intended purpose, there are good reasons for believing that the trouble lay in the fact that objects seen through it not only appeared smaller but also appeared farther away. This fact is itself not clearly understood. The rays of light reaching the eye are essentially parallel, so that the lens of the eye would tend to flatten out as in viewing objects at a great distance. But the accommodation cue alone is ordinarily not thought to be as potent as the effect in question seems to be. A possible explanation is that the accommodation cue, together with the cue created by the diminutive images of familiar objects, may conjointly produce the impression that they are quite far away.

But whatever the cause of the distance effect, one can see how it could operate to nullify adaptation to a minified image. If the greater apparent distance of the objects seen through the device is taken into account, then the apparent size of the objects will be boosted precisely as occurs in yielding constancy in daily life. If an object appeared twice as far as it actually was, then its half-sized image would be expected to yield a percept normal in size. As a matter of fact, many observers did report that what they saw appeared farther away but not necessarily smaller. The same impression is gained in looking through field binoculars in reverse. Hence our observers were not exposed to stimulation in which the half-sized visual angles at first signified half-sized objects at a certain distance. Rather they were confronted with information that the half-sized visual angles signified more or less normal-sized objects at greater than their actual distances. Consequently, one cannot study adaptation to altered size because the constancy function is already present in the subject's repetoire.[14]

A solution that finally suggested itself was to use a convex mirror. A convex mirror yields reduced, virtual images of objects as does a negative lens, but it does not seem to create the impression that objects are farther away than they actually are. The reason for this may be that a convex mirror is optically equivalent to a negative lens alone, rather than to a lens *system* such as is described above. The mirror can be placed at a distance such that the virtual images are easily accommodated, and a large mirror can be used to provide an adequate field of view. Minification will allow the observer to see a fairly large region of the environment within the mirrored scene. Binocular vision can be used without any of the problems encountered with lens systems. In our experiments, the mirror was 12 inches in diameter with a radius of curvature of 48 inches. For objects located about 2 feet in front of the mirror, virtual images of about half size were formed at a distance of about 1 foot beyond the plane of the mirror.[15]

The procedure for exposure to the optically reduced scene was to require the subject to sit at a table and view objects placed on the table

[14] Of course, one could study adaptation to altered distance perception, but that is a totally different problem.

[15] The position of the virtual image is given by the formula $1/q = 2/R - 1/p$ where q is the distance of the image from the plane of the mirror, R is the radius of curvature of the mirror, and p is the distance of the object (24 inches in this case). With $R = 48$, q is -12. The size of the image is given by the formula $S_i = S_o \times q/p$ where S_i = size of image and S_o = size of object. For an object of 12 inches, $S_i = 6$ inches. In addition to this computation, an empirical determination was made of the apparent size and apparent distance of a 12-inch luminous line resting on the table about 2 feet from the mirror. The line was observed through the mirror in total darkness and then matched to a variable line seen in full illumination. Following several such matches, the line's apparent distance was judged also in full illumination. The average length of the line for 10 subjects was 6 inches. The average distance was 37.4 inches. Since the mirror was about 24 inches from the subject's eyes, this corresponds rather closely with the computed value of 36 inches (24 + 12).

through the mirror. He could not see anything except through the mirror. To accomplish this he viewed the scene through a large tube as depicted in Figure 5–5. The interior of the tube was the only part of the scene that was directly visible, i.e., not viewed through the mirror, but pains were taken to prevent any illumination from reaching it, and it was lined with black felt. However, the subject's own face seen *through* the mirror at the end of the tube *was* visible as a silhouette. In addition to seeing his face through the mirrored tube, the subject saw a portion of his trunk below the tube, his hands and arms, and the objects used which were placed on the top of the table.

The problem of how to measure adaptation to the minified image proved to be a difficult one. Presumably, objects seen through the convex mirror would, at the outset, appear quite small. Following a period of exposure, they should appear somewhat more normal in size or, if adaptation were complete, completely normal. This suggested presenting a standard of some specific length for judgment both before and after the exposure period. How should the size judgment be made? Obviously if the standard were matched to a variable object, this would tell us nothing about the subject's impression of the phenomenal size of either (the El Greco fallacy). Measuring adaptation in the case of size is a difficult problem, because there is no distinctive or unique size that can be relied on. One way of getting around the problem is to use some non-visual response to the standard. Judgments could be made by touch, and this method was tried. The danger here, however, is that spatial perception via touch may itself undergo adaptation (see Chapter 7). In that case proprioception would yield spurious information about vision, as Harris has shown for the pointing response.[16]

What seems to be required then is to ascertain the apparent size of a standard based upon some particular phenomenal size the subject carries in memory. For example, the subject could be asked to set a line equal to a standard unit of measurement before and after the adaptation period. Before adaptation, a given length, such as a 12-inch line, should be estimated more or less correctly. Following adaptation to a minified image, assuming it to be complete for purposes of discussion, a 12-inch line should now appear to be 24 inches long (a negative aftereffect), so that the line would have to be set much smaller, namely 6 inches long, in order to appear 12 inches long. This method is acceptable, and it was used in preliminary work, but it was discovered that many people are very

[16] C. S. Harris, Adaptation to displaced vision: Visual, motor, or proprioceptive change? *Science*, 1963, **140**, 812–813.

inaccurate in estimating length in terms of standard units of measurement.

There is one other point to be made clear about the methodology. The test line should be exposed in isolation, which is easily achieved by using a luminous line in total darkness. If this is not done, if for example the line is seen in a fully articulated environment, one can hardly expect much of an effect to manifest itself. It seems unlikely that a 12-inch line, seen in a normal room following the exposure period, could be expected to appear to be 24 inches long. For that to be true the entire room would have to appear twice its size. Otherwise, the size of the line relative to other visible objects provides a cue that would tend to counteract any adaptation effect.

The method that finally evolved was first to present a standard object, a line, which the subject then judged from memory.[17] In order to provide ample exposure to the standard line and to establish a base line of judgments of its length prior to adaptation, the following procedure was adopted. The line (12 inches long and $\frac{1}{16}$ inch wide) was presented on the wall with the lights on for 10 seconds. The subject was positioned 2 feet from the wall. He was told to look at it and note its length. The room lights were turned off, and the subject had to indicate when the line (now luminous) was the same length as the just-seen standard. It was varied in short steps by the experimenter at a constant rate in either an ascending or descending direction. The subject was allowed to request reversal of direction, and he was encouraged to make any adjustment necessary to satisfy himself on the correctness of his match. In later variations the subject himself adjusted the line. He was then blindfolded, the line was set again at 12 inches, the room lights were turned on, and another view of the standard given. Following this, another match was made in the dark. After every judgment the standard line was exposed again. Altogether eight judgments were made, four ascending and four descending in an ADDA ADDA or DAAD DAAD order. The average

---

[17] Another method that was tried and that has much to recommend it was as follows. The subject was asked when a variable-sized familiar object appeared to be normal in size. A graduated series of luminous pictures of a familiar object such as a playing card was presented in the dark. The subject had to indicate which picture was normal in size. This method relies on the fact that memory for the size of a familiar object of a certain constant size is quite good. Following adaptation, the subject would presumably perceive the normal-sized card as too large, because a smaller image has become identified with that particular phenomenal size. Hence he should select a smaller card. Because different subjects had varying past experience with playing cards (as would be true for virtually any such object), the procedure was modified by showing the subject a normal-sized card shortly before the experiment began. This presentation also served as a more recent exposure to the object in question.

of these eight settings can be taken as a pre-adaptation base line, but it was felt that an average of the last two of the eight settings would also be a valid measure to use, because these settings were based on the greatest amount of experience with the standard and were closest in time to the post-adaptation judgments. Following the period of exposure to the mirrored scene, the subject was brought back to the same position near the wall. He now judged the luminous line in terms of his memory of the line as seen previously. One ascending and one descending setting was made. More judgments would have added reliability to the measure, but it was felt that the adaptation effect might wear off with the passage of time.[18] Order of ascending and descending trials was systematically varied from subject to subject, as was their order during pre-adaptation trials.

The subjects in the first series of experiments reported here were boys and girls of high school age.

Results of Experiments

Control Experiment

In the control experiment a plane mirror was used instead of a convex mirror. Since these conditions are identical with those of the other experiments to be reported, except for the factor of minification, the ability to judge the line's length from memory can be assessed in the most relevant way. A further purpose of this control experiment was to provide a base line against which to measure the effect of exposure to minification. If minification is expected to yield a reduction in the judged size of the line following exposure, it must be shown that such a reduction does not occur or is not of the same magnitude when conditions are otherwise comparable but minification is not present. During the exposure period, as in the main experiment, the subject engaged in the three activities already described, each for one third of the time.

The results were as follows. The mean of the eight pre-exposure mean judgments for the nine subjects employed was 10.71, revealing a tendency to underestimate the 12-inch standard line, a tendency shown in virtually every experiment performed using this method. This constant error undoubtedly is based on the difference in appearance of a luminous and

---

[18] In a few experiments, more than two post-exposure settings were obtained, and it was found that the adaptive effect was indeed beginning to disappear as a function of time.

non-luminous line, the former appearing larger when objectively equal to the latter. However, subjects are fairly consistent in their judgments. An average range of a little over 1 inch for the last two pre-exposure judgments or the two post-exposure judgments was obtained, which is impressively small if one keeps in mind that ascending and descending trials typically yield a substantial spread.

T A B L E 5–1 *Results of Control Experiment*

Subject	Difference 1 *	Difference 2 **
1	+.87	+.22
2	+.37	+.25
3	+.38	+.26
4	+.50	−.03
5	−.62	+.28
6	+.25	−1.23
7	0	+.60
8	−.50	−.22
9	−.25	.43
Mean	+.11	−.03

* Difference 1 = difference between mean of last two pre-exposure judgments and mean of two post-exposure judgments.

** Difference 2 = difference between mean of all pre-exposure judgments and mean of two post-exposure judgments.

The main results are shown in Table 5–1 under the columns headed Difference 1 and Difference 2. Taking the average of the last two pre-exposure trials as the base line, there is little change over time. The average of the two post-exposure trials is 10.68, a value almost identical to the 10.57 average of the last two pre-exposure trials. The same is true taking the average of all pre-exposure trials as the base line. One might have assumed that the pre-exposure judgments would be fairly consistent (since they were based on immediate memory of the standard), but the results of the post-exposure trials are gratifying in that they show that the phenomenal length of the standard was preserved in memory with considerable accuracy. These results, therefore, set the stage for the proper evaluation of the subsequent experiments.

Exposure to a Minified Image

The general procedure has already been described. In this experiment, as in the previous one, the subject engaged in three successive activities, each for 10 minutes. In doing so, he moved his arms and hands freely on the table and moved the objects at will. His head and trunk did not move very much because it was necessary to maintain the position of the head inside the tube. However, there was no attempt to restrict movements except to ensure that the subject never withdrew from the tube during the exposure period. Once this period began, all possible precautions were taken to make sure the subject could not see anything other than the mirrored scene until the post-adaptation measures had been secured. Otherwise, there was the possibility that the adaptation would be canceled out.

T A B L E 5–2   *Results of Experiment on Minified Image*

Subject	Difference 1	Difference 2
1	0	+.26
2	−1.00	−.90
3	−.75	−1.85
4	−1.50	−1.60
5	−2.75	−1.31
6	−2.50	−2.40
7	−1.37	−1.90
8	−.88	−1.38
9	−3.20	−2.40
10	−.25	+.50
11	−2.87	−2.50
12	+.13	−.52
13	−1.12	−1.93
14	−.75	−.73
15	−1.38	−.66
Mean	−1.35	−1.29

The results were as follows. The variability was somewhat higher in this experiment, but still reflected considerable consistency in judgment. The main findings shown in Table 5–2, in which the mean differences are given under columns headed Difference 1 and 2, indicate a substantial adaptation effect. From an average pre-adaptation value of 11.57 inches, the mean estimate of the standard length following adaptation fell to 10.22, a decline of 1.35 inches.

It can be seen from the table that many individuals have large negative difference scores. If the variability of the control group (SD = .5) is taken as an index of the variability of a population of subjects for whom the mean difference score is zero (i.e., no adaptation), then a difference of ±1 for any randomly selected subject could only be expected to occur 5 per cent of the time. If so, there are many subjects in the experimental condition whose difference score clearly implies they have adapted.

Adaptation without Movement

In the light of the controversy about the role of active movement in yielding adaptation effects, it was thought desirable to ascertain whether visual changes based on the observer's movement played any role (or possibly a necessary role) in adaptation to altered image size. However, when an optical device such as a convex mirror which does not move with the head is used, the kind of information (discussed earlier) that may be provided by movement is not available. That is, if the head moves through an angle of 30°, the retinal image of the scene reflected through the mirror will displace by 30°, *not* 15°, as is the case with minifying lenses that move with the head. Consider an object in the field which physically subtends an angle of 60° and appears to subtend an angle of 30° seen through the mirror. When the head moves 30° it will go from one end of that object to the other. Therefore, any information based on head movement will actually confirm the fact that the object is one which *does* subtend an angle of 30°, rather than inform the subject that the apparent 30° angle is actually one of 60°. If this is correct, the head movement permitted in the previous experiment on minification would, if anything, oppose adaptation. Therefore, in the experiment now to be described, where head movement is eliminated, there is certainly no reason to expect any lessened effect.

The observer was told to remain absolutely stationary. He rested his arms on the table, and they were seen through the mirror along with the other objects in the field, namely, checkers and checkerboard, newspaper,[19] and playing cards. His chin was placed firmly on a metal bar at the bottom of the viewing tube. The subjects were observed carefully throughout the 30-minute exposure. Those who shifted their positions at any time were disqualified. Occasional rest periods were permitted in which the subject could move freely while he was blindfolded. Otherwise, the procedure for the entire experiment was like those already described.

The results were as follows. The mean Difference 1 score was −1.11, and the mean Difference 2 score was −.99. There was thus a substantial reduction in the length of the line the subject considered equal to the

[19] In this and various other experiments, reading a newspaper took the place of the picture-drawing activity used during the exposure period in the previously described experiments.

standard following the exposure period. These values are significantly different from zero and are not significantly lower than those obtained in the main experiment on minification. Nine of the ten subjects showed a decline; eight showed an appreciable decline. Hence it is quite clear that an adaptation effect is produced without movement of the observer. Since no effect of movement is to be expected when minification is produced by a mirror, this experiment serves primarily as a repetition and confirmation of the earlier findings. However, the reader's attention is called to footnote 5 on page 152, which describes preliminary research utilizing a lens system worn on the head. Here an effect of movement *is* to be expected, but none was obtained.

Variations in Duration and Method of Measurement

Following the research reported above, certain changes in procedure were introduced. One such change was to permit the observer himself to vary the length of the luminous line. A short handle was attached at right angles to the narrow band of cardboard on which the luminous line was painted. By moving it to the left or right, the visible line was lengthened or shortened. Since prior to each judgment the experimenter set the line to some value arbitrarily shorter or longer than 12 inches for ascending and descending trials respectively, the subject could not gauge his setting by the remembered extent of movement from previous trials.

In the same experiment the exposure period was reduced to 10 minutes. There was no way of determining precisely how much exposure was necessary to yield an effect, and the choice of 30 minutes in the previous experiments was more or less arbitrary. Work on adaptation to a displaced image has indicated that significant effects can be obtained in even shorter periods. The only other change in procedure from that of the earlier experiment on minification was the inclusion of all objects in the scene throughout the exposure period (rather than introducing them one at a time), although one third of the time activity was centered on cards, checkers, or drawing pictures, respectively.

The results indicate that permitting the subject to adjust the line himself increases the reliability of the measure, judging by the reduced variability of the settings. The accuracy of judgment seems to improve as well with this method, since the average pre-settings are closer to 12 inches. The average Difference 1 score was $-.85$ for ten subjects, and the average Difference 2 score was -1.04. These values are significantly greater than zero. Seven subjects show a sizable decrease in their judgments.

Is adaptation quantitatively less in 10 minutes than 30 minutes? The mean difference score of −.85 is not significantly lower than that of the earlier experiment (−1.35), but the two experiments are not identical in procedure. A few subjects who had participated in other experiments and had shown adaptation were rerun with 2-hour exposure periods. There was no clear trend except that they all again gave evidence of adaptation. Hence from the data at hand it is not possible to say anything about progressive adaptation over time.

"Miniature World"

The procedure of these experiments is adequately described in the chapter proper. The results are given in Table 5–3.

T A B L E 5–3 *Results of Experiments on a "Miniature World"*

GROUP A			GROUP B		
Subject	Difference 1	Difference 2	Subject	Difference 1	Difference 2
1	−1.62	−1.12	1	−.62	−.81
2	−.87	−1.31	2	−1.00	−1.19
3	−.75	−.91	3	−.62	−.91
4	+.25	+1.59	4	−.87	−1.04
5	−.50	−.47	5	+.75	+.53
6	−2.00	−2.03	6	−.75	−.97
7	−.50	−.48	7	−.75	−.97
8	−2.25	−2.80	8	+.50	+.56
9	−.88	−.85	9	−1.62	−1.66
10	+.87	+1.47	10	−1.62	−1.29
11	0	−.59	11	−2.25	−1.66
12	−1.38	−1.22	12	+1.12	+1.34
Mean	−.80	−.73	13	+.25	+.12
			14	−.12	+.12
			15	−.62	−.54
			16	+.12	+.34
			17	0	+.15
			18	−.50	−.34
			19	+.75	+.47
			20	−.50	−.41
			21	−.50	−.72
			22	+.12	+.03
			23	0	−.63
			24	+1.00	+1.03
			25	+1.00	+.53
			Mean	−.27	−.32

Control for a Distance-Adaptation Effect

Is it possible that the effect we obtained is due to some change in distance perception rather than a change in size perception? Since size and distance perception are ordinarily inextricably related, this possibility must always be considered. Suppose, for whatever reason, adaptation affecting distance perception occurred during the exposure to the convex mirror, so that objects tended to appear farther away after the exposure period. The test line would look longer (if it appeared farther than it actually was), in keeping with Emmert's law. This is precisely what was found, namely, a negative aftereffect resulting in the subject's selecting a smaller line to compensate for the effect. Thus the result could conceivably be an artifact of adaptation to altered distance cues.

Is there any basis for such an effect to occur? Although the situation is complicated, the possibility exists that there is. The virtual image created by the convex mirror is located only about half as far away from its surface as the objects it reflects. The objects located on the top of the table were about 2 feet from the mirror, but their reflected images would be only 1 foot from it. If, therefore, the subject at first mislocated objects as nearer than they actually were, he might in time adapt. Adaptation would then consist in his interpreting distance cues as signifying greater distance than before. The complication here is that the scene in question is a mirrored one, so that when we say "nearer" or "farther" we mean with respect to the plane of the mirror. What is "farther" from the mirror is nearer to the observer. Hence it would be foolhardy to make a definite prediction as to what, if anything, might be expected to happen. Certainly no subjects reported that anything about the distance of things seemed awry.

Nevertheless, as a check on a possible change in the interpretation of distance cues, an experiment was performed which was identical with that of the size-adaptation procedure, except that distance judgments were obtained before and after the exposure period, rather than size judgments. In the pre-exposure measure, the subject was shown a line on the wall from a fixed distance, as in the preceding experiments, with the room lights on. Then in the dark he moved his chair forward with his feet (in descending trials) or backward (in ascending trials) until he gauged the distance to the line to be the same as before. Eight such trials were given, half descending (subject moved far from wall prior to judgments), half ascending (subject moved near to wall prior to judgment). The size of the line was varied from trial to trial to avoid utilization of remembered size as a basis of judgment in the post-exposure measures. The subject's head was stabilized in a chin rest. The pre-exposure measures were intended to afford a base line for judgment of distance when such judgment must be made in the dark. Following the exposure period of 30 minutes, which was conducted in the same way as the size-minification experiments, the subject was again brought before the wall in the dark. Now he was given one ascending and one descending trial in which he had to gauge from memory when a small luminous circle was the same distance from himself as the lines seen previously in the light had been (a small circle rather than a line was used to discourage utilization of remembered size rather than distance).

If distance cues now signified a greater distance than previously, the circle, when at the correct distance, would appear too far away. To compensate, the subject would have to position himself nearer to the wall than he did in the pre-exposure measures. The results did not substantiate such a prediction. Four of five subjects tested positioned themselves slightly farther away afterwards than before. One subject did show a decrease of around 5 inches. However, no subject revealed a change that might be considered to be significantly outside the range of judgments made before the exposure period. Hence one can only conclude that if there was any change in distance perception, we were not able to detect it with our method.

Adaptation to

Optical Distortion

of Form

CHAPTER SIX

What is the relationship between the specific shape of the image and the phenomenally perceived shape? Consider the problem of the perception of curvature. The question is essentially this: Is an image that is straight the stimulus correlate of a phenomenal straight line, and, similarly, is an image that has a certain value of curvature the correlate of a phenomenally curved line of a corresponding value? For an adult, the answer of course is "yes" and, if we restrict our discussion to a frontal plane, a straight line in the environment yields an image that is straight, and a curved line yields an image that is correspondingly curved. Hence perception of curvature is quite veridical. The environmental line, its retinal image and the phenomenal line are all congruent.

But what the question is getting at is whether it is *necessarily* the case that an image which is straight must be the correlate of a straight phenomenal line. It seems to have been assumed by many that the geometry of the retinal or cortical pattern of excitation is sufficient to explain the corresponding phenomenal geometrical properties of the object. The discovery of the orderly cortical mapping of the retinal image seems to have done away with interest in the origin of the spatial attributes of retinal local signs, such as existed at the time of Helmholtz.[1] Many nativists have felt that there can be no answer to the question of why a square looks the

[1] Hebb is a notable exception. (See D. Hebb, *The organization of behavior,* New York: Wiley, 1949.)

176

way it does and a circle looks the way it does. One can only point to the geometrically different cortical patterns in the two cases. The realization that forms are transposable in position and size served further to under-score the crucial role of geometrical relationships between the elements of the image of a figure as the essential correlate of shape. Therefore it has been implicitly assumed that the perception of a shape quality such as curvature is directly given by the shape of the image.

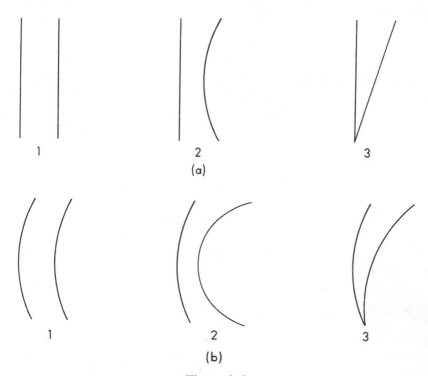

Figure 6–1

However, if phenomenal shape is essentially based on the spatial relationships of the elements of a figure to one another, then, following the same logic as in the cases of orientation and size, the specific curva-ture of any element of the retinal image of a figure ought not to be crucial. That is to say, if the entire image were to be consistently transformed —for example, curved in one direction as by a wedge prism [2]—the spatial *relationships* between elements would remain invariant. Thus, in Figure

---

[2] Light entering the prism from above or below has a different angle of incidence than light entering from straight ahead, such that different regions of a vertical line will be displaced differentially. The result is that a straight line yields a curved image.

6–1, in each pair, *b* is such a transformation of *a*. If we consider only the spatial separation between the two lines along the horizontal direction in each *a* figure, this separation is exactly maintained in the corresponding *b* figure. In Pair 1, the vertical lines are parallel to each other in both *a* and *b*; in Pair 2, they curve away from each other by the same magnitude in both *a* and *b*; in Pair 3, they diverge from a common point at the bottom at the same rate in both *a* and *b*.

Hence, insofar as such intra-figural characteristics are concerned, the *b* images should be as informative or accurately representative as the *a* images. Yet it is also clear that the *a* and *b* versions do not look alike. They are discriminable with respect to the degree of curvature of each line element. Apparently, then, what we mean by degree of curvature is not something that can be defined solely in terms of the manner in which lines relate to other lines. In fact, this must be true because an impression of the curvature of a line is immediately present even in viewing it in isolation, as in the case of a luminous line seen in the dark, with no other lines to relate it to.

Is it possible to say anything about the characteristics of a phenomenal straight line as compared to a curved one, or is the perceived shape of a line as irreducible a quality as color or taste? It would seem that there are certain characteristics which can be specified. One of these has to do with the apparent direction of points on a line with respect to the observer. If an observer stands in front of a large curved line, as shown in Figure 6–2, only a small region of it appears to lie straight ahead. Other parts lie off to the side and increasingly so for points farther up or down the line. If the observer were to move up or down, he would no longer be directly in front of any region of the line. All this, of course, would be different if the line were straight. Hence, one characteristic of a phenomenal straight line is that all points on it are simultaneously straight ahead of the observer when it is vertically aligned in the sagittal plane, or all points are simultaneously at eye level when it is horizontally aligned in the plane of the eyes. More generally, regardless of where the line is in a frontal plane or what its orientation is in relation to the observer, points on it alter their positions with respect to the observer's sagittal or horizontal axis at a *constant* rate only if the line is straight.

There are other properties of straight lines that also are related to the way lines behave, so to speak, when we perform certain operations. A straight line can be viewed from different vantage points or rotated about one of its ends without changing its projected curvature; a straight line projects as a point when seen head on; a straight line is seen when a string is

pulled taut or a plumb line is dropped; the shortest phenomenal line connecting any two points is a straight line.[3] The closer a curved line is to a
straight one, the closer it comes to behaving in accordance with these properties. It would seem then that these characteristics "define" phenomenal
straightness and, therefore, a line which has these properties ought to appear straight.

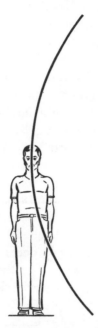

Figure 6–2

The first three of these properties have to do with the relationship of
line to observer (direction of points on line from the observer; constancy
of projected curvature; projection as a point when viewed head on) and
the next two (taut string, plumb line) clearly refer to rather infrequently
occurring events which can hardly play a very significant role. This fits
with the conclusion reached above, that there does not seem to be any
basis for distinguishing "straight" from "curved" purely in terms of how

[3] This criterion parallels the one that geometers might be expected to emphasize.
However, in Euclidean geometry there is no rigorous way of defining a straight line.
It is impossible to do so without already assuming one knows intuitively what it is. A
physical operation for determining "shortest distance," such as pulling a string taut,
is not acceptable as a mathematical definition. How is "shortest distance" otherwise to
be determined since measuring instruments already presuppose "straightness"? Natu-
rally a straight path would be shortest if shortest is determined by a straight ruler.

one line relates to another. Thus it would seem that there are two aspects of shape that ought to be distinguished. One is the purely *object-relative aspect,* by which I mean the manner in which line elements relate to one another; the other the purely *subject-relative aspect,* by which I mean the manner in which lines relate to the observer. Both *a* and *b* versions in Figure 6–1 are alike from the standpoint of the object-relative aspect, but they differ with respect to the subject-relative aspect. It is plausible that the object-relative aspect of shape is directly given by the intra-figural spatial relationships and does not require learning.[4] The attribute of straightness or curvature on the other hand is a subject-relative aspect of shape which is based on relationships such as those described above, between the line and the observer.[5]

Are the characteristics of a straight line given on the first encounter such that it is intuitively evident that a given line either is or is not straight? We tend to think so because the attribute of straightness or curvature is phenomenally as immediate and as sensory an experience as, say, color. "Straightness" is in the "look" of a thing. Yet if phenomenal straightness is indeed defined by the characteristics listed above, it is clear that at least some experience is required before the necessary information would be available that would enable an observer to perceive the shape of a line. If apparent curvature is largely dependent on the perceived direction of points along a line with respect to the self, then the development of perceived curvature must parallel the learning of radial direction. In other words, until the neonate has learned that points *A, B,* and *C* in Figure 6–3 are each straight ahead, i.e., in the sagittal plane, the imaginary line connecting them will not have the phenomenal attribute of straightness. The basis for the learning of radial direction was outlined in Chapter 4. Awareness of egocentric orientation plays a role in the process, and this too is a function of past experience (see Chapter 2). As to the

[4] Logical considerations and recent evidence favor the belief that learning is not necessary for the existence of segregated and discriminably different shaped entities in the visual field. For a discussion of this problem, see C. B. Zuckerman and I. Rock, A reappraisal of the roles of past experience and innate organizing processes in visual perception, *Psychol. Bull.,* 1957, **54,** 269–296. For more recent evidence, see R. Fantz, Form preferences in newly hatched chicks, *J. comp. Physiol. Psychol.,* 1957, **50,** 422–430; R. R. Zimmermann, Analysis of discrimination learning capacities in the infant rhesus monkey, *J. comp. Physiol. Psychol.,* 1961, **54,** 1–10.

[5] After this chapter was completed, a paper by Held and Hein came to my attention in which a somewhat similar distinction is drawn between two aspects of perceived shape: On the modifiability of form perception, Chapter in *Symposium on models for perception of speech and visual forms* (J. C. Mott-Smith, W. Wathen-Dunn, H. Blum, and P. Lieberman, Eds.), Cambridge: Mass. Inst. of Techn. Press, in press.

change or lack of change of the curvature of the image and the projection of the image when a line is seen head on, these properties depend upon movement of the observer. Hence they too entail at least some prior experience to be realized. If the observer is stationary, therefore, the information upon which these defining properties of the shape of a line is based would necessarily depend upon past movement that somehow makes its influence felt via memory.

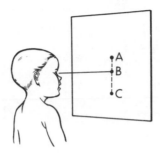

Figure 6–3

For a hypothetical subject born with a prismatic optical system, a specific retinal curvature, say convex to the left with a particular radius of curvature, would represent straight lines (Figure 6–4*a*). On the basis of the discussion above, I can think of no reason why this curved retinal image should not very soon yield an impression of a line that is "straight." The reason I say "very soon" is that, at the outset, no retinal curvature ought to signify any specific phenomenal impression of curvature. But because lines that produce this particular curved image (namely, physically straight lines) will behave in accordance with the defining properties of straight lines, that curved image should soon yield an impression of straightness. The corollary is that a straight retinal image, Figure 6–4*b*, will appear curved, convex to the right, by precisely the same amount that line *a* appears curved to the left to us now.

Any commerce our hypothetical subject has with his environment will yield information that the retinal image *a* has the properties associated with straightness. If the line which yields the image *a* is physically in the sagittal plane, then all points on it are in the straight-ahead direction (because the physical line in question *is* straight). It must now be assumed that egocentric orientation is established on the basis of a curved retinal direction, and radial directions are established in accordance with this curvature. As a result, all points on that curved retinal image will yield an impression of being straight ahead. A straight rod viewed from any vantage point or rotated about an end will yield a curved image whose curvature never deviates from *a*. An actual line with the shape of *a* when viewed without prisms from varying positions or when rotated will, of course, project varying curvatures, including that of its own mirror image when it is rotated 180°. But a straight environmental line that yields an image such as *a* will continue to yield that same image regardless of the position from which it is viewed and, therefore, would never project the mirror image of that curvature. When a straight rod is viewed head on without prisms, it will project as a point and, of course, this will be true even when the image is prismatically curved.

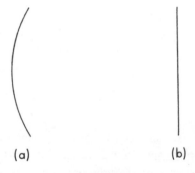

(a)   (b)

Figure 6–4

What about the criterion that the shortest phenomenal line connecting any two points is a straight one? Is it necessary for a naïve observer to find out which path is the shortest or does a particular path immediately look shortest? One might think that the path between *x* and *y* in Figure 6–5*a*, which yields an image that is straight when viewed through prisms, *b* (solid line), ought to be seen as shorter than the curved path described by the image of the prismatically viewed straight line (dotted line) if the organism is capable of discriminating relative extensity from birth (as was assumed in the last chapter).[6] But this presupposes that the shortest physical distance across the retina or cortex is innately linked with the shortest phenomenal distance, and it is by no means clear that this is the case. In any event, as a result of experience of the kind described above, the path of the dotted line will begin to appear straight and, therefore,

[6] As will be pointed out later, however, such size or extent discriminations may be innately given only along the same retinal-cortical direction and not between two different directions.

it will undoubtedly begin to appear to be the shorter path, and the solid line will begin to appear to be the longer one.[7]

Consequently, it would seem correct to conclude that the specific curvature of the image of a line need not necessarily signify any specific phenomenal curvature. The curvature it does signify is based on learning. Since our hypothetical observer will experience an isolated straight line as curved and a particular curved line as straight, even while remaining stationary, it would seem necessary to conclude that, for him, an image of a specific curvature has become the correlate of phenomenal straightness.

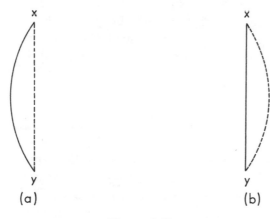

(a)   (b)

Figure 6–5

Once again, therefore, it is necessary to invoke the notion of a memory trace that is faithful to the specific nature of the proximal stimulus, in this case the shape of the image. It is on the basis of this stimulus-copy aspect of traces of varying curvature that lines come to have an immediate

[7] A physically straight line is unique in certain respects (e.g., in a Euclidean world, it is the shortest physical path between two points). A phenomenally straight line displays various of these unique properties, and in addition, it is a line of neutral curvature. That is to say, it is the curvature that seems to be zero in the continuum from convex left to convex right (*d* in the figure below). It divides space into two symmetrical portions, whereas a curved line does not. It is, therefore, a convenient reference for specifying degree and direction of curvature. Two lines of equal curvature deviation from a straight line, but of opposite signs, will look like mirror images of each other. This is not true for any other line. What happens if some image other than the straight one becomes the correlate of a phenomenally straight line? That image would become the neutral point in the continuum, and curvature of other lines would be judged in relation to it. Two lines of equal curvature-deviation in opposite directions from that one would now look like mirror images of each other. For example, in the

sense of specific curvature, which is what I mean by the subject-relative aspect of shape perception.

The analysis presented here leads to a reconsideration of the nativism-empiricism controversy in form perception. Consider the data summarized by von Senden bearing on the question first raised by Molyneux as to whether a person blind from birth would be able to distinguish a sphere from a cube on gaining his sight.[8] The argument has rightly been made that it is not plausible to expect such a person to know which visual object is the cube and which the sphere merely because he previously could distinguish them by touch. The question would have to be rephrased to ask whether the cube and sphere are discriminably different from one another.[9] In suggesting the question be put in this way, it was presupposed that the cube and sphere would look the way they do to a normal adult (namely, square and round respectively), although the subject would not yet know which was called the sphere and which the cube. Based upon the present analysis, however, I would now add that the cube and sphere would not necessarily look the way they do to a normal adult, because the qualities of "straightness" or specific curvature are not given directly by the curvature of the images of lines. Hence, although the sphere and cube would undoubtedly be discriminably different, because the cube has sudden changes of curvature at the corners while the sphere does not or because seen side by side their curvatures differ, they would not appear different in the way they do to us. Since one could not be said to be "straight" and the other "round," they might appear less different from one another than they do to us.

Assuming all I have said thus far to be true, what should be the consequences for an adult of viewing the world through prisms that do

figure below, if *c* became the retinal correlate of a straight line, *b* and *d* would look like mirror images of each other.

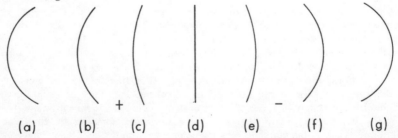

[8] M. von Senden, *Space and sight* (trans. by P. Heath), Glencoe, Ill.: The Free Press, 1960.

[9] C. B. Zuckerman and I. Rock, op. cit.

alter the curvature of all images? In one sense, based upon the fact that all curvatures will be altered to the same degree, the apparent shapes of things ought not to be altered (the object-relative aspect of shape). A shape such as a rectangle seen through the prisms, as in Figure 6–6, does retain many of its figural attributes. But by virtue of a record in memory of images of specific curvature that are associated with specific phenomenal curvatures, it appears to bulge, its sides are curved, and its angles do not all appear equal. Therefore the prisms would have a very different effect in an adult than in our hypothetically naïve observer. But adaptation to the prismatic image should be possible. The observer will obtain information that the seemingly curved direction is one that can be

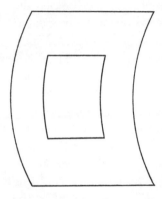

Figure 6–6

aligned with his own egocentric vertical axis, and otherwise meets all the criteria of straightness I have suggested. When the curved direction in Figure 6–6 becomes phenomenally straight, the angles of the figure, ipso facto, become phenomenally right angles. The curved image then deposits its own stimulus-copy traces signifying that that curvature and not zero curvature is straight.

The Evidence

The Gibson Effect

The classic experiment on adaptation to optically altered form was performed by Gibson in 1933, in which observers viewed the environment through a wedge prism.[10] At the outset, straight lines appeared quite

[10] J. J. Gibson, Adaptation, after-effect, and contrast in the perception of curved lines, *J. exp. Psychol.*, 1933, **16**, 1–31.

curved. Although Gibson had originally planned to study modifications in auditory and kinesthetic space habits resulting from the displacement, his subjects reported an adaptation to the curvature of straight lines and a negative aftereffect (straight lines appearing curved in the opposite direction) on removing the prisms. Hence, Gibson focused on this adaptation-to-curvature phenomenon.

The apparent curvature of straight lines before, during, and after exposure was measured by requiring the observer to estimate how far the mid-point of the line seemed displaced from the imaginary straight line connecting its end points. In some experiments, a scale running through the mid-point at right angles to the line helped the observer to estimate. Activities during the exposure period varied depending upon the experiment, but by and large the observer remained more or less stationary. Gibson's findings can be summarized as follows: (1) A measurable decrease in apparent curvature of prismatically viewed straight lines occurred even within 10 minutes, and an equivalent increase occurred in the curvature of straight lines viewed directly after removal of the prisms. (2) The same effect of the same magnitude was obtained without the prisms using an actually curved line as the inspection object—that is, it appeared less curved after exposure, and a straight line subsequently appeared curved in the opposite direction. (3) These effects occurred without reaching or grasping movements of the arm and with or without fixation. (4) A similar effect was found in the realm of kinesthetically experienced curvature. (5) The adaptation effect is localized in the region of the retina where the image of the line impinged. (6) Approximately 52 to 82 per cent of the adaptation effect transfers from one eye to the other.

The important finding for our present purposes is the second, namely, that an actually curved line yields the same effect as a prismatically curved one. In this case, there is no information that the curved line is anything but curved, so that the effect is clearly not one of prism adaptation such as I have been discussing in this book. Since, moreover, the magnitude of the effect was the same as that obtained with prisms, it is gratuitous to assume that anything additional was going on in the prism situation. In fact, the conditions of inspection in the prism experiments were probably not conducive to an adaptation effect based on information. The subject was stationary and, therefore, had no way of knowing whether he actually faced a curved line or not.

What kind of effect, then, did Gibson discover? His own conclusion was that it was a tendency toward the normalization of the stimulus, that is, a tendency back toward the norm or neutral point (e.g., straight line) of which the inspection stimulus (e.g., curved line) is a departure. Once normalization occurs, that is, once a curved line is seen to be less curved than it is, thereafter a straight line would have to appear curved. The subjective scale of curvature would have changed. As to why such a normalization should take place, Gibson's assumption was that a persistent quality may tend to become the neutral or normal quality, as in color adaptation. Since color adaptation (with negative after-image) is localized on the retina, Gibson found it natural to assume that curvature adaptation was localized too. (One contradiction Gibson does not seem to take cognizance of is that he did obtain his effect with eyes continuously moving up and down the curved line, which means the localization of the image on the retina is not as specific as ordinarily is the case with fixation. In fact he reports the effect is somewhat *better* with eye movements.)

Later Köhler and Wallach believed they had demonstrated that Gibson's curvature aftereffect was a special case of their displacement effect.[11]

Figure 6–7

(See Chapter 2, pages 74–75.) As is reflected in what they call the distance paradox, the maximum displacement effect ordinarily occurs at a certain distance from the inspected line rather than in the identical locus. If a test line (T) falls on the retina in a position adjacent to the position in which a curved line had previously fallen (I), then, as shown in Figure 6–7, the distance between the end points of inspection and test lines is such as to yield a displacement effect whereas the lack of distance between points at the center is not. Hence, the test line would appear to curve in the opposite direction. They were able to show that, following inspection of a *straight* line, a curved test line would appear *more* curved,

[11] W. Köhler and H. Wallach, Figural after-effects: An investigation of visual processes, *Proc. Amer. Phil. Soc.*, 1944, 88, 269–357.

yet there could hardly be any normalization of a straight line. As to the problem of change in the appearance of the inspection line itself—that is, the adaptation effect proper—Köhler and Wallach could argue that there is more satiation of the area on the concave side of the line than on the convex side. The concave side is more "surrounded" by the line. Hence the line would tend to be displaced away from the concave side, which means, in effect, that it would appear to be straightening out.

One major difficulty with this hypothesis is that the curvature effect occurs with continuous changes of fixation. Hence it cannot be explained entirely in terms of the particular theory of satiation developed by Köhler. Since Held has found that figural aftereffects also occur with changing fixation,[12] Gibson's effect could be considered to be a special case of figural aftereffects, but we are left without any general theory for such effects.

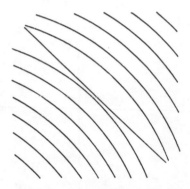

Figure 6–8   (*Courtesy the American Psychological Association*)

An important clue in explaining the negative aftereffect, I believe, is found in Gibson's demonstration that a very similar effect occurs in simultaneous contrast, as illustrated in Figure 6–8. The straight line appears curved in a direction opposite to that of the curved lines, and the magnitude of this effect is about of the same order as the negative aftereffect. That being the case, a contrast theory, either simultaneous or successive, seems to be indicated. Presumably the curved lines in the figure do not change their apparent curvature. Hence normalization is not a necessary precondition for the contrast effect and, therefore, is probably not necessary for the negative aftereffect.

As suggested above, it would seem plausible to believe that the object-

[12] R. Held, Adaptation to re-arrangement and visual-spatial aftereffects, *Psychol. Beitr.*, 1962, **6**, 439–450.

relative aspect of shape is given innately, since it is based on the position of line elements within the retinal image relative to one another. If true, this aspect of shape is present even before the absolute or subject-relative significance of any retinal curvature is acquired. If curvature *difference* is a primitive type of experience, then one might say that what is revealed in Figure 6–8 is the experience of the critical line *curving away from* the other lines. With respect to the contextual lines as frame of reference, the critical line is "curved." This would also hold for Gibson's negative aftereffect considered as a *successive* contrast effect. In other words, as far as curvature *difference* is concerned, the critical line in Figure 6–8 is identical to that in Figure 6–9. Each curves away from its

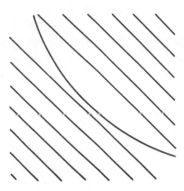

Figure 6–9

context to the same extent.[13] That they do not appear equal is, of course, due to the powerful influence of the subject-relative aspect of shape according to which the critical line in Figure 6–8 is straight and in Figure 6–9 is curved. Nevertheless, they appear less different than they would if each were seen in isolation.

A very powerful effect of this kind is illustrated in Figure 6–10 in the form of an illusion. The center line in *a* has the same curvature as in *b*, but they look quite different. In *a* it is more curved than the surrounding lines, in *b* it is less curved, and hence they look different. Many illusions of curvature can be explained in this way. Here again, however, the

[13] Assuming that the explanation offered here can account for Gibson's contrast effect or his negative aftereffect, it does not as such do justice to the adaptation effect proper. Perhaps prolonged exposure to a particular curvature leads to some breakdown in the communication with the trace of that curvature, such that its absolute curvature is no longer so clearly given by memory (analogous to the satiation of meaning with repetition or other satiation effects). That leaves the line somewhat non-specific as to its curvature, there being no other lines nearby to give it any relative curvature.

absolute or subject-relative curvature is given via memory processes and would be present even for an isolated line. As a result of our awareness of the curvature of each line on this basis, only moderate illusory effects occur.

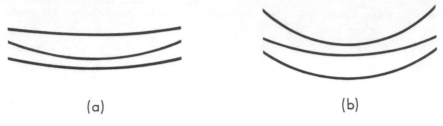

(a)   (b)

Figure 6–10

There is an important fact about the perception of curvature which my students and I noticed in constructing figures such as those shown above. Phenomenal curvature is a function of length of arc, other things being equal, as is illustrated in Figure 6–11. Both *a* and *b* have the

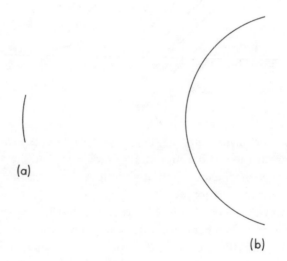

(a)

(b)

Figure 6–11

identical radius of curvature, but *b* is a longer segment than *a*. They appear quite different.[14] Conversely, in Figure 6–12, *a* and *b* have very different radii, but they appear more or less equal.

[14] Since becoming aware of this fact, I have seen reference to it in only one place, namely, in a book on optical illusions by a physicist: S. Tolansky, *Optical illusions*, New York: Pergamon Press (Macmillan), 1964.

Apparently, phenomenal curvature is to a large extent a function of the configuration. We spontaneously react on the basis of apparent angle or arc of circle. Thus, in Figure 6–11, b is a much greater segment of a circle than a, whereas in Figure 6–12, b is the same segment of a circle. It may be that we compare any curve to an imagined straight line and, that being the case, the smaller the segment of arc (other things equal), the less does it depart from a straight line. Only equal segments of a circle, regardless of their radii, form the same "angles" with respect to a straight-line standard.

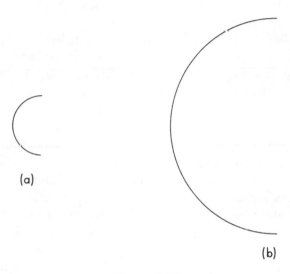

(a)

(b)

Figure 6–12

This fact should not be surprising in view of the more general fact of the transposability of forms in the size dimension. In Figure 6–12, b is a transposition of a. If perceived curvature were to be a simple function of radius of curvature, then whenever a figure containing curved-line components was transposed in size it would have to appear to be different in shape. And, what amounts to the same point, whenever we approached such a figure it would change its shape, because the radius of curvature of the retinal image would undergo a transformation. However, the fact that the phenomenal curvature of even an isolated line is configurationally determined sets certain limits on the extent to which we should expect its apparent shape to be influenced by the context of other lines as in Figures 6–8 and 6–10.

The effect of context on curvature is analogous to similar effects in orientation and size perception. The orientation of a line is to a great extent a function of its direction relative to a frame of reference, and the apparent size of a line is a function of its size relative to its frame of reference. I have observed a very strong effect of the surrounding field on the apparent curvature of a line: A wire is first bent so as to compensate exactly for the curvature produced by a given prism. Seen through the prism it will now yield a straight retinal image, and it will appear straight when placed in front of a homogeneous background. When, however, the background is a typical scene such as the interior of a room, the line appears markedly curved, in a direction opposite to that of the vertical of the room. Presumably this effect would occur if a room were constructed in such a way that all vertical lines were actually curved in the same direction. The effect appears to be greater than the type of contrast effect illustrated in Figure 6–8, and therefore suggests once again a role of familiarity with objects, in this case their shape.

Given this fact, there would seem to be a further analogy between curvature, orientation, and size perception. In all three cases it is possible to arrange the objective scene so that the resulting retinal image will be comparable to that which results from viewing a scene through prisms or lenses: prism curvature and actual curvature; the Stratton and Wertheimer paradigms in orientation; the mirror-minification procedure and the "half-sized world" procedure in the case of size perception. In all cases there are immediate effects which are not adaptation effects—in the Wertheimer paradigm a surrounded line does not appear as tilted as it actually is, an object in the "half-sized world" does not appear as small as it actually is, and a curved line among the other curved lines does not appear as curved as it actually is. In all these cases familiarity with objects in the scene plays a role. In the case of orientation and size, however, I have argued that although a situation arranged to yield the same proximal stimulus as is created by optical distortion may produce an adaptation effect, the effect is certainly not the same as that of optical distortion. Only in adaptation to optical distortion is the relationship between objects and the self transformed. The same, therefore, ought to be true for curvature.

As noted above, Gibson did not create suitable conditions for prism adaptation to occur. At the outset he was interested in other problems, and when he did become interested in the curvature effect, he discovered it could be produced without prisms. This meant to him that the effect had nothing to do with adaptive learning—how could it if the effect with actually curved lines was non-veridical? Since the effect was of the same magnitude with curved lines as with straight lines curved by prisms, his deduction was plausible, and he thereafter veered away from what I believe is quite a different phenomenon, namely, prism adaptation. The subsequent interest in the figural aftereffects continued to focus on the purely configurational aspect of Gibson's findings.

Prism Adaptation to Curvature

Fortunately, the work of Erismann and Ivo Kohler led to a reconsideration of the meaning of Gibson's initial procedure.[15] These investigators were concerned with the long-term effects of wearing prisms and other optically distorting devices. Their subjects wore the prisms for days, weeks, or even months. All those who wore prisms for any length of time reported a diminution in the curved appearance of straight lines and a striking curvature of straight lines on removing the prisms. The problem before us is this: Can we assume such adaptation is reducible to Gibson's effect, or does it represent genuine prism adaptation to the curved images based on information that such environmental lines are straight? To be sure, the Gibson effect should be expected to occur for Kohler's subjects, and therefore it ought to be subtracted from the total adaptation effect obtained. Unfortunately, although we know the magnitude of the Gibson effect for limited exposure periods (up to an hour), we do not know what it is for extended periods. However, it is a fair guess that this effect does not increase substantially over time. To the extent that it is a contrast phenomenon, it does not require prolonged exposure. We do know that the Gibson type of adaptation to *tilted* lines (cf. the Addendum to Chapter 2) does not ever seem to become greater than about 2°.

The precise quantitative extent of the adaptation obtained by Kohler and Erismann is difficult to gauge, but it is quite clear that what they found goes beyond the Gibson effect. Only in one experiment is anything approaching quantitative data given, and that is a special experiment involving the use of prisms in the upper half of the spectacle frame. In that experiment, although the subject could view the world normally (i.e., not through the prisms) at will, by looking downward, a cumulative build-up of adaptation to the prismatically curved lines nevertheless occurred. The effect was measured by periodically presenting slides of lines of varying curvatures and asking the subjects to indicate which one appeared straight and to rate each line for curvature. The prisms used had a 10° angle at the apex, which means they were relatively weak, the angle of deflection of an object straight ahead being about 5°. Although

[15] I. Kohler, The formation and transformation of the perceptual world (trans. by H. Fiss), *Psychol. Issues*, 1964, **3**, 1–173.

numerical values are not given, it can be seen from their graph of the results that, by 4 or 5 days, vertical lines appeared only about half as curved as they did at the outset, and the negative aftereffect was about half of the curvature created by the prisms. Although the experiment continued for 40 days, the adaptation to curvature reached a plateau by about the fifth day. In any case, there is an appreciable effect despite the fact that prismatic stimulation is intermittent. The dependency of the effect on location of objects above eye level (a situational aftereffect) would surely rule out explanation merely in terms of contrast or normalization.

In other experiments, no quantitative data are given, but it is quite clear that substantial adaptation to curvature occurred. A recent repetition of this work by Pick and Hay with somewhat stronger prisms (20 diopters, deflection of about 11°) did fortunately include quantitative determinations. For curvature, the effect in terms of per cent of total adaptation possible was 11.2 per cent after 3 days and 30 per cent after 42 days.[16] With these prisms it is probable that a configurational adaptation effect based on mere inspection of lines would be no more than would require a prism strength of 3 diopters to nullify. The effect measured after 42 days required a prism strength of 6 diopters to nullify. It should be pointed out that an effect of this magnitude is not very great as far as apparent curvature is concerned. A straight line viewed through a prism of 6-diopter strength does appear curved, but not very curved, particularly if the line inspected is short. Viewed through a prism of 2-diopter strength, the curvature is no longer very readily discernible. Nevertheless the inference is probably safe, even on the basis of these experiments, that adaptation to prismatic curvature is of a magnitude not encompassed by the Gibson effect and, therefore, represents a phenomenon in its own right. Definite proof on this point, however, has recently appeared. What is required is a procedure in which the subject views the world through prisms, but is not stimulated by curved lines. Held and Rekosh accomplished this by using a method similar to that used by Mikaelian and Held, in which a random pattern of irregular spots fills the entire field (see p. 58).[17] Since such a field remains random when viewed through the prisms—i.e., one does not see lines, either curved or straight—it fulfills the conditions for distinguishing purely configurational effects from prism adaptation effects. Their subjects either walked around in the cylindrical

[16] H. L. Pick, Jr., and J. C. Hay, Adaptation to prismatic distortion, *Psychon. Sci.*, 1964, 1, 199–200.

[17] R. Held and J. Rekosh, Motor-sensory feedback and the geometry of visual space, *Science*, 1963, 141, 722–723.

room containing the spots on the wall (active condition) or were wheeled around in it (passive condition) for a half hour. Before and after exposure the subjects were required to adjust a variable-strength prism until lines seen through the prism appeared straight. The difference in apparent curvature before and after exposure for the active observers was reflected by a change in the strength of the prism adjustments which averaged 3.35 prism diopters. Since the prisms were of 20 diopters strength, the effect is 17 per cent of complete adaptation. This is impressive if one considers that there were no lines at all visible to the subjects. They could not have had any conscious appreciation that apparently curved lines represented objectively straight lines. The passive observers did not adapt at all.

Another method for separating the Gibson effect from genuine prism adaptation is to present subjects with a curved line that appears straight when first viewed through a prism. Here there is no basis for predicting normalization, since the line already appears to be straight. However, given adequate information as to the actual curvature of the line, one would have to predict that such a line would in time come to appear curved. Gibson reported using this method with two observers without effect, but apparently the observer's head was stationary. If the head is stationary, and all the observer can see is the line, there is in all likelihood no information available that the line is anything but straight. In a carefully designed experiment, Malcolm Cohen has recently shown that one does get adaptation under these conditions if the head is permitted to move but not if it is held stationary.[18] In the same experiment, adaptation to an objectively straight line seen through a prism was greater with head movement than without such movement (presumably representing the combined effect of Gibsonian *and* prism adaptation), whereas adaptation to an objectively curved line not seen through a prism was the same with or without head movement (since only the Gibson effect, which does not depend upon head movements, could then occur). When the inspected object was a small dot seen through a prism, Cohen also obtained an adaptation effect if the head was permitted to move but not if it was held stationary.

Hence we can safely conclude that prism adaptation to curvature occurs over and above the Gibsonian configurational effect. As to the necessary conditions for achieving it, the experiment by Held and Rekosh and the one by Cohen both demonstrate the crucial role of movement, the

[18] M. Cohen, Visual curvature and feedback factors in the production of prismatically induced curved line aftereffects. Paper read at Eastern Psychological Assoc., New York, April 1963.

former also indicating that the movement must be self-produced to be effective, in line with Held's theory. That movement should be important for adaptation to prism-produced curvature follows from consideration of the question of how information could be imparted that the apparent curvature is other than it at first appears to be. If the observer is stationary, he has no way of knowing that a prismatically curved image emanates from an objectively straight line, provided the scene contains no familiar objects.

In adaptation to tilt, displacement, or minification, what was considered necessary was information about the relationship of the tilt, direction, or size of external objects to the phenomenal self and, in principle at least, one way information concerning this relationship could be obtained was by mere inspection of the scene with parts of the body visible. In the case of curvature, however, it would seem unlikely that the sight of the body through the prisms provides information to the effect that things are not as curved as they appear.

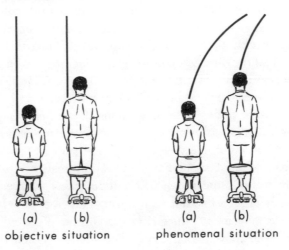

(a)   (b)   (a)   (b)
objective situation   phenomenal situation

Figure 6–13

The self enters in not as a visible object but in the more subtle form alluded to in other chapters. Suppose, for example, the observer is viewing a long vertical line directly in front of him while seated. (See Figure 6–13a.) He now gets up. The line remains straight ahead (b), which ought not to be the case on the basis of its apparent curvature unless the observer were moving in a curved path, which he knows he is not. Otherwise expressed, when the observer moves along a straight path, points on the retinal image of that path displace along the curved image of the path. Hence this act informs him that what appears to be a curved path in space is actually aligned with his egocentric vertical axis. It would seem plausible that either movement of the entire body or the head would be necessary in order to begin learning about the differentially altered radial direction of high and low points in contrast to those at eye level. Otherwise there is no reason why objects cannot remain localized where they seem to be. Movement is also necessary before the shape of external objects can be revealed by the behavior of the proximal stimulus. For example, a vertical rod seems to bulge to the left. If the observer now walks around it, the direction of curvature is expected to change until eventually it bulges to the right, but instead it will continue to appear to bulge to the left. Hence this action would yield the information that the line is not curved at all. Only a straight line retains its apparent curvature with such changes in vantage point. (However, as noted in previous chapters, strictly speaking, if some movement is perceived in the line with movement of the observer because of the component of abnormal displacement of its image, it can be argued that no information about the true shape of the line is provided. Such information may depend upon the prior re-establishment of complete position constancy.)

In the experiment by Cohen, head movement alone yields an effect even when the sole object visible is a dot. This finding suggests that information as to the true radial direction of points in various positions in space suffices for adaptation to prismatic alteration of shape. In other words, when the dot is above or below eye level it appears radially off to the side. Head movement supplies the information that in these positions it was actually in the sagittal plane. Therefore, this experiment is an extremely important demonstration of the subject-relative basis of the phenomenal experience of the curvature of a line.

Further evidence is provided by the results of an experiment by Taylor and confirmed by an as yet unpublished experiment by Festinger, in which observers wore contact wedge prisms which moved with the eyes.[19] Straight lines at first appeared curved. In order to continue fixating the line, the eyes must move along a straight path because the line is objectively straight. In other words, because the prisms are attached to the eyes, the path of eye movement must be faithful to the objective path to be followed, not the path of the retinal image, as is the case in daily life or when prisms are worn in spectacles. The observer continuously sweeps

[19] J. G. Taylor, *The behavioral basis of perception*, New Haven: Yale Univ. Press, 1962; L. Festinger. Paper read at the Conference on Adaptation, Massachusetts Institute of Technology, June 1965.

his eyes back and forth along the line. The result for Taylor, who was his own subject, was that the curvature completely disappeared after an hour, and a negative aftereffect was obtained on removing the prism. In a later session, he reported complete straightening after only 20 seconds of scanning. For Festinger's subjects, the line appeared less curved after a while, as indicated by the curvature then selected as looking straight. It would seem that the straight path of eye movement alone provides information that the line is straight. Festinger believes that the information in question derives from a central copy of the neural command to the eye muscles, not from afferent feedback, the existence of the latter now being very much in doubt.[20]

[20] It is doubtful whether proprioception alone could be responsible for the adaptation that occurs with eye movement, even if there were evidence that such proprioception existed. If the eyes scanned a straight line that appeared curved, let us say as a result of an optical illusion, based on the dominance of ·vision it is not improbable that the observer would "feel" his eyes moving in a curved path even if they moved in a straight path. Therefore, if this were the only basis of adaptation, the line would probably never straighten out, despite the continued "information" that the eyes moved along a straight path. There are many cases in perception where we misinterpret what the eyes are doing, based on the manner in which the external objects are phenomenally experienced (see, below, the example of misinterpretation of diagonal eye movement in the half-prism experiment). In the example under discussion, however, if the observer begins to move his eyes along a curved path in order to scan the line, a curious thing happens. The line moves out of the foveal region. Hence the observer must *intend* to move his eyes along a straight path, not a curved one, if he is to continue scanning the line. This efference type of information could conceivably be the basis of the adaptation reported by Taylor and by Festinger.

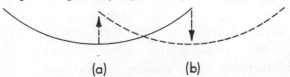

(a)   (b)

There is, however, another possible source of information that the eyes are not moving along a curved path. If an observer wearing a contact prism scans a straight line that appears curved, the image of the line undergoes a continuous transformation, as shown in the figure above. A point on the line (*a*) that at one moment falls in the fovea will displace not directly to the side of the fovea as the eyes move horizontally, but obliquely; a point on the line (*b*) that had been in the periphery in an oblique direction will displace obliquely so as to fall in the fovea. Thus *a* will seem to move upward and *b* downward as the eye moves to the right. The same type of transformation occurs in looking through a spectacle prism, not a contact prism, when the head moves along the path of a straight line. Therefore, it could not be the case that the eye (or head) movement is actually along the phenomenally curved path of the line. If the eyes (or head) were to scan a curved line, the image of the line would not undergo such a transformation. Point *b* would displace in the direction indicated if the eyes were moving obliquely upward, but then point *a* would *not* simultaneously displace in a totally different direction.

The fact that, logically and empirically, movement seems to be extremely important for adaptation to prismatic alteration of curvature fits in with the analysis of curvature as the subject-relative aspect of phenomenal shape. In other words, if phenomenal straightness or curvature depends upon the properties of a line that have to do with the position of the points making up that line in relation to the observer, then (1) adaptation should be possible, because what matters in this respect is the objective shape of the line, not the shape of its retinal image, and (2) movement should be crucial, because the properties that define subject-relative curvature require movement to become manifest.[21] Adaptation implies that retinal curvatures, different from those of the past, have become the signs of specific phenomenal curvatures, presumably on the basis of an association between a given retinal curvature and information concerning phenomenal curvature which endures in memory.

As to the question of active vs. passive movement, here again there is no question that a passively moved subject will still perceive that he is moving, although he will experience rubbery transformations and he may perceive changes of curvature of lines in the environment as he moves. However, this will also be true for actively moving subjects. It is possible that in passive movement the observer is not adequately aware of which way he is being moved. For example, if in Figure 6–13 the observer were passively moved and did not get adequate information to the effect he was being moved straight up, then he might possibly experience himself as moving along the phenomenally curved path of the line. That is, in passive movement, the information is ambiguous. The apparent displacement might be the result of actual movement along a curved path, in which case there is not an adequate basis for "believing" the environment is not what it appears to be.

Nevertheless, the possibility of conveying the necessary information without active movement should be explored. The Held and Rekosh experiment is the only one thus far to focus on this issue. Based upon the analysis offered in this chapter, one might predict that wheeling the subject around vertical columns would convey the information that the apparently curved columns were straight. The direction of curvature would remain unchanged. Transporting a subject around horizontally

---

[21] There is another way in which movement can provide information as to the prismatically created curvature. If the subject tilts his head, a straight vertical line changes from maximum curvature when the head is upright to zero curvature when it is tilted 90° (for a base-left or base-right position of the prism). Conversely, a straight horizontal line changes from straight to maximally curved with a 90° tilt of the head.

oriented rods (with prisms mounted base up or down) might permit
adaptation because the rods could be seen alternately from the side and
head on. In fact, with the prisms mounted this way, so that horizontal
lines appear curved, merely wheeling the subject around or rotating him
back and forth in any normal environment ought to suffice. It would become evident that all points along a seemingly curved path remain at eye
level during movement, although peripheral points along the path had
at first seemed higher or lower. Thus the egocentric "horizontal" would
be seen to be parallel to the, at first, phenomenally curved lines.[22] The
fact referred to in footnote 20, that the images of points on a straight line
simultaneously displace in different directions when the observer moves
through space, may also serve as information to the effect that he is *not*
moving along a curved path.

It is not beyond the realm of possibility that some degree of adaptation
to prismatic curvature could take place even for a stationary observer.
Familiarity with typical environmental scenes in which walls, buildings,
and the like are known to be straight might conceivably yield an effect
above and beyond the Gibsonian normalization expected. This could be
tested by comparing the effect of exposure to a familiar indoor scene with
that of exposure to an equally articulated but meaningless array of vertical and horizontal lines.

The "Situational" Aftereffect

I have not yet discussed a most important discovery by Erismann and
Kohler concerning adaptation. In addition to changes of curvature, the
prism optically distorts shape in certain other respects. Because of the
differential amount of displacement depending upon angle of incidence,
objects to the left and right are deflected more than those straight ahead.
This results in a compression of objects on the left (assuming the prism is
base left, which deflects light to the right) and an expansion on the right.
The explanation for this is made clear in Figure 6–14. All three points are
deflected to the right, but A and C more than B because of their greater
angle of incidence. If A is deflected more to the right than B, then its

---

[22] In line with the analysis above, it would seem that the most directly relevant
information concerning curvature when prisms are worn base left or right derives
from vertical movements of the observer. This may explain the negative results in the
passive condition of the Held and Rekosh experiment. The subjects may rarely have
moved their heads up and down while being transported in the cart, whereas they
may have done so in connection with walking movements in the active condition
(despite instructions to keep the head stationary). A repetition of the experiment with
prisms base up or down seems indicated.

image is now closer to B than it would be otherwise (compression); if C is deflected more than B to the right, its image is now farther from B than it otherwise would be (expansion). Another differential effect of the prisms is that horizontal lines above eye level appear to slope downward toward the base side of the prism and those below eye level seem to slope upward, so that, taken together, they seem to converge. With vertical head movements, the slopes of horizontal lines at first appear to change.[23]

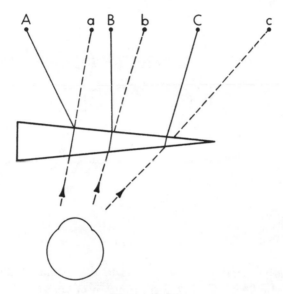

Figure 6–14

Hence at the outset, a configuration such as *a* in Figure 6–15 will appear distorted as shown in *b*, and the field undergoes rubbery transformations with head movement. However, the observer is perfectly free to move his eyes. Presumably the frequency of fixation to the left and to the right or above or below eye level is approximately equal. Yet, in time, adaptation does occur, according to Ivo Kohler. His data are primarily qualita-

[23] The explanation of the tilting of horizontal lines which are above or below eye level would seem to be as follows: Light from above or below is deflected by a prism both horizontally and vertically because the deflection is a function of the angle formed by the ray of light and the normal to the surface where the ray intersects the prism. Although the normals on both faces of a base-left or base-right prism are horizontal, they are not parallel to each other, as would be the case for a glass with parallel sides. Therefore the vertical component of displacement will not necessarily be equal for light entering and light leaving the prism and the direction of this difference is not the same for light entering from the left and light entering from the right.

tive and are concerned mostly with the observer's report of what things look like *during* movement. The main effect is that the awareness of the rubbery transformations is reduced. This would imply that the expansion and contraction and tilting of images is increasingly discounted. On removing the prisms, objects appear to expand and contract with lateral head movements, and horizontal lines appear to tilt with vertical head movements. These effects occur regardless of whether the observer is looking straight ahead during the test or is looking directly at the object on the left or right.

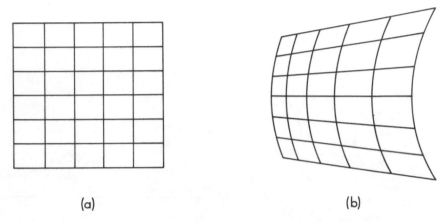

(a)   (b)

Figure 6–15

No quantitative data are presented as to the extent of these effects,[24] but in a study by Pick and Hay, a diminution of compression and expansion with head rotation of between 5 and 10 per cent after 42 days is reported.[25] Their measurement was based upon the diopter value of the prism required to nullify the impression of contraction and expansion or tilting of horizontal lines *during movement* of the observer. The effect in the case of tilting was considerably greater, the diminution being in the vicinity of 25 per cent after 42 days. Only one of their measures was concerned with the appearance of things with the observer stationary, namely, a test in which a quadrilateral was adjusted by the observer until it ap-

[24] Except in the half-prism experiment (described further below), in which several types of measurements were taken, such as the distortion required to make a quadrilateral appear square and the curvature required to make a line appear straight. These measurements revealed that considerable adaptation had occurred, and it was clearly a function of whether the stimulus object was located above or below the head.

[25] H. L. Pick, Jr., and J. C. Hay, Gaze-contingent adaptation to prismatic distortion, *Amer. J. Psychol.*, in press.

peared to be square. This measure did reveal at least as much, if not more, adaptation to the tilt of horizontal lines as did the measure taken with head moving. They also required three subjects, while stationary, to equate the length of a line seen to the left with one to the right. An effect was obtained, but the magnitude is not given.

Hence the effects are definite but modest considering the long period of time involved. I am assuming the Pick and Hay data are more reliable in this respect because they used eight observers, whereas Kohler used only himself and Erismann. Also Pick and Hay were able to obtain quantitative measurements. Kohler calls this a situational aftereffect, because what occurs seems to depend upon the position of the eyes. He argues that it cannot be explained in terms of a local retinal-cortical effect, such as is possible in classical color adaptation, because it is not the case that one side of the retina is consistently exposed to compression and the other side to expansion. That would only be true if the eyes remained stationary.[26]

[26] Perhaps the best-known situational aftereffect is the reported adaptation to colored spectacles in which the left halves were colored yellow and the right halves blue. Notwithstanding the fact that eye movements back and forth would presumably cancel out local retinal adaptation to one color, Kohler reported obtaining a weakening of blue and yellow sensations and, when the spectacles were removed, negative afterimagery of yellow and blue. However, there have since been two attempted replications of Kohler's experiment, both negative (T. L. Harrington, Adaptation of humans to colored split-field glasses, *Psychon. Sci.*, 1965, 3, 71–72; C. McCollough, The conditioning of color perception, *Amer. J. Psychol.*, 1965, 78, 362–378). McCollough suggests that Kohler's results were based on: (1) classical color adaptation in the periphery of the retina that did receive predominantly either yellow or blue light, and (2) a simultaneous contrast effect from the thus-adapted periphery to the foveal area.

A similar argument could be made in the case of the compression-expansion effect, namely, that one side of the retina is predominantly exposed to compression and the other to expansion. The greater density of contours on the compression side could conceivably lead, according to the Köhler-Wallach theory, to greater satiation in this portion of the field in comparison to the other, thus tending to offset the compression effect and leading to a negative aftereffect. It is unlikely, however, that an explanation of this kind is adequate to explain the situational aftereffects of compression-expansion or tilting of horizontal lines, since these effects are presumably observable in the centrally fixated region of the field which is exposed equally to the opposite prismatic distortions.

Another finding of Kohler which has aroused much interest is that there is adaptation to the prismatically created color fringes produced at the boundaries of objects in the field and, upon removal of the prisms, "phantom" color fringes or negative aftereffects are seen at such boundaries. Since the eyes are free to move, the adaptation and aftereffects could hardly be based upon local retinal adaptation to a specific color. Celeste McCollough has now shown that this effect is probably due to color adaptation of orientation-specific edge-detectors. (C. McCollough, Color adaptation of edge-detectors in the human visual system, *Science*, 1965, 149, 1115–1116.)

Kohler interprets this effect as one of eye position influencing what shape is perceived with a given retinal shape, and this interpretation has been accepted by most workers in the field. In fact, Kohler prefers the term "conditioned" aftereffect. A new perception is conditioned to the eye-position stimulus. Thus, with prisms on, different retinal images ultimately come to signify the same phenomenal impression, depending upon eye position: with eyes left, a narrow image yields the same-size impression as a wide image with eyes right (assuming for the sake of discussion the effect to be complete). On removing the prisms, with the eyes turned left, one sees something in a particular way (for example, wide); with eyes turned right, an image of the same width yields a different phenomenal impression (for example, narrow).

However, I believe this way of describing the effect fails to make clear its true meaning. What the subject learns is that objects *to the left of his head* are wider than they appear to be and objects *to the right of his head* are narrower than they appear to be. Just as changes of eye position do not affect the perceived radial direction of objects in space, by the same token they do not affect the operation of this learned "principle." As long as the object is to the left of the subject's head, it is wider than it appears. This derives from the fact that, as long as the object is seen through the prism located to the left of the sagittal plane of the head (whether viewed foveally or peripherally), it is optically compressed. Since the physical objects are not compressed, the principle "things to my left are wider than they appear" is veridical and when perception is based on it, it too will be veridical.

In other words, constancy of direction already exists for the subject, and he makes good use of it in the prism situation. Changing eye position in no way changes the optical fact of compression of objects located phenominally to the left of the head. Hence, what must be learned if adaptation is to occur has to do with radial direction in space and not with retinal locus per se or eye position per se. In a manner of speaking, therefore, one might say that the subject learns to pay no attention to eye position. The learned effect would be identical if the eyes remained stationary throughout, but we might not realize the significance of it, i.e., that what was learned relates to phenomenal and not retinal location. Perhaps the point can be made clearer by going back to what Kohler says, namely, "eyes left, see expanded; eyes right, see compressed." This is not quite correct. One would have to rephrase it to say "eyes left, see *foveal object* expanded; eyes right, see *foveal object* compressed." When the eyes are turned, the object that had been fixated and which now is in the periphery does *not* change its appearance at all. Hence, changing eye position does not lead to phenomenal change, but only to what one can see clearly by virtue of foveal vision. Therefore, the conditioning model is incorrect.

If this analysis is correct, then anything that could affect apparent radial direction would affect shape in such an experiment, even if the eyes remained stationary. For example, a luminous object that is actually straight ahead appears to be off to the side if placed at the edge of a large luminous rectangle in an otherwise dark field (Roelof's effect). Hence, for a subject who had been wearing prisms, I would predict its shape would be affected in the same way as an object which actually was off to the side. Or if by induced movement a stationary object were made to appear to move in a particular direction, its phenomenal shape ought to appear to alter. These predictions stem from the suggestion that what is relevant is phenomenal location with respect to the observer's head, not position of the eyes.

In one of Kohler's experiments, the subject wore prisms in the upper halves of the spectacle frame only. To the extent that he saw objects through the prisms, therefore, the situation was essentially like that of the full-prism experiment. Thus this might be considered a compound "situational" design. There was compression to the left and expansion to the right, but only for objects located above the plane of the eyes. A complicating feature of this design is that negative aftereffects of adaptation to the prism should manifest themselves in the lower non-prism portion of the field, as indeed they did in the early stages of the experiment. In time, however, the distortions wrought by the prisms began to adapt out, and also the aftereffects in the lower field began to disappear. Thus perception became more veridical regardless of the location of objects in the field. Furthermore, with the spectacle frame off, aftereffects were increasingly a function of where objects were located—namely, up and left, expansion; up and right, contraction; down, no effect. However, adaptation was never complete, even after 50 days.

This experiment is also of interest with respect to a phenomenon such as curvature, which in the upper half of the field is not "situational." All vertical lines are curved, whether they are to the left or right. But adaptation to curvature becomes situational since it depends upon whether the line is located above or below eye level. With spectacles removed, straight lines seen above eye level appear more curved than those seen below eye level, and a long vertical line seems to bulge in its upper portion. The dependency of the aftereffect on perceived location provides evidence of the fact that more is going on here than a mere Gibsonian contrast effect resulting from a previously seen configuration. Again, it should be emphasized that what is crucial is phenomenal location of lines, whether above or below eye level. Eye position as such is unimportant.

Of special interest in this experiment is the fact that the upper portion of the field was displaced relative to the lower, and that at the outset this was quite noticeable to the subject. If adaptation to displacement were to occur, therefore, it would mean that an object above eye level in the sagittal plane, which stimulated the retina to the left of the fovea when the eyes were straight ahead, would eventually be located as phenomenally straight ahead. Yet that same object, if seen below eye level, would be located straight ahead only if it stimulated the fovea. As shown in Figure 6–16, a long vertical line yields a bifurcated image, both portions of

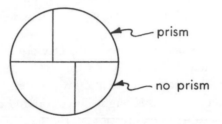

Figure 6–16

which would have to be perceived as straight ahead if adaptation were complete. Does this mean the line must appear straight and continuous? The facts seem to be as follows: There was a general tendency to avoid looking directly at the region dividing the prism and non-prism field. The subject preferred to keep his eyes up or down. When, however, he did look there, he saw just as much of a displacement at the end of the experiment as at the start. Nevertheless, both half images had the same radial location for the subject, and a corollary of this is the fact that an object was not seen to jump from one position to the other with vertical movements of the head or eyes. Conversely, with spectacles removed, a fixated point straight ahead did seem to jump laterally with vertical head or eye movements. Objective tests with prisms off indicated beyond a shadow of a doubt that two different physical directions had both come to signify the "straight ahead" direction. This is perhaps the clearest illustration of a situational aftereffect.

This aspect of the half-prism experiment is primarily relevant to the problem of displacement discussed in Chapter 4. Information is available that objects seen through the prisms are not displaced as they at first seem to be. An object straight ahead can be seen directly only by turning the eyes (or head). Therefore, for objects above eye level, the combination "image foveal, eyes turned" must come to signify that a foveal object is straight ahead; whereas, for objects not seen through the prisms, the pre-experimental state of affairs still governs apparent radial direction. What is new in this experiment is the finding that both of these can be true simultaneously. Before the combination of retinal locus and eye position is fully interpreted, the location of an object in the up-down direction is taken into account. As a result, when the eyes move up or down in scanning a vertical line, the subject ceases to be aware of lateral shifting necessitated by the prism. Otherwise expressed, a diagonal shifting of the eyes comes to be experienced as a vertical movement of the eyes. On removing the spectacles, the subject experiences truly vertical eye movement as diagonal. Consistent with the analysis presented in Chapter 4, I would argue that the cause of adaptation to displacement here is the assimilation of information as to where objects are located in relation to the self. The reinterpretation of the direction of eye movement is a necessary concomitant of adaptation. If a thing *appears* to be straight ahead when fixated, then it follows that the eyes must be directed straight ahead. Since with diagonal movement the eyes continue to be directed at a point that appears straight ahead, it "follows" that they are moving vertically.

There are several problems raised by the work on the situational adaptation effects which warrant discussion. One has to do with the manner of testing for these effects; the second has to do with alterations of phenomenal shape other than curvature; a third is the problem of how it is possible for an adaptation effect to be tied to a specific location in phenomenal space. As to the first, it would appear that most of the evidence thus far attesting to the existence of situational effects derives from dynamic testing conditions, i.e., what the observer sees when moving his head. While the question of whether or not the perceived world will cease to undergo rubbery transformation during movement of the observer is an interesting one, I believe there is a danger of obscuring the central issue by focusing on this aspect of adaptation.

What we want to know is whether a compressed image and an expanded image (or lines tilted in opposite directions) can simultaneously come to signify the same thing because each is tied to a specific phenomenal location in space. When we test for awareness of change during movement, it is not altogether clear that we are answering this question. Perhaps because the re-afference that occurs—for example, expansion or compression of the images of objects—is concomitant with movement of the observer, it is more and more discounted. As a matter of fact, when the head moves to one side, the images of all objects, whether to the left or right, either expand or contract, but not both simultaneously. In other words, it is not the case that the compressed images on one side and the expanded ones on the other behave differently. The compressed ones expand and the expanded ones expand more as the head moves in one direction; similarly with regard to the tilting of the horizontal lines. Hence, the principle could be adduced: Discount expansion of all images with head movement to the right; discount compression of all images with head movement to the left. If so, the effect would not be situational at all, at least not in the sense of a different perception of objects as a function of their location. It is, of course, possible that the adaptation in question is not based only on such a discounting principle, but rather reflects a situational change in the phenomenal width of objects to both sides. If compressed images on one side signify the same width as expanded ones on the other, then there should be no rubbery change with movement. In order to find out whether the latter explanation is the correct one, it is desirable to test with the observer stationary by presenting objects in different locations. In the few cases where this has been done, situational effects were obtained, but there are scarcely any data of this kind, particularly for the compression-expansion effect.[27]

The second problem—that of alterations of shape—arises because the type of transformation of the image under discussion is quite different from curvature, the only type of transformation of shape with which I have thus far dealt. It might be well first to consider this problem apart from the situational aspect of the adaptation, namely, whether it is plausible that a rectangular or trapezoidal image can ultimately signify a square, as is implied in these experiments (leaving aside as well the curvilinear shape of the sides of the image in this discussion). Is it not the case that this kind of transformation is of the object-relative type and, if so, should adaptation be possible? In other words, since it would seem that a rectangular image conveys the information that one axis is of a different extent than the other or, in the case of a trapezoidal image, that one side

---

[27] Another reason why tests *during* movement of the observer may be misleading is that it is difficult to control for eye position and, in fact, in the work reviewed here, no restrictions on eye position were imposed. This means that the aftereffects thus observed could conceivably be based upon the predominant type of stimulation that different regions of the retina have received during exposure to the prisms. (See the preceding footnote.) This possibility is eliminated when testing is done with observer stationary and under instructions as to where to turn his eyes.

diverges from the opposite side, one might think that it would never be possible to see the corresponding object in any other way than as rectangular or trapezoidal.

As already noted, the evidence is rather fragmentary concerning the extent to which such alterations of shape do occur. Also to the extent they do occur, such transformations are situationally determined in the experiments under discussion, a fact which may require a different type of explanation than would be the case if everywhere in the field a square were to be represented by a rectangular image. I will return shortly to the problem of dealing with the situational type of changes. Supposing for the moment, however, that an experiment had been performed entailing alteration of size of image along one axis only, everywhere in the field, and that the rectangular image eventually came to signify a square, how might we account for this?

The problem reduces itself to a modification of size, but only in one direction. Thus the analysis presented in Chapter 5 on adaptation to size is relevant here. That is to say, all the information about size along one axis is consistently transposed. This includes any visible portions of the body. Since specific size is a function of the relationship of images of various sizes to one another, the information is available concerning true size along that axis. Therefore, to the extent that comparisons are restricted to one axis at a time, within the foreshortened axis an apple continues to appear proportionately larger than a grape and smaller than a grapefruit. It continues to appear hand size. But comparisons between the two axes would nevertheless suggest that, let us say, horizontal dimensions were smaller than equivalent vertical dimensions. Information as to the equality of vertical and horizontal extents with one another would, however, be provided whenever the observer tilted his head by 90° or objects were rotated 90°. The point is illustrated in Figure 6–17. Assuming the horizontal dimension of the picture in *a* is foreshortened by the optical device, in *b* both hand and rectangle appear long and narrow. In *c* the hand and rectangle are seen with head tilted 90°. The hand now appears short and squat. But in *b* and *c*, both axes of the rectangle remain the same size in relation to the hand as they are in *a*. As a result of seeing hand and rectangle in the different orientations, traces faithful to the horizontal width of the image of rectangle and hand in *b* ultimately might signify the same size as traces faithful to the (egocentrically) vertical width of the image of rectangle and hand in *c*.

It is also possible that an altered interpretation of visual angle along the changed axis could take place based upon head movements. That is to say,

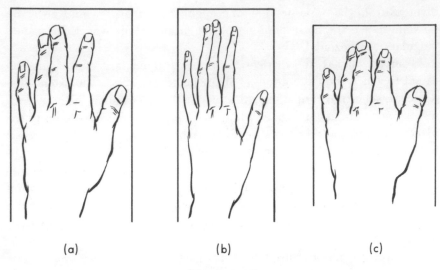

(a)   (b)   (c)

Figure 6–17

the observer could learn that what appeared to subtend an angle of, say, 45° in the field was actually 90°, because the head has to turn through 90° to move from one end of that arc to the other. Head movement along the other axis would not lead to any such change.

But does such possible modifiability imply that the geometric relationship of elements of a figure to one another (the object-relative aspect of shape perception) is not innately determined, as suggested earlier in the chapter? There are two possible answers to this question. One is that there is no innately built-in equivalence between *different* retinal directions. Therefore, while it might be evident without any learning which line was longer in *a, b,* or *c* in Figure 6–18, because both lines of each pair are parallel to one another, it might not be evident in *d* or *e*. The other possible answer is that, regardless of what may be innately given concerning the object-relative aspect of shape, the subject-relative aspect can, via learning, override it. If the two lines in *d* did innately appear of differ-

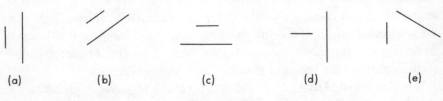

(a)   (b)   (c)   (d)   (e)

Figure 6–18

ent length, still it is in principle possible to learn that they signify the same length.

The third problem is that of the situational aspect of the effects reported. How does it come about that the location of an object can influence the manner in which it is perceived? The clearest example, I believe, is the effect on radial direction of the location of a point above or below eye level in the half-prism experiment. Under ordinary circumstances, memory traces specific to each eye position are associated with particular phenomenal locations of objects whose images fall on the fovea. For the effect with half prisms, it is necessary to assume in addition that the trace refers both to eye position and to the location of things with respect to the observer's eye level. Hence, the trace combination "eyes straight ahead, object above eye level" comes to signify that a fixated object is to the left, whereas the trace combination "eyes straight ahead, object below eye level" signifies that a fixated object is straight ahead.

The same logic can be applied to situational effects that entail changes of shape. There are certain phenomena in perception in which something akin to location affects shape. For example, tilting back an object into the third dimension (within certain limits) will not alter its appearance, despite change of the projected retinal image (shape constancy). The phenomenal shape is affected by taking slant into account. Less well known is the effect of phenomenal orientation on shape. As described in the Addendum of Chapter 2, it has been demonstrated that, even with no change whatsoever in the orientation of an image on the retina, changing the perceived orientation of the object in space will significantly affect its shape (see page 65). Gestalt psychology has emphasized that we rarely perceive anything strictly in accord with the isolated retinal image per se. The perceptual constancies and many other phenomena attest to the correctness of the Gestalt critique of the constancy hypothesis—the assumption of a one-to-one correspondence between a local retinal stimulus and phenomenal experience. Hence it should not be considered alien to what we know about perception that a retinal image of a certain shape can yield different phenomenal shapes depending on its perceived location.

As a result of movements of the head or entire body, an object that at one moment is off to one side of the head and appears compressed will, the next moment, appear quite different when it changes its location. When the object is centered in the sagittal plane of the head, its shape will be perceived more or less veridically. When it is located off to the other side of the head, it will appear to be stretched out. Such movement therefore provides ample information that the way objects appear is a function of their location with respect to the observer's head. It is possible that the appearance of objects when they are straight ahead serves as the norm or index of their true shape with respect to which perception is "corrected" when objects are located to the side of the head. Whereas for non-situational effects (e.g., curvature) the stimulus-copy trace alone eventually signifies a specific phenomenal shape, in the situational after-effect, that trace plus a trace component of radial location does so. In other words, ordinarily a trace of an image such as *a* in Figure 6–19 comes to signify a square. For the subject wearing prisms, a trace containing two components—a copy of the image shape *and* a representation

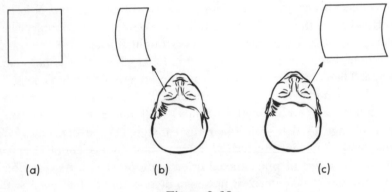

(a)   (b)   (c)

Figure 6–19

of its location vis-à-vis the head—comes to signify a square (*b* or *c* in Figure 6–19). The stimulus-copy shape component of the trace varies depending upon the location component.

As noted, the situational aftereffects and the perceptual constancies are very similar. In both cases there is a "taking into account" by the nervous system of information about the external situation above and beyond that given in the circumscribed retinal image. If the situational aftereffect is indeed another constancy, the following question arises. Some psychologists have noted that, despite the presence of constancy, the capability also remains of perceiving in terms corresponding closely to the state of affairs given in the retinal image. For example, in the case of size perception, one can, with certain instructions, elicit judgments of size approximating changes in the visual angle. William McDermott and I have recently shown that observers can equate objects on the basis of visual angle, even when one of the objects compared is seen to have a definite objective size.[28] That is, observers are capable of abstracting a sensation of pure extensity from the total impression of an object of a certain size at a certain distance. Hence the Helmholtzian notion of a sensation of size based on visual angle accompanied by an unconscious inference of size based on taking distance into account rings true to some extent. In the case of shape constancy, we may well be aware of the elliptical "sensation" yielded by a circle at a slant, while at the same time evidencing constancy for the objective shape of the circle.

If this way of describing the constancies is correct, does it apply to the situational aftereffects? If it does, it means that in a certain sense the observer continues to "see" the object to his left as narrow and that to his right as wide. But this sensory core, which remains unchanged over time, is supplemented by a "taking into account" type of objective experience precisely as in the constancies. This interpretation, if correct, places in a somewhat different perspective the problem raised above as to how a rectangular or trapezoidal image could yield an impression of a square, and it may render unnecessary the speculations offered concerning that problem. The fact that such images can lead to the experience of a square under certain conditions in prism adaptation is no more or no less a problem than the fact that an ellipse can lead to the experience of a circle under certain conditions in daily life.

The evidence on this point is not sufficiently clear-cut. Much of the data is concerned with how the world appears during movement of the observer, but there is some evidence that does suggest changes of shape may be a function of the location of the object. However, these impressions of shape could have been of the "objective" type that subjects typically employ in constancy situations. In other words, although it is possible for subjects to focus on the appearance of objects as given by the retinal image, they usually do not do so, and certainly don't do so in experiments in which they are asked such questions as "How big *is* that (distant) triangle?" or "What *is* the shape of this (tilted) form?" As noted, appropriate instructions can affect what the subject reports about his perceptual experience. Therefore, we don't know if the outcome would differ in experiments on "situational" prism adaptation if the subjects were instructed to be more analytical about what they were seeing. In any case, it would seem advisable to leave this as an open question. Since it has not been raised previously, research has not been directed toward answering it. One final point on this question. The similarity between the situational aftereffects and

[28] I. Rock and W. McDermott, The perception of visual angle, *Acta Psychol.*, 1964, **22**, 119–134.

the constancies lends support to the view that the constancies are also learned.[29]

SUMMARY

The question was posed as to the relationship between the shape of the retinal image and phenomenally perceived shape. It was argued that the manner in which lines in the environment relate *to one another* spatially is correctly represented by the normal retinal image, but it would also be correctly represented by an image that is consistently transformed, as is the case in viewing the world through wedge prisms. Although prismatically viewed objects do appear similar to their normally viewed counterparts, they also appear different. The difference resides in the apparent curvature of the component lines, straight lines now appearing curved and curved lines appearing either more or less curved or straight.

An attempt was made to uncover the perceptual properties of curved and straight lines. It was suggested that a phenomenal straight line is defined by the apparent direction of its locus of points with respect to the observer and by the behavior of its retinal image with changes of the position of the line in relation to the observer. The aspect of shape concerned with "straightness" or "curvature," therefore, seems to be essentially subject-relative in contrast to the aspect concerned with the spatial relationship of line components to one another (object-relative). Based on prior experience in which images of specific curvature have always represented lines of specific phenomenal curvature, memory traces representing this association are deposited. This explains why the apparent curvature of all lines is altered on first viewing the world through prisms. In the prism world, straight lines are represented by curved images, but these images now reflect the perceptual properties of straight lines. Adap-

---

[29] That is, they may be learned where a "taking into account" process operates. Research just completed in our laboratory by Donald Heller demonstrates that size constancy is not present in rats reared under conditions of visual deprivation, but is present in the same animals following a period of exposure to conditions of normal illumination. In achromatic color constancy, on the other hand, Hans Wallach has shown that constancy results from the determination of achromatic color by the intensity-ratio of neighboring regions, which ratio does not change with changes of illumination. (H. Wallach, Brightness constancy and the nature of achromatic colors, *J. exp. Psychol.*, 1948, **38**, 310–324.) It would be difficult to understand how illumination could be taken into account in view of Hering's paradox, namely, that there would seem to be no way of determining whether light reaching the eye is from a surface of low albedo in high illumination or of high albedo in low illumination.

tation, therefore, consists in the establishment of new associations between image curvature and information concerning phenomenal curvature.

In his classic experiment on adaptation to prismatically created curvature, Gibson discovered that if the observer inspected actually curved lines the lines also tended to straighten out, and a straight line seen thereafter appeared curved in the opposite direction. It was suggested that this aftereffect is a case of successive contrast, which is based on the tendency to perceive curvature in terms of the spatial relationship of lines to one another (the object-relative aspect). Certain geometric illusions were examined from this point of view. It was noted that the phenomenal curvature of an isolated line is a function of length of arc, other things being equal.

The Gibson effect is based on configurational relationships of the inspection and test patterns. The work of several other investigators, on the other hand, clearly indicates that, above and beyond the adaptive change predictable in terms of the Gibson effect, there is prism adaptation to curvature, based on information as to the properties of objects in the environment. In all such research thus far performed, movement of the observer or his head or his eyes alone was a necessary condition for adaptation, as is to be expected on the basis of the defining properties of subject-relative curvature. Feedback from movement provides the crucial information that points are not located where they at first appear to be. There is evidence which suggests that *active* movement by the observer is a necessary condition. If further research confirms this finding, the explanation may lie with the ambiguity of information about the direction of movement of the observer when such movement is passively imposed. However, procedures were suggested by which passive movement would be expected to yield adaptation to prismatic changes of curvature, and it was pointed out that familiarity with the scene might produce an effect even in a stationary observer.

Kohler and Erismann discovered that certain adaptation effects are a function of the location of objects with respect to the observer, since there are certain optical effects of a prism that are a function of such location (the situational aftereffects). However, these effects are not a function of eye position as Kohler and others seem to think, but rather of the phenomenal location of objects with respect to the observer's head. These effects have been confirmed, but they are rather small. Several problems are raised by these findings, chief among which are: (1) The method of testing thus far employed has been primarily a dynamic one—how things appear *during* the moving of the head. The meaning of the situational effects would be clearer if it can be shown that the phenomenal shape of objects differs depending on their apparent location under static conditions of testing. (2) Certain changes of shape are reported that are not readily explained (e.g., rectangular images yielding the impression of square objects). If such changes are found under non-situational conditions, an explanation in terms of the modification of size signified by the image along only one axis would seem to be required. (3) Change in appearances as a function of phenomenal location is in keeping with other well-known perceptual phenomena, notably the constancies. To account for situational aftereffects in terms of the theory offered in this book, it is necessary to assume the memory trace includes a component representing phenomenal location of objects with respect to the head, in addition to one that is a copy of the proximal stimulus pattern. Since it is known that the specific character of the proximal stimulus is to some extent available to conscious awareness in the case of size or shape constancy, it is possible that this is also the case in the situational aftereffects. If so, then these effects are essentially like those obtained in experiments on the constancies, namely, based on a tendency to perceive in terms of an objective attitude (what the external object *is*) rather than an analytic attitude (what the proximal stimulus or sensation *is*).

ADDENDUM

The Cortical Representation of the Retinal Image

As already noted, the cortical mapping of the retinal image is one of topological representation rather than geometrical congruency or similarity. Largely as a result of a disproportionately great amount of cortical area representing the relatively small foveal area of the retina, there are gross distortions in the geometry of forms. A square on the retina may project in the cortex as a quadrilateral whose sides are curved rather than straight. Yet the phenomenal experience of the shape is in excellent accord with the shape of the image, and is veridical with respect to the shape of the object.[30] Since it is primarily the cortical event that underlies or parallels the experience, how can a particular geometrical pattern in the cortex give rise to a rather different pattern in experience, and why does the latter happen to correspond with the image and with the object?

Some have puzzled about this fact, but others have taken the position

---

[30] In this discussion I am restricting the analysis to two dimensions.

that it is a pseudo-problem. Why, they ask, need there be a geometrical similarity between cortical event and phenomenal event? Earlier I argued that it makes little sense to believe there need be an identity between cortical orientation and phenomenal orientation or cortical size and phenomenal size. Yet in the case of form, there are certain reasons why one might think there ought to be a similarity between the geometry of the cortical pattern and the perceived shape. The shape has certain geometrical characteristics that it is reasonable to assume derive from the geometry of the cortical pattern. For example, a circle is symmetrical. One would think this characteristic derives from a symmetry in the cortical event underlying the perception of the circle and that that in turn derives, at least in part, from the geometry of the pattern of excitation. Do those who speak of a pseudo-problem here believe that the perceived shape has nothing at all to do with the geometry of the cortical pattern of excitation? Could the latter be triangular and the former circular or rectangular? Why then is there any cortical map of the retinal image? Why isn't there random distribution of fibers such that adjacent retinal points are not even adjacent in the cortex?

I would like to suggest that in certain respects there is truth in both positions, i.e., the position that the cortical pattern is merely a coded representative of the phenomenal pattern and bears no particular geometrical similarity to it and the position that the geometry of the cortical pattern does play a role in determining the phenomenal geometry. In the first place, it must be made clear that many proponents of the "code" hypothesis would agree that geometry *is* the relevant determinant of phenomenal geometry but merely claim that the geometry need not be similar. For example, one might say that a kidney-shaped cortical pattern yields a phenomenal circle. Hence it is the kidney-shape that is crucial, not intensity, size, or some other factor. Whenever a pattern of that shape occurs, a circle is seen.

What, then, according to this view is the correlate of an ellipse? Could it be any geometrical shape? It would seem plausible to think that if *a* in Figure 6–20 is the cortical correlate of a circle, then *b* is the correlate of an ellipse with the horizontal axis longer and *c* an ellipse with the vertical axis longer. In other words, a sensible code would be one based on some principle that would apply with consistency to all shapes. If *a* yields a circle, then apparently the axes *x* and *y* signify equal phenomenal lengths. If so, then an ellipse in the same approximate region of the retina whose horizontal axis is longer than its vertical would have to be based on a cortical pattern in which the correlate of the horizontal axis was longer than x, and similarly for the y axis with respect to a vertical ellipse. Hence the correlate of an ellipse in that region of the retina would have to be a curvilinear pattern whose width-to-height ratio is different from that ratio which represents circles.

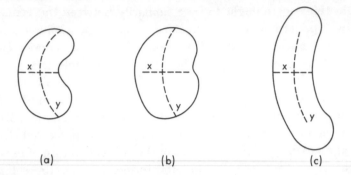

Figure 6–20

If cortical extents of varying magnitude in different orientations signified (either innately or via experience) the identical phenomenal extent, this would amount to a code that could be consistently applied to all shapes. Thus, suppose in Figure 6–21a that the cortical extents 1, 2, 3, and 4 all signify equal phenomenal extents. Then it would follow that a pattern of excitation such as 1 in *b* would appear perfectly circular, and one such as 2 in *b* would appear elliptical or egg-shaped. Although 2 appears circular in the figure (as it would if its cortical pattern could be directly seen), the fact is—according to our assumption—that its vertical diameter signifies a much smaller extent than its horizontal diameter. In *c* the triangle would appear *equilateral*, not isosceles, and so forth.

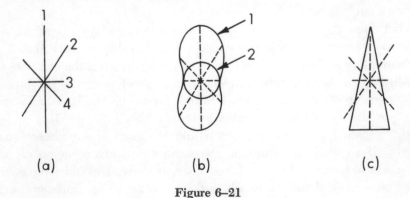

Figure 6–21

If this is approximately correct, there remains the problem of explaining how cortical patterns can represent such different phenomenal patterns, and how the distinctive phenomenal properties of specific shapes are accounted for by their corresponding cortical patterns. Obviously we cannot expect to unravel this complex problem fully at this stage of our knowledge, but there are a few relevant ideas that come out of the analysis in this chapter.

1. At birth, shape is primarily a function of intra-figural relationships, so that if the cortical image is a transformation of the retinal image, shape would not necessarily be altered. To the extent that the entire retinal image is transformed in the cortical projection in such a way that the relationships between parts of the figure are preserved, the object-relative aspect of form perception would not be affected. All that matters at the outset is the manner in which lines approach and recede from each other without regard to their directions relative to the self. Thus, for example, if the *a* patterns in Figure 6–1 represented the retinal image and the *b* patterns the cortical "image," such a distortion would not constitute a problem.

2. Certain absolute phenomenal properties of figures, such as straightness, do not require straight images and, in fact, do not exist at all at the outset. Hence the curvilinear nature of cortical lines representing straight phenomenal lines or the straightness of cortical lines representing phenomenally curved ones is not a problem.

3. Based upon the ability to assimilate information as to the actual state of affairs in the environment, even if it were the case that a cortical pattern initially gave rise to a non-veridical percept, that state of affairs may be subject to change. Thus a curved cortical line will come to signify a straight phenomenal one; two cortical lines of different length in different orientations can perhaps ultimately signify equal phenomenal extents.

4. A last point concerns a hypothesis I would like to suggest concerning the fact that projected patterns of the identical image vary with the location of the image. This fact constitutes a problem for both points of view. For those who advocate an isomorphism, it is puzzling that so many different cortical patterns can all signify the same phenomenal shape. Köhler and Wallach tried to solve this problem with the suggestion that there is a greater permanent satiation in the periphery because projected patterns would be denser in the smaller cortical area allotted to peripheral vision.[31] Greater satiation would lead to increased functional distance between cortical points, thus offsetting the smaller

[31] W. Köhler and H. Wallach, op. cit.

physical distance. For those who advocate a code, it is a troublesome complication that there is no one cortical pattern that consistently yields a given phenomenal shape. I would like to suggest that the equivalence of different cortical patterns in different locations may be the end-product of past experience, such as occurs in the situational aftereffect. To illustrate, suppose that a vertical straight line *x–y* falls on a vertical retinal meridian when its center falls on the fovea (Figure 6–22a). The projec-

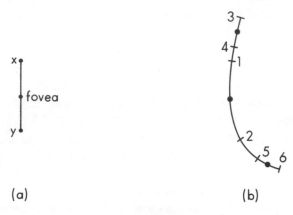

(a)   (b)

Figure 6–22

tion of this image to the cortex is illustrated in *b* (1–2). The cortical line is somewhat curved. This pattern in this retinal-cortical location becomes identified with a straight line of a given extent in the manner discussed in this chapter. If, now, the eye turns up, the line falls in the upper periphery of the retina and yields a cortical pattern of a somewhat different length and curvature (3–4 in *b*). Still the line will not change its radial direction (constancy of direction), so that it is clear it is the same object that a moment previous appeared quite different, and information as to its properties is available as before. Furthermore, there is the tendency to discount the stimulus change based upon the fact that it was wrought by eye movements. There are, therefore, reasons why that cortical pattern in that location will also be identified with a straight line of the same length as 1–2. Similarly for other cortical patterns yielded by the location of the image in other retinal locations (e.g., 5–6 in *b*). This hypothesis is almost identical to the one outlined in the chapter in connection with the Erismann-Kohler situational effects, except that here it is the varying retinal-cortical locations that might be said initially to signify different shapes and extents; whereas, in their work it is the varying locations relative to the head which do so. According to this hypothesis, early in life each eye movement would yield the transforming rubbery impression that in the Kohler experiment occurred only with head movement. Presumably these phenomenal transformations would soon die out. The distinctive cortical pattern for each retinal location would come to signify the same phenomenal shape.

The Role of
Proprioception in
Visual Adaptation

CHAPTER SEVEN

When vision is altered by prisms or lenses, any physical contact with objects could be thought to inform the observer of the true nature of these objects. Touch remains veridical.[1] What could be more plausible than to suppose that visual adaptation is based on tactual information? In its more general form, the thesis that we learn to see the world the way we do via touch has always been a popular one. In adapting to displacement, it is tempting to assume that it is via the correct proprioceptive information of the hand's location that we learn to reinterpret the altered visual information. Touch could also be thought to be the source of information that leads to adaptation to altered visual shape and size.

There are, however, good reasons for believing this argument to be incorrect. Most obvious is the empirical fact that adaptation has been obtained under conditions where there is no physical contact with objects in the environment. In many of the experiments on displacement or tilt, in which subjects are permitted to walk freely about in the environment,

[1] The words "touch" or "tactual" are used here in the dictionary meaning of perception based on physical contact with objects (generally manual), rather than in the narrower meaning of sensations based on stimulation of the skin surface. Clearly, appreciation of spatial properties of objects via touch is based on proprioceptive information deriving from the position of the fingers relative to one another or of other parts of the body to one another.

222

although there is locomotion, there is no contact with objects. Even more to the point are the positive results of experiments in which the observer is moved passively in a wheel chair or is completely stationary. Another reason for rejecting this argument is that vision is a much more precise and accurate sense than touch, and there is some evidence that vision is dominant when the two senses yield contradictory information.[2]

An Experimentally Created Conflict between Vision and Touch

In our laboratory, work has been in progress for many years on the relationship between vision and touch, a brief report of which has already appeared.[3] The main features of the research will be described here and a more detailed account will be given in the Addendum. The experiments were designed to answer the question: If contradictory information is given to two sense modalities as to the spatial properties of an object, what will be experienced? By means of optical distortion, an observer can be given a visual impression of an object that is at odds with his tactual impression of it. Will the observer be aware of this conflict or will one unified impression be experienced? If a unified impression is experienced, will it be a compromise between the visual and tactual sensations or will one sense dominate?

Experiments were done on distortion of shape and distortion of size. In all experiments, the subject views the visually distorted standard object through an optical device while at the same time grasping it with his fingers. The only object visible is the standard. To prevent sight of the hand—which might lead to a loss of experimental naïveté—the subject grasps the standard from behind through a thin cloth. In the experiments on distortion of shape, the standard is a small square which appears to be a rectangle whose height is twice its width when seen through the optical device.

In a control experiment, the observer looks at the standard through the optical device but does not touch it. Here, as expected, perception is governed by the distorted visual appearance so that, by and large, subjects judge the standard to be a rectangle whose sides are in about the same ratio to each other as in the distorted retinal image of the square yielded

[2] J. C. Hay, H. L. Pick, and K. Ikeda, Visual capture produced by prism spectacles, *Psychon. Sci.*, 1965, 2, 215–216.

[3] J. Victor and I. Rock, An experimentally created conflict between vision and touch, paper read at Eastern Pscholological Assoc., Atlantic City, April 1962; I. Rock and J. Victor, Vision and touch: An experimentally created conflict between the two senses, *Science*, 1964, 143, 594–596.

by the optical device. In another control experiment, the observer grasps the standard but does not see it. Here, as expected, perception is governed by tactual information so that the standard is, by and large, judged to be square.

In the experimental or conflict condition, the standard square is grasped and seen simultaneously. It was found that in this conflict situation, with vision and touch providing discrepant information, judgments of the shape of the standard are governed by its visual appearance. In fact, there is little evidence that touch plays any role at all. (Various methods of measuring what the observer experiences are employed, as described in the Addendum. All gave consistent results indicating the dominance of vision.)

Parallel experiments were performed for optical distortion of size. The standard square is viewed through a minifying lens system that reduced the size of all dimensions of the image by a factor of about two. (See Figure 7–1.) When the square is seen, but not touched, size perception is

Figure 7–1

essentially a function of the minified image; when touched only, the standard square is judged to be somewhat smaller than its actual size; when both seen and grasped in the conflict condition, the square is judged in terms of its visual appearance. Again, touch has very little influence.

In short, the results of the shape and size experiments seem to show that for subjects who remain naïve, with few exceptions, the visual impression is completely dominant. An experimental procedure added at the end of some of the experiments will serve to illustrate another important point about the dominance of vision. The subject was asked to look at and grasp the standard. While still grasping it, he then was told to close his eyes and open them again. The experimenter then asked him if the standard felt any differently when his eyes were open or closed: 23 of 38 subjects tested in this way reported that the object "felt" larger when their eyes were closed. The remainder did not report any definite impression. In other words, vision is so powerful a cue in relation to touch that the very touch experience itself undergoes a change. The object actually feels the way it looks (visual capture) and that is why, apparently, most subjects were unaware of a visual-tactual conflict in the experiments reported. This is precisely what Gibson found to be the case when subjects felt a straight rod which prisms made appear curved. "It was discovered . . . that in actual fact the kinesthetic perception, insofar as it was consciously represented, did *not* conflict with the visual perception. When a visually curved edge such as a meter stick was felt, it was felt as *curved*. This was true as long as the hand was watched while running up and down the edge." [4]

Although about one subject in five in our experiments did become aware of the conflict, it is remarkable that there were so few, from the standpoint of the discrepancy between the visual and tactual information. For example, the visual object is about one quarter of the area of the tactual in the size experiments. (There was a tendency for the aware subjects to resolve the conflict more in the direction of touch than do naïve subjects.) Note that reporting a conflict does not necessarily indicate a spontaneous registration of contradictory perceptions. The subject may have been suspicious of the apparatus or (and this occasionally did occur despite efforts to prevent it) may have looked away or up, thus obtaining an uncontaminated tactual impression of the standard which led to an awareness of the conflict. In any event, the answer to the starting question as to whether a unified impression would be experienced in the conflict condition is a qualified "yes." Generally the subject is unaware of the conflict, which means he does have a unified impression. Further, that impression is dominated by what he sees.

Adaptation to Contradictory Information from Vision and Touch

That vision dominates perception when vision and touch are pitted against one another is only indirect evidence that touch is not the cause of visual adaptation. With continuous exposure to the new relationship, vision could begin to undergo change. If, early in life, vision had been

[4] J. J. Gibson, Adaptation, after-effect, and contrast in the perception of curved lines, *J. exp. Psychol.*, 1933, 16, 4–5.

educated by touch, it may nevertheless have become dominant thereafter by virtue of its greater ability to give information about distance and its over-all versatility.

Hence the direct test would be one in which a possible change in the spatial properties signified by vision and by touch is studied, following a period of exposure to contradictory information from the two senses. In the work on size perception, described in Chapter 5, where the observer was permitted to manipulate the objects he saw, adaptation to the altered visual angle was obtained. Assume for the moment that, had we tested it, the interpretation of size via touch alone would not have undergone any change. In that case we would have had a situation in which, given exposure to contradictory information from the two senses, vision fell into line with touch rather than touch falling into line with vision.

But this interpretation would be unjustified, because that experiment did not isolate touch as the only possible cause of visual adaptation. Other information was available and, in fact, we obtained visual adaptation in an experiment in which the observer did not grasp anything, remaining stationary throughout. Furthermore, in those experiments the visually perceived objects did not appear half size even from the beginning, because to some extent there was an immediate correction effect operating. Hence it is not clear what change to expect, if any, in the size signified by touch. That is to say, if a one-inch square appeared to be one-half inch, then the feel of a one-inch square could ultimately come to signify a half-inch square. But if, for whatever reason, it appears visually to be one inch in size (despite the optical minification), it is difficult to see why there should be any change in touch perception. Even if it did not *appear* to be true size, the subject clearly knew the true size because familiar objects were used. This kind of knowledge could stand in the way of any change in size signified by touch.

Therefore, this is not the correct paradigm to test the question at issue, and the majority of experiments performed on perceptual adaptation cannot be considered relevant to this question. The correct design is precisely the one that involves a conflict situation described in the preceding pages. Here the only information about size other than the immediate visual impression is given by touch and the only information other than the immediate touch impression is given by vision.[5] This is so because only a single visual object is presented, and this object could conceivably

[5] The only other experiments in the literature which seem to fulfill these conditions are those in which the observer views only his arm through a wedge prism. Here vision informs that the arm has one location and proprioception that it has another.

be of *any* size, since it has a neutral square shape. Neither size relationships nor familiarity can serve to indicate the true size. The vision-control experiment established that the object did indeed appear to be about half size. Similarly, the touch-control experiment established that by touch alone the object was perceived more or less veridically. It is true that touch is veridical in the situation described, but this is irrelevant. (There is no obvious way of directly distorting touch sensations.) Since there is no other source of sensory information than that given by either vision or touch, there is no a priori reason why touch could not undergo change, even though the change would be in a non-veridical direction. The question we are asking, then, is this: What would be the effect of continued exposure to this conflict situation? Would continuous palpating of the square begin to yield visual adaptation? Would visual size begin to change as a result of the flow of veridical information from touch? Or would the opposite occur, would the significance of size via touch begin to accommodate itself to the altered visual size? The experiments described below attempted to find out.

The basic plan of the experiments followed the adaptation paradigm: First there was a pre-exposure test to establish base lines, then exposure to the conflicting information from the two senses, and finally a post-exposure test, the results of which are compared with the pre-exposure test. As a first step, we sought to ascertain whether there would be any change at all in the cross-modality equivalences that existed prior to exposure. In other words, for adults, vision and touch roughly correspond, in the sense that a one-inch visual object is considered about equal to a one-inch tactual object.[6] During exposure to visual minification, however, an object that appears visually to be one inch yields a tactual impression of a two-inch object. What we wished to find out first of all is whether the one-to-one equivalence might change in the direction of the one-to-two equivalence. If this sort of change occurs, then we may ask which modality is responsible for the change. If this change does not occur, then there would be no reason to pursue the problem further. The pre- and post-exposure tests designed to answer this question were cross-modality comparisons. Either a visual standard object was given which had to be matched by a tactual comparison object (V-T) or a tactual standard had to be matched by a visual comparison object (T-V). (Either of these methods alone might be considered sufficient, but we felt it wise to cross-check by including both. However, only one of these methods was used

[6] There are certain constant errors in the "equivalences" that exist between these modalities, but I am ignoring them in this discussion.

for any one subject.) Needless to say, in these tests visual objects could not be felt and tactual objects could not be seen.

An Experiment on the Length of a Line

In an experiment done in collaboration with Arien Mack, the question arose as to what activity the subject should engage in during the exposure period. In order to provide continuous exposure to the contradictory information from the two senses, we simply required the observer simultaneously to grasp an object and view it through the lens system throughout the period. But this provided no task for the subject, and his attention soon waned, which, in turn, led to moments when the observer looked away from the object. At such moments he often became aware that the object was larger than it had appeared, a state of sophistication we sought to avoid. We then arrived at the idea of having the subject draw lines and rectangles of various sizes while viewing his own drawing through the minification lens. To prevent his hand from being seen, the subject drew his lines from underneath translucent paper with a thick marking pen which insured that his own drawn lines and nothing else were visible to him. He could see the lines growing in size as he drew. Thus any line he drew simultaneously yielded proprioceptive information as to its length and erroneous visual information to the effect that it was half its true length. This was precisely the kind of exposure condition desired. The subject was kept busy doing this for 30 minutes. The apparatus was essentially identical with that described in connection with the conflict between vision and touch in size perception.

Since the perception of length via proprioception during the exposure period was based on a temporal development in drawing lines rather than a simultaneous act of grasping an object, it was decided to make the pre- and post-exposure tests equivalent in this respect to the exposure task. In the V-T procedure, the subject was shown a line that was made to increase gradually to a length of 25 mm. by means of a children's toy. When a knob is turned a line appears and grows in size as a function of continued turning of the knob. He then was asked to draw a line of that length with his eyes closed. In the T-V procedure, the subject proprioceptively experienced a length of 25 mm. by drawing a line between two fixed edges of a slit cut in a cardboard. He then opened his eyes and adjusted the knob of the aforementioned toy until the line appeared to have a length equal to the previously felt length. Thus, if the drawing activity during exposure has led to a change in the proprioceptively given sense of length associated with a particular visual impression of length, it should be revealed by a change from the pre- to post-exposure cross-modality equivalency response. Specifically, the proprioceptive impression of length while drawing lines may become associated with a shorter visual length than previously. In the V-T procedure this would be revealed by the subject drawing a longer line in the post-exposure than in the pre-exposure test; in the T-V procedure it would be revealed by his producing a shorter visual length on the toy in the post-exposure than in the pre-exposure test.

For each subject, the average of his pre-exposure trials was computed and his post-exposure setting was subtracted from this average to yield a difference score. In the V-T procedure, the mean difference score for 8 experimental subjects was +6.0 mm., a value significantly different from 0. (In order to establish that the change was indeed caused by exposure to the conflicting sensory information, a control experiment was performed with 8 different subjects. For this group the procedure was identical in every respect but one, namely, a tube with plain glass was substituted for the minification lens system. The mean difference score was +.1 mm., signifying no systematic change at all.)

In the T-V procedure, the mean difference score for 14 subjects was −2.4 mm., a value that could be expected to occur by chance only one time in ten, were the population mean difference score 0. In this case, however, the mean difference score for 15 control subjects was +1.5 mm., a value not significantly different from 0, but which does reflect a definite trend in the opposite direction. Hence, whatever the cause of this trend, we may presume it was operating for the experimental subjects as well. The difference between mean scores for the experimental and control group is significant. As to the magnitude of the effect, assuming complete adaptation would result in doubling the pre-adaptation length of the line drawn in the V-T procedure, the increase represents a change of 28 per cent; assuming that complete adaptation would result in halving the pre-adaptation length of line reproduced in the T-V procedure, the decrease represents a change of 15 per cent.[7]

[7] The only previous attempt to study the consequences of exposure to an altered size relationship between vision and touch was by Weber some years ago. C. O. Weber, Visual-motor coordination in concave and convex mirror space, *Amer. J. Psychol.,* 1931, 43, 254–260. Weber's observers viewed rectangular shapes through concave or convex mirrors and had to draw them. A concave mirror magnifies and a convex mirror minifies visual size. Since the observer's hand was only visible through the mirror, he had to draw a rectangle larger than it appeared to be in order to match the standard when looking through the convex mirror, and he had to draw one that was smaller when looking through the concave mirror. In essence, this is quite like the procedure we employed, except that our observers could not see their hand and therefore had no idea about the optical distortion to which they were being subjected. As a test of the

In our experiment, both ways of testing for adaptation, namely V-T and T-V, indicate that it has taken place. However, we are not in a position to determine from these measures alone whether it is touch, vision, or possibly both that has undergone a change. The same outcome would be predicted if touch had succeeded in educating vision as if vision had educated touch, namely, selection of a larger tactual line to match a given visual line or selection of a smaller visual line to match a given tactual line. Therefore one purpose of the experiment described next was to include certain tests designed to answer the question: Which modality is responsible for the effect obtained? A further purpose was to use a different type of proprioception from the one thus far studied, namely, one involving grasping objects between the fingers. In daily life the apprehension of spatial properties such as size or shape by touch undoubtedly is more typically achieved by encircling the object with the fingers and, if necessary, shifting them around.

An Experiment on the Size of a Square

In the following experiment, done in collaboration with Laurence Adams and A. Lewis Hill,[8] there were several important changes in the procedure, namely, (1) touch was accomplished by grasping a square

---

effect of this exposure, Weber required his subjects to draw one-inch squares without looking, and also to select one-inch squares visually. They did this before and after the exposure to the mirror. These measures depend upon memory for standard units of size, which we have found to be quite unreliable.

Weber's results are hard to interpret. For one thing, he did not seem to understand that the outcomes for vision and touch should be in *opposite* directions. He seems to assume that because a concave mirror enlarges visual size it ought to enlarge the subject's phenomenal conception of size in both the vision and motor spheres (and contrariwise for a convex mirror). Hence he was not puzzled by his results, which seem to point in this direction. The reason I say "seem" is that there is a general tendency to draw or select successively larger rectangles during the pre- and post-exposure testing (for both concave and convex mirror observers), and this tendency obscures the meaning of the results. The cause of the tendency is unknown, but underscores the importance of control groups in this paradigm, groups unfortunately not included in Weber's study. Even allowing for such an upward tendency, however, the results do not consistently go in the directions expected on the basis of exposure to conflicting information from vision and touch. The only clear finding in Weber's study is that, quite apart from the effect of exposure to the distorting mirrors, a striking constant error in the vision-touch equivalency was obtained. Subjects drew squares about 50 per cent smaller than their visual selections when giving their impressions of an inch during the pre-exposure tests. We encountered a similar tendency to overestimate extent by touch.

[8] I. Rock, A. Mack, L. Adams, and A. L. Hill, Adaptation to contradictory information from vision and touch, *Psychon. Sci.*, 1965, 3, 435–436.

rather than by drawing a line, (2) a new procedure for the adaptation exposure was devised, (3) tests were included to measure vision and touch per se, in addition to tests to determine the cross-modality equivalences, and (4) all tests involving vision were conducted in complete darkness.

The problem that troubled us in the previous experiment, namely, how to occupy the subject with a meaningful task during the exposure period, was now solved in a different way by the simple expedient of placing a comparison object under the reduction lens in addition to the standard object. The subject was required to compare the standard with comparison objects in terms of size, while both viewing and grasping each alternately. The comparison objects were squares of increasing size arranged along the edge of a wheel which the subject rotated with his other hand so as to advance the different squares into a central position under the lens (see Figure 7–2). The subject could grasp the standard or compari-

Figure 7–2

son square from below, through a cloth and, thus, he did not see his hand. By using several different size standards, the subject was kept busy making comparisons throughout the 30-minute period, and yet all his experience entailed exposure to the contradictory information from the two senses. Very few subjects consciously realized there was a contradiction between visual and tactual size impressions. It is important to be clear that, since both standard and comparison squares were minified and since both were grasped tactually, the observers had no difficulty comparing them with one another.

The pre-exposure and post-exposure tests varied for each of the four different conditions employed. In the V-T procedure, the subject was shown a 27-mm. luminous standard square in the dark and had to match it by grasping, without viewing, a series of comparison squares (those along the wheel shown in Figure 7–2). In the T-V procedure, the subject was required to grasp, without viewing, a 27-mm. standard square and then to match it to one of a series of luminous visual comparison squares presented to him in the dark. The square in the center of the series was 27 mm. and matched the standard.

To determine whether any change occurred in vision, the same method was employed here as in the work on size described in Chapter 5. The method entails memory for a specific size introduced as a standard at the beginning of the experiment. To review, the subject is first shown the standard (in this case a 27-mm. square) with lights on. He then matches it, from immediate memory, in the dark, to one of a series of luminous squares. The standard is again shown in the light and once again matched in the dark. Several such trials are given. This procedure serves to provide ample exposure to the standard and a base line against which to measure post-exposure judgments. Following the exposure period, and without seeing the standard again, the subject must select a luminous square he believes is the size the standard square had been. If touch has altered the impression of size yielded by a given retinal image, a square smaller than that selected in the pre-exposure trials should now be chosen, because it ought to appear larger than it is. In appearing larger, it should match the remembered size of the previously seen standard. The reason for conducting all tests involving vision in the dark is the same as that mentioned in describing the work on size adaptation. It is unlikely that the entire scene would signify a different size than it had before, and the size of a single object would undoubtedly be very much influenced by its size relative to all other visible objects, thus working against any change.

A similar test was employed to study the fate of touch perception. The standard 27-mm. square was presented to the subject, and he was allowed to see it while grasping it. Immediately thereafter he had to select by touch alone a comparison square that equaled the standard. This sequence was repeated several times. Following the exposure period, he had to select from memory, by touch only, a square he believed was equal in size to the previously felt standard square. If tactual size has undergone a change in the predicted direction, then the observer should select a larger square after the exposure period than before it. The reason why the observer was initially allowed to see as well as grasp the standard was that in preliminary work it was discovered that memory for tactual size alone was quite imprecise and variable, thus tending to obscure any adaptive change. By permitting vision of the standard, the memory trace was apparently more definite and hence more stable. Since, however, the issue is not one of memory, but of perception via a given modality after exposure, the fact that in this condition the post-exposure test was conducted by touch alone guarantees that we are measuring the size perception via that modality. The "before" and "after" tests both entail matching by touch alone.

The inclusion of the four different measures described seem to make separate control groups unnecessary, particularly in the light of the rather clear-cut effects obtained.

The results of the cross-modality matches will be considered first. Table 7–1 gives the difference score between the average pre-exposure match and the mean of the first two post-exposure trial matches for each subject. Two difference scores are given, one based on the mean of the subject's last two pre-exposure selections (Difference 1) and one based on the mean of all pre-exposure selections (Difference 2). The units are the steps along the comparison series. In the V-T procedure, if exposure to the conflicting information had an effect, one should expect that after the exposure a larger tactual size would be matched to the visual standard than before it. Inspection of the results indicates that this

T A B L E 7–1   *Difference Scores: Pre-Adaptation Minus Post-Adaptation Means*

Vision-Touch Difference		Touch-Vision Difference		Vision Difference		Touch Difference		Touch Replication Difference	
1*	2*	1	2	1	2	1	2	1	2
+1.0	+.5	−1.5	−1.0	+.5	+.38	+1.0	+1.0	+2.5	+2.38
+2.0	+1.75	−.5	−.25	+1.0	+1.0	0	−.75	−.5	−.37
0	+.5	−3.5	−3.25	0	−.12	−.5	+.63	0	0
+.5	+.5	−2.0	−1.5	−.5	+.50	+1.0	+.63	0	+.13
−.5	−1.25	+1.0	+1.25	+.5	+.63	+1.0	+.88	+1.0	+.63
+1.5	+1.25	0	+.5	0	−1.25	0	−.50	+.5	+.25
0	+.25	−.5	−.5	−.5	−.62	0	+.63	+1.0	+1.63
+1.5	+2.0	−.5	−.5	0	0	+1.0	+1.13	+1.0	+.88
+1.0	+1.25	−2.0	−1.75	+1.5	+1.25	0	+.38	+1.0	+1.13
+3.0	+3.75	−1.0	−.75	0	−.12	+2.0	+1.50	−.5	−.25
Mean									
+1.0	+1.05	−1.05	−.78	+.25	+.16	+.55	+.55	+.60	+.64

* Difference 1 is based on the average of the last two of the pre-exposure judgments minus the average of the first two post-exposure judgments. Difference 2 uses the average of *all* pre-exposure judgments from which is subtracted the average of the first two post-exposure judgments.

is what took place in the great majority of subjects. The mean difference scores are both significantly different from 0. In the T-V procedure, an effect in the opposite direction is to be expected: After exposure to the conflicting information, a smaller visual size should be matched to the tactual standard than before. Again this is what occurred for the overwhelming majority of subjects. The mean Difference 1 score is significantly different from 0, and the mean Difference 2 score falls just short of significance.

I turn now to the more direct measures of size perception in each modality. If a change has occurred in the size signified by vision, the subject should select a smaller visual square after the exposure period than before it, because he would have learned that a seemingly small visual object is actually larger. In point of fact, the change that does occur is (non-significantly) in the opposite (+) direction, as can be seen in Table 7-1 in the columns under "vision." If a change has occurred in the size signified by touch, the subject should select a larger tactual square after than before the exposure period, because he would have learned that a seemingly large tactual object is actually smaller. This did occur for a majority of subjects, and the mean difference score of +.55 is significantly different from 0. Since, however, the result was not as striking as in the V-T or T-V cross-modality comparisons (4 subjects showing no change), the experiment was replicated with 10 new subjects. A virtually identical outcome was obtained, the mean difference scores being significantly different from 0. The combined data are convincing because 11 subjects show a change in the predicted direction as compared to only 3 in the opposite direction (or 15 to 4 using the Difference 2 scores). The results of the four different tests support the conclusion that an adaptive change in the relationship of the tactual and visual modality to each other has taken place, and that this change is based on an altered significance of size via touch.[9]

As to the magnitude of the effect obtained, the cross-modality measures revealed a change of approximately one step along the comparison series, which is approximately 12 per cent in length. This represents a change of about 20 per cent in area. Considered in relation to what would be com-

---

[9] The reader can now understand why I rejected a particular method in studying adaptation to a minified image (Chapter 5), namely, one in which the observer estimates the visual length of an object that is grasped but not seen, before and after the exposure period. Although in certain respects this would be superior to the method we did employ, it is subject to possible adaptation of size in the realm of touch. If touch perception itself undergoes change, it can scarcely be considered a stable indicator of visual size.

plete adaptation (selection of a 13.5-mm. square in the T-V measure or a 54-mm. square in the V-T measure), the effect is approximately 22 per cent in the former case and 11 per cent in the latter case. The effect is somewhat less in the direct measure of touch perception, but the cross-modality measures are probably more accurate indices of the actual change obtained, since they do not depend upon memory.

Visual Space and Haptic Space

In the light of our results, the implication is clear that for sighted individuals the spatial significance given by touch derives from correlated visual experiences during development. Thus we conclude that vision educates touch and not touch vision, the opposite of the traditional empiricist claim about the origin of various perceptual qualities in vision. As lucidly summarized by Hochberg, the classical structuralists sought to derive the world of perceived objects in space from elementary sensations by assigning a crucial role to memory images based on proprioception.[10] In 1709, Berkeley had enunciated the doctrine that "visible figures are the marks of tangible figures, and . . . it is plain, that in themselves they are little regarded, or upon any other score than for their connection with tangible figures, which by nature they are ordained to signify." [11] This point of view has not lost its appeal with the passage of time, as is illustrated by what John Dewey said two centuries later: "Ultimately visual perception rests on tactual . . . Spatial relations are not originally perceived by the eye, but are the result of the association of visual sensations with previous muscular and tactual experiences." [12]

If we were to assume that the same dominance of vision over touch obtains for the infant as for the adult, then the fact that objects are often simultaneously grasped and seen would permit learning to take place. In time, a given tactual impression alone would, by association with vision, signify a given size or shape.[13] In fact one might argue that, for the sighted person at least, there is no separate spatiality indigenous to touch at all.

[10] J. Hochberg, *Perception*, Englewood Cliffs, New Jersey: Prentice-Hall, 1964.

[11] G. Berkeley, *An essay towards a new theory of vision*, London: J. M. Dent, 1910, p. 77.

[12] J. Dewey, *Psychology* (3rd ed.), New York: American, 1898, p. 165.

[13] There is evidence in the literature that points to the role of prior visual experience in the apprehension of spatial properties of objects by touch. In one study it was shown that sighted subjects when blindfolded judge form more accurately than blind subjects, and accidentally blinded subjects are, in turn, superior to those born blind. See P. Worchel, Space perception and orientation in the blind, *Psychol. Monogr.*, 1951, **65**, 1–28.

What there is, is a particular complex of proprioceptive sensations which, by association, conjures up visual imagery of shape, size, and the like. For example, if I grasp an apple with my eyes closed, based on the configuration of my hand in grasping it, I visualize the apple's shape and size. If this reasoning is correct, it would explain the phenomenon of visual capture, namely, that in cases of a conflict between the two modalities the *felt* impression actually conforms with the visual one. That is to say, if touch yields spatial impressions via visualization, then the intersensory conflict situations we described can be thought of as a conflict between direct vision on the one hand and visualization mediated by touch on the other. It is no wonder then that vision is completely dominant; obviously what one sees directly would take precedence over what one merely visualizes. And the spatial aspect of the proprioceptive experience would tend to conform with what one actually sees the hand doing in the case of a conflict situation.[14]

Perhaps it is a mistake to think that there are as many "spaces" as there are sense modalities. Certainly we can quickly dispose of the idea that modalities such as audition have their own separate "spaces." The capacity to locate an object in space by means of audition does not imply there is an auditory space. A sounding object is localized in *space*. If the object is also seen, that space is visual. If it is not seen or if the eyes are closed, it is localized in imagined space. For a sighted person, that imagined space is essentially visualized, but for a congenitally blind person, there is no doubt also an imagined three-dimensional manifold in which objects are phenomenally localized with respect to the self and to one another.

Instead of thinking of multiple "spaces" corresponding to the several modalities, perhaps we should think of space as a basic category of mind, as Kant suggested. In other words, there is only one space that is trans-sensory, so to speak. However, vision is a modality that directly yields spatial information—extensity and the simultaneous location of points with respect to one another. It is questionable if other modalities yield

[14] In addition to visual capture and the evidence reported in this chapter concerning the dominance of vision over *touch*, there is evidence of the dominance of vision when it conflicts with other kinds of proprioceptive data. For example, in his work on movement perception, Duncker has reported that when illusory movement is induced in a stationary target by moving its surroundings, the observer feels his *eyes* to be moving as he fixates the target. In the experiments of Asch and Witkin, subjects often report that they feel their own (upright) *body* to be tilted in accord with the visual impression of their body's position. When the room is rocked back and forth, observers often experience an induced rocking of their body in the opposite direction, which may easily lead to nausea. The so-called haunted-swing illusion, famous in European carnivals, was based on the dominance of vision over proprioception.

such information, with the possible exception of touch. At any rate vision would seem to be so superior in this regard that, for the sighted, impressions of size, shape, and location are rendered visually, and when vision is not directly used, such impressions are visualized even when the objects are sensed in modalities other than vision.

It is interesting to consider in the light of our findings the belief of philosophers over the centuries that touch is the reality sense par excellence. This belief is no doubt based on the fact that in touch we make direct contact with the material world and on the fact that a distance receptor such as vision is subject to illusions. Our findings make amply clear that, in point of fact, adults spontaneously rely on vision, not touch, when the two are at odds, despite the fact that touch "does not lie." Of course it is no doubt true that if told about the contradictory information one would place greater reliance on touch if one had to make a judgment about the actual properties of the object rather than about the apparent properties. This is no doubt based on the realization that there are ways of tampering with visual information but not with tactual information. If the argument is that we *ought* to rely on touch whether empirically we do or do not, then the question arises whether touch by itself can yield reliable information about the world. Perhaps the existence or non-existence of an object or its surface texture can most reliably be established by contact via touch, but an appreciation of its spatial properties via touch may, if my reasoning is correct, depend upon the prior education of touch by vision.

Implications for Studies of Adaptation

If touch adapts itself to vision, then it is hardly plausible to explain visual adaptation on the basis of tactual information. The findings described in Chapter 4 on adaptation to displacement, in which the observer views his moving hand, are in line with this conclusion. If a subject sees his own hand displaced by a wedge prism, it is logically possible that the veridical tactual information as to its location could play a role in bringing about a new interpretation of the proximal visual stimuli relevant to location. But on the basis of the dominance of vision and our finding that touch adapts to vision, one would have to predict that (1) the hand would immediately feel as if it were where it visually appeared to be (a state of affairs hardly conducive to a causal role for touch) and (2) in time, with vision eliminated, the direction signified by the complex of proprioceptive sensations provided by a particular position of the hand and arm would be non-veridically interpreted. For example, when the arm pointed straight ahead, it would be felt to point to the side. These effects are, of course, precisely those that have been found to occur.

The same reasoning would apply to adaptation studies of phenomena other than radial direction. We now know that adaptation of various kinds can occur in the absence of tactual information concerning the external state of affairs. But it is nevertheless instructive to consider whether such information could be considered a sufficient condition for adaptation. The implication of our work in this chapter is that it could not. Consider adaptation to curvature. If an observer runs his hand along a straight rod which appears curved through a wedge prism, can the veridical tactual information yield visual adaptation? We would have to predict that when simultaneously seen the rod would actually *feel* curved (see Gibson's observation, p. 225) and that in time the proprioceptive sensations yielded by the hand moving along a straight rod would give rise to an impression of curvature even when the eyes are closed.[15] Harris reports precisely such an after-effect.[16]

In the case of orientation, suppose an observer, looking through a prism system that tilted the image of the scene, simultaneously grasped a vertical rod with both hands. According to the traditional view, the proprioceptive complex ought to tell him the rod is upright, but it would look tilted. However, I would predict the rod would feel tilted as well and that he would not necessarily experience any conflict. In time, with eyes closed, a vertical rod would no longer proprioceptively be felt to be vertical. Since this example has to do with orientation, it is interesting to consider the implications for Stratton's theory of adaptation, namely, that it is based upon the re-establishment of harmony between vision and touch. The prismatically tilted rod would, according to Stratton, look tilted because the tactual complex of sensations yielded by grasping the upright rod would lead the observer to imagine a visual orientation different from the one actually seen. In time, the felt rod would cease to suggest that visual direction and instead suggest one such as is yielded by the prismatically viewed vertical rod. This, says Stratton, is the meaning of uprightness. Over and above the reasons given in Chapter 2 for rejecting Stratton's explanation, one now can add the prediction mentioned above, that the

---

[15] I am assuming in all these examples that no other information is available which would lead to visual adaptation. Once visual adaptation occurs, the situation is changed and the prediction would have to be modified.

[16] C. S. Harris, Perceptual adaptation to inverted, reversed, and displaced vision, *Psychol. Rev.*, 1965, 72, 419–444.

prismatically tilted rod when grasped would no longer yield the felt quality usually associated with uprightness. It would "feel" tilted. Hence intersensory harmony would be established immediately, but the rod would still appear to be tilted.

The exact meaning of harmony or disharmony between vision and proprioception is in need of clarification. I have argued that what we get from proprioception is a sense of the position of parts of the body with respect to one another. To this extent, there is no connection whatsoever between visual and tactual localization. The feet may *feel* to be at one end of the body, but that says nothing about where they ought to appear visually. Therefore, if this were the whole story, it would be inappropriate to speak of a harmony or disharmony between the two senses. That the felt body could be localized *anywhere* in the visual field is suggested by a relatively unknown experiment of Stratton's in which he viewed the world through a combination of mirrors which yielded the impression that he was looking at his body from a point about two feet above his head. This head-on view of his body was localized horizontally in space, directly in front of his eyes.[17] The question at issue was whether in time the felt and seen location of the body would become harmonious. Stratton concluded that they would. The experiment dramatizes the fact that initially sensations in the two modalities are unrelated as far as spatial significance is concerned, but also brings out the fact that they do become related to one another via experience.

The fact is that whatever the position of parts of the body, they are both seen and felt in the sighted individual. Therefore, for any given combination of proprioceptive sensations, a particular visual location of all visible parts of the body will obtain and, as a result, the sensations from the two modalities are experienced as emanating from one and the same object. (The interesting question arises as to how the neonate knows which seen part of the body is the same as which felt part of the body. Is it the simultaneity of the two events, for example seeing the visual hand move at the same time as feeling a part of the body move?) This association will ultimately lead to the tendency to visualize from proprioceptive data alone not only how parts of the body are positioned relative to one another, but to where in the visual field they would appear, if seen. That being the case, in viewing through an inverting optical device there will be a conflict between the visualized location of a proprioceptively sensed part of the body and its seen location. Stratton reported that in time this conflict disappeared. This finding is in accord with the data pre-

[17] G. M. Stratton, The spatial harmony of touch and sight, *Mind*, 1899, 8, 492–505.

sented in this chapter and the findings of Harris and others that, in the case of a conflict between vision and touch, there will be a tendency for vision to dominate immediately and for touch to accommodate to the altered visual state of affairs. In the case of a reversed image, however, the conflict is rather extreme. The hand on the left is seen on the right. To be felt on the right, the subject has to suppress the visualization that it is on the left and instead to visualize it on the other side. Assuming for the moment no change in the rest of the body, sense could only be made of this impression by visualizing the left hand as stretched across the chest to the right side, which of course requires quite a distortion of the actual state of affairs. Perhaps this explains why visual capture is not as immediate or as complete in the case of optical inversion of the image as it is for other changes, such as displacement, minification, or the like. Of course, in an experiment such as Stratton's, even if visual capture were as effective as in these other cases, it would only apply to parts of the body visible at any given moment. Visualization of parts not in the visual field— and which may suddenly enter the field—would be in terms of the pre-existing associations until such time as new associations might become established.

In any event, it does seem to have been the case for Stratton and others who repeated his experiment that harmony between vision and touch was eventually re-established. In time it may have come to pass that the felt location and direction of movement of a limb conformed with the altered vision when the limb was not directly visible. For example, movement of the left hand across the body to the right side gave rise to the feeling (or, as I would maintain, visualization) that it was moving from the right to the left side. This could explain, Harris observes, how visuomotor coordination to the re-erected image ultimately became automatic. At the beginning it would require a deliberate effort to move the left hand to the right in order to grasp an object that is actually on the right but appears on the left. But if in time a rightward movement of the left hand was felt (visualized) as going leftward, the movement could run off without creating a sense of conflict.

Yet it must be borne in mind that such accommodation of proprioception to vision is not the same as would exist if visual adaptation to the inversion had occurred instead. For in that event, an intersensory harmony would exist that was complete and that would not entail any difficulties concerning the need to visualize physically improbable positions of one part of the body with respect to others. Every felt part of the body would be visualized to be located precisely where it was seen to be located through the lens system. For example, the feet would be visualized as being in the lower part of the field and that is where they would appear if the lower region of the retina had now come to signify egocentrically "down." Whereas, without such visual adaptation, by association, the proprioceptively experienced feet might correctly be expected to appear in the region of the field where they now always did appear, but that region would remain egocentrically "up."

The Contribution of Proprioception to Visual Adaptation

When a visual object is simultaneously manipulated by hand or when the hand alone is viewed, information via touch does not lead to visual adaptation. But what about those cases in which visual adaptation *does* occur? A major basis for adaptation of all kinds is derived from movement, namely the transformations of the retinal image that occur when the observer moves. Yet, as has been noted in previous chapters, were it not for information as to precisely how the body is moving in space, the meaning of the transformations of the retinal image would remain ambiguous. For example, in the case of a prismatically tilted image, points in the image displace in a direction parallel to the direction in which the observer is moving. If, therefore, the information is centrally registered that an animal is walking forward, the flow of the image of points on the ground along an oblique retinal direction implies that this retinal direction is one that signifies the egocentric "vertical" orientation. If, however, the animal without prisms were walking obliquely (that is, moving its legs in a direction oblique to the sagittal axis of the body), that same direction of flow of the image would have an entirely different implication, one that would not be expected to lead to visual adaptation. Consequently, some non-visual information concerning how the body is moving through space is required to render the visual information unambiguous. This information may be proprioceptive or it may be based upon a copy of the efference signals required for the movements in question.

The need for such supplementary non-visual information also seems to arise in cases where adaptation results from viewing the stationary body. For example, in the experiment of Wallach *et al.* in which a stationary observer views his body through a wedge prism, visual adaptation to a displaced image can only be predicted if the information is available that the head is not twisted to the side. If it were, the unusual visual position of the trunk would be accounted for.

Why is it that proprioception sometimes plays an important role in bringing about visual adaptation while in other cases (those explored in this chapter) it does not lead to visual adaptation, but rather itself undergoes adaptive change? Perhaps the first point to make is that the cases in which proprioception itself changes involve manual exploration (as summarized by the term "touch perception"), while the instances in which proprioception contributes to visual adaptation entail information as to how the observer is displacing through space or how the head is positioned in relation to the rest of the body. A second point is that the dominance of vision over touch arises when a part of the body such as the hand is both seen and felt or an external object is both seen and felt. Now, in the example of an observer wearing tilting prisms, he may not see his body at all, but if he does he certainly will not see it moving obliquely as he walks, because it is *not* moving in this fashion. He will therefore see that his movements are in a direction congruent with the sagittal plane of his body. Hence there is no strong reason for the actual nature of the walking movements not to be registered proprioceptively in a veridical fashion.

The case of a stationary observer viewing his body through a prism is admittedly similar *in principle* to the case of viewing only the hand. Yet it may not be correct to predict that the feel of the body will swing into line with the apparent visually displaced location of the body, with the result that the torso will be felt to be displaced with respect to the head. My reason for saying this is that the straight-ahead radial direction is largely based upon the sight of the body so that, when a major portion of the body is seen displaced, the "straight ahead" tends to shift to where the body is now seen to be. That being the case, vision and proprioception are not as much in potential conflict with one another as when only the hand is seen. This is a third possible explanation of why proprioceptive information may be completely ineffective in some cases and contributory to adaptation in other cases.

It should be borne in mind that proprioceptive (or efference-derived) information as to the position of the head with respect to the body, or the manner in which the body is moving through space, is not *always* a necessary factor in visual adaptation. It does not play a role in adaptation to optically altered size when such adaptation is based upon sight of the body or of familiar objects. Proprioceptive information as to *how* the observer is moving does not contribute to the re-establishment of position constancy and, in fact, might be said to oppose it at the outset. The true rate or direction of head movement must be suppressed if the field is once again to appear stationary. However, it is true that information must be registered centrally that the organism *is* moving. In visual adaptation to tilt based on sight of the *entire* body, as in seeing it in a mirror, no contribution from proprioception is involved. There would be no ambiguity concerning the meaning of the tilted image which requires proprioceptive information to resolve. The direction of movement of the eyes, head, or entire body may not be ambiguous in adaptation to prismatically created curvature, because the manner in which points on the curved image of a straight line displace (that is, simultaneously in different directions) is such as to indicate the observer is not traversing a curved path.

Even where proprioception does contribute necessary information, it is probable that it does so by virtue of how it leads the observer to *visualize* his body, at least for the person who has had prior visual experience. For example, if his head is not tilted, proprioceptive signals lead the observer to visualize it as straight with respect to the trunk. It is this visualization that renders the prismatically displaced image of the body unequivocal information to the effect that the visual straight-ahead is now signified by a different combination of retinal locus and position of the eyes.

SUMMARY

Since the information provided by touch remains veridical when vision is optically distorted, it has seemed plausible to many that the source of information that leads to adaptation is proprioception. There are, however, logical and empirical reasons for doubting the correctness of this argument. Experiments were described in which a conflict between vision and touch was created as to the shape or size of objects. It was found that not only was vision completely dominant but that the observers tended to report that objects felt precisely the way they looked.

To test more directly the hypothesis that vision is educated by touch, further experiments were conducted in which the adaptive consequences of exposure to contradictory information from vision and touch were studied. While viewing an optically minified object, the observer was simultaneously given continuous proprioceptive information concerning its size. Conditions were such that the only possible source of information that the object was larger than it appeared visually was proprioceptive. And, of course, the only possible source of information that the object was smaller than it felt was visual. Measures of change were based on comparison of pre- and post-exposure tests of cross-modality equivalency, as well as on tests of visually perceived size and tactually perceived size. The results clearly demonstrated that adaptive change in the relationship of the tactual and visual modality to each other does take place, but it is not based on an alteration of visual size. Rather it is based on an alteration in the size signified by tactual stimulation.

Thus the implication is that rather than vision being educated by touch in infancy, touch is educated by vision. For sighted individuals, the spatial dimensions of objects signified by touch could derive from prior experience with correlated visual information. It was suggested that—at least for the sighted—there is no separate spatiality for touch, that the complex of proprioceptive stimuli lead to a visualization of the spatial properties of objects. If true, the dominance of vision and visual capture can be understood in terms of the victory of direct vision over what is merely visualized. The chief implication of the findings for work on perceptual adaptation is that touch cannot be the basis of visual adaptation but—where visual information is limited—vision can be the basis of proprioceptive adaptation. However, proprioceptive information concerning the position of the head with respect to the body, or that the body is in motion and how it is moving through space, does play a contributory role in visual adaptation wherever the purely visual information is ambiguous as to what it signifies.

ADDENDUM

Procedure and Results of Experiments on Conflict between Vision and Touch

Experiments on Shape

Several experimental procedures were used. In all experiments, the subject viewed a standard object through a transparent plastic optical element that was bent so as to compress the image along its horizontal axis only, thus changing the object's visual shape. While the subject was looking at the object, he was also instructed to reach behind it and to grasp it through a black silk cloth. The subject viewed the object through an eyepiece set into the front of a box. He saw it within the small field provided by a circular opening in front of the optical element. The subject placed his right arm around to the rear of the box and, through a large opening and through the cloth, grasped the object—a 25-mm. white square, 1 mm. thick, made of a hard plastic material attached to a thin black metal stem set vertically in a hole in the bottom of the box. The retinal image of the width of the object was optically reduced by approximately one half, which means that the square appeared to be a rectangle whose vertical to horizontal sides were in the ratio of 2:1.

The question of how to measure what the subject experienced was an interesting one. After viewing and grasping the standard, the subject could be asked to select a comparison object which he judged to match the standard. But how should the comparison object be presented, visually or tactually? Eventually we decided on three different experiments: (1) visual comparison only, (2) tactual comparison only, and (3) a quite different method in which the subject was asked to draw a picture the same shape as the standard. In this last method, one may assume that the subject utilized both visual and proprioceptive senses in making his reproduction. Different subjects were used for each experiment. In all experiments, the subject was instructed either to draw or to match in accordance with his "impression" of the standard. In this way no bias was introduced that might have favored vision or touch, as would have been the case if we had asked the subject to match what he had "seen," or what he had "felt."

In each experiment there were three conditions. In the experimental condition, the subject viewed the standard at the same time that he grasped it. Pains were taken to ensure that he simultaneously viewed and grasped the standard and that he never performed one maneuver without the other. He then selected or drew a rectangle that seemed to correspond in shape to the standard. This was the main condition in which vision and touch yielded conflicting information. The subject was not told what his task was to be until after he had been exposed to the standard. This prevented him from using his fingers to measure or otherwise to engage in judgmental efforts at accuracy. Such efforts, in preliminary experiments, had often led to an awareness of the experimentally created conflict. In the vision-control condition, the subject only viewed the standard. This afforded an empirical check on the distortion produced by the optical element and provided a base line of what was to be expected in the drawing or matching task when the standard was seen but not touched. In the touch-control condition, the subject only grasped the standard. This provided a measure of the central tendency and accuracy of shape discrimination by touch alone and provided a base line of what was to be expected when the standard was experienced by touch only. In Figure 7–3, the plan of the experiments is given. Each row represents an entire self-contained experiment, with a particular method of testing what the subject experiences when he is exposed to the standard. The three columns under "condition of exposure of standard" represent the three ways of exposing the standard, namely, the experimental or conflict condition and the vision and touch-control conditions respectively. In all conditions, 5 seconds were allowed in which to perform the experiment. Only one judgment was obtained from each subject, since additional judgments could not have been made without destroying the desired naïveté.

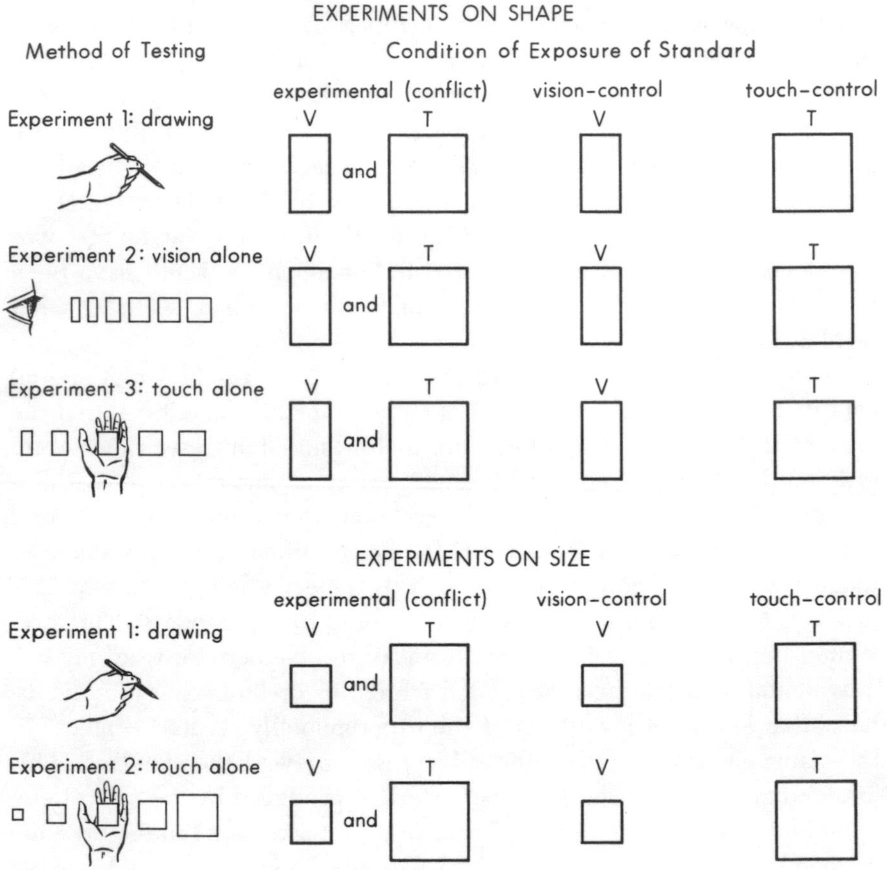

Figure 7–3

In the first experiment, in which the subjects made drawings of their impression of the shape of the standard, the drawings were carefully measured at the top and bottom for width and these two values were averaged. The two sides were then measured in the same way to determine the length. The proportion of the length to the width was the measure used to represent the perceived shape. The mean proportion of length to width for the 10 subjects in this experiment was 1.85; the vision-control subjects yielded a mean of 1.9; and for the touch-control subjects, the mean proportion was 0.98. In this experiment, the same subjects served as controls for both touch and vision after the conflict condition, the order of the two being counterbalanced among the 10 subjects. Since the objectively correct drawing should have been a square, the fact that the experimental subjects were drawing a rectangle of almost a 2:1 ratio (which was exactly what they did, on the average, in the vision-control condition) indicates that vision was completely dominant.

In the second experiment, the method of selecting a comparison match by vision alone, under one experimental and two control conditions, was utilized. In this and the remaining experiments, separate subjects were used for the two control conditions. The match was made from a rack that had a series of rectangles on stems set in holes in its base, with varying widths but identical height (namely, 25 mm.). In the experimental condition, the subject selected a comparison stimulus he considered to be the same width as the standard. He only looked at the comparison object, although he looked at and grasped the standard. This procedure may be thought to favor a visual resolution, since the subject selected by vision alone. However, since he was not aware during inspection of the standard that he would have to make a visual match, he would have no reason to concentrate more on vision than touch in his perception of the standard. It could also be argued that it should not make any difference what comparison technique was used since, if the subject received a unitary impression, this impression would be communicated by whatever type of comparison he made. That is, once he "decided" what he had experienced, it should not be crucial which method or modality he employed to tell us what he had experienced. The mean width obtained for the experimental condition was 14.1 mm. ($N = 10$); for the vision-control condition, the mean width obtained was 13.4 mm.; and for the touch-control condition, the mean width was 23.1 mm. The results clearly show a favoring of a visual resolution. There is not too much difference between the average vision-control match and the experimental (or conflict) match. The optical element yielded an image that should have appeared to be about 12.5 mm. wide. Two subjects who gave experimental matches in the direction of touch account for the slight difference that was obtained.

In the final experiment, comparison with the standard was made by touch alone. Again, one experimental and two control conditions were used. The rack used in the second experiment was also used in this one. The subject could grasp the first rectangle and then move his hand along the rack, feeling each rectangle in turn. But he could not see them. The rack was so placed that selections were made in an ascending order for half of the subjects and in a descending order for the remaining subjects. If the previous experiment can be considered biased toward a vision resolution, then this experiment should, if anything, be biased toward a touch resolution. Again, however, it could be argued that matching by touch or vision should give the same results.

For 10 subjects, the mean for the conflict condition was a width of 14.5 mm.; for the vision-control condition, the mean width was 14.1 mm.; and for the touch-control condition, the mean width was 20.5 mm. Although the majority of subjects showed complete dominance of vision in the conflict condition, two subjects revealed a compromise and one showed dominance of touch. However, the possibility exists that these last three subjects thought that the rectangle they selected corresponded with a narrower visual size. In other words, they may have experienced the standard in the conflict situation as quite narrow (i.e., vision may have been dominant), but they may have tried to match their tactual experience of it with their tactual experience of the comparison object. They may not have realized that their tactual experience did not *belong* with their impression of the rectangle as narrow. In other words, an adaptation effect may have occurred in which a tactual impression now signified a shape different than it had before. Some support for this conclusion is derived from a check of the subject's tactual choice, in which he was asked to select visually an object he thought matched his tactual choice.

Experiments on Size

In the experiments on size, the same general method was used except that the visual image of the standard square was reduced in size by a factor of two by a minifying lens system.[18] The subject looked through a cylinder (containing the lenses) mounted in a wooden crosspiece above the standard. The subject grasped the standard through the black silk cloth below. The standard protruded through the silk in a horizontal plane and was attached by a vertical screw to a wooden crosspiece below. It was a 25-mm. white square, 6 mm. thick, which was reduced to approximately half size by the lens. The standard was viewed within a large area

[18] The problem of changes in apparent distance in viewing through such an optical device, discussed in Chapter 5, was not encountered in the work on sensory conflict, possibly because all the observer could see was a single square. In any case, the vision-control data indicate that the standard did appear about half size through the lens system. However, see footnote 19.

surrounded by black felt so that the observer could see nothing else in any direction. (See Figure 7–1; also see Figure 7–3 for the plan of the two experiments described below on size.)

In the experiment utilizing drawing, there were 10 experimental subjects and 8 subjects for each of the two control conditions. The results for each subject was expressed in terms of the average length of the four sides of the drawing. The mean length for the experimental condition was 15.3 mm.; for the vision control, it was 14.5 mm.; for the touch control, it was 18.0 mm. A value of 12.5 mm. was expected for the vision-control condition, since this would be half of 25 mm. and, of course, a value of 25 mm. was expected for the touch-control condition. In another experiment that required drawing, utilizing 16 subjects as their own controls, the mean size was 12.3 mm. for the conflict situation; for the vision control, it was 12.6 mm.; and for the touch control, 17.7 mm.[19] The results of this size experiment thus also show that vision is completely dominant. The subjects draw a figure in the experimental condition that is essentially no larger than the one they draw in the vision-control condition.

In the only other experiment performed on size, the comparison with the standard was made by touch alone. The selection was made from a series of squares varying in size mounted in sequence on a cardboard. The subject could rapidly move his hand along the card from one square to another. Twenty subjects were used. The means were as follows: for the conflict condition, 16.2 mm.; for the vision control, 15.8 mm.; and for the touch control, 22.8 mm.

[19] Thus, in the first-mentioned experiment, in absolute terms, the drawings were slightly larger than the 12.5-mm. value to be expected on the basis of the optical arrangement intended. This may be the result of the placement of the lens at a distance not sufficient to yield the full 2:1 reduction. But in the second experiment on size mentioned above, the distance was somewhat greater, and the average judgments were closer to 12.5 mm. In the shape experiments, the visual control data suggest that the optical compression may not have been fully one-half. The drawings for the touch-control condition were clearly smaller than the objectively correct value of 25 mm. With the vision control yielding a value greater than 12.5 mm. in many experiments, and the touch control a value considerably smaller than 25 mm., predictions based on dominance of touch or vision are no longer as far apart as originally desired. Nevertheless, the dominance of vision is clear from the results.

Theoretical Considerations

CHAPTER EIGHT

Summary of the Theory

It may be helpful to summarize those features of the theory that are common to all the areas discussed.

1. The essential information from which the perceived spatial attributes of objects in the world are derived is provided by the relationship of the retinal images of objects to one another. Since such relationships are independent of the absolute nature of the entire retinal image, it follows that optical transformations which alter the entire image in some consistent fashion should not result in changes of the perceptual attributes in question.

2. The relationship of objects in the field to the self as an object in the field is of central importance. This relationship is also not affected by optical transformations of the entire retinal image, as is most clearly evident when the body is a visible object in the field. However, even when the body is not visible, the way in which it relates to all other objects remains unchanged by optical transformations, although this information will then generally become available only when the organism moves.

3. The conclusion that optical transformation should not result in perceptual change is valid only for a completely naïve subject. For one who has had experience prior to such optical transformation, it does typically lead to phenomenal distortions of one kind or another. To explain this, I

have suggested that memory carries some record of the specific or absolute nature of the stimuli that previously gave rise to the experiences in question (the stimulus-copy aspect of the memory trace, in contrast to the representational aspect of the memory trace). By virtue of such traces, the transformed proximal stimuli lead to non-veridical experiences such that objects now appear to be upside-down, tilted, diminutive, or curved, depending on the nature of the transformation.

4. With continued exposure to the optically altered image, however, traces congruent with the new stimuli take the place of the original traces. Since the relationship between retinal images has not been altered, the necessary information about size or shape or orientation is conveyed just as in the past. This information can be supplied either by (a) direct sight of the body, (b) movement of the observer, or (c) the presence of familiar objects whose size, orientation, or shape is known. An association, therefore, is formed between the new proximal stimulus and the relevant properties of the distal stimulus (for example, tilted retinal image and "parallel to head" or curved retinal image and "straight line"). As comparisons with the pre-experimental traces begin to be replaced by comparisons with the new traces, perceptual adaptation will be evidenced. The optically transformed image now leads to normal perception because traces of the transformed image have been associated with veridical information about the properties of objects. Once this association has been formed, it will of course play its role in perception even when sight of the body, movement of the observer, and familiar objects are no longer present.

5. Changes of the retinal image concomitant with movements of the body tend to be discounted (i.e., not seen) as changes in the environment, provided information is available that the organism is moving. Such information may be supplied by a central copy of efference signals, by proprioception, or by visually induced apparent movement of the self. This discounting tendency is central in adaptation to optically altered rate or direction of displacement of the image with movement of the body (i.e., in the re-establishment of position constancy), and plays a role in other types of adaptation.

6. Transpositions of the entire retinal image of a kind that simulate the transformations achieved by optical devices often yield immediate impressions similar to those conveyed by optical transformations. Exposure to these simulated stimulus patterns may give rise to perceptual adaptation. The preservation of the customary relationship between familiar objects conveys the impression of normalcy. The clearest examples of this

type of effect are the tilted room and the "miniature world." In the long run, however, effects of this kind are distinguishable from those based on optical transformations because, in these cases, the self is not included in the transformation. Hence the information is not conveyed that objects are normal in relation to the body of the observer, as is the case with actual prism adaptation. (In addition to such effects, there are certain circumscribed effects of inspecting line patterns, similar to those generated by optical transformations—configurational effects—which complicate the picture but which can be experimentally isolated.)

7. Visual adaptation is based primarily on visual information. In fact, under conditions where visual information is restricted and contradictory information from vision and touch is given, based on the dominance of vision, a change in the interpretation of proprioceptive sensations occurs, such that perception via touch is realigned with vision. However, where visual information is ambiguous, proprioceptively given information (or a central record of efference signals) concerning the body or how it is moving through space is a factor in the visual adaptation achieved.

Stimulus Copy vs. Representational Aspects of the Trace

Logical considerations and experimental findings have led to the assumption that the memory trace contains an aspect that is faithful to the specific or absolute nature of the stimulus and not merely to the phenomenal experience produced by the stimulus. In other words, the trace preserves a copy of the retinal image, not just the perception that was produced by the retinal image. Many psychologists would indeed readily accept the notion that the trace is something of a replica of the proximal stimulus with regard to such features as its location, orientation, size, and shape.[1]

But the memory-trace concept is usually invoked for the purpose of doing justice to prior experience, of *representing* the prior experience at the time of recall. Hence it has been assumed that the trace is a record of the phenomenal content of the prior experience. That is certainly also true. Obviously one would not expect phenomenal content to be directly given by the specific physical attributes of the trace, or how could the size of

---

[1] This is the simplest possible assumption we can make about the trace and there is some fragmentary evidence that supports it. See H. Wallach and P. A. Austin, Recognition and the localization of visual traces, *Amer. J. Psychol.*, 1954, **67**, 338–340; and I. Rock and W. Heimer, The effect of retinal and phenomenal orientation on the perception of form, *Amer. J. Psychol.*, 1957, **70**, 493–511.

objects in the world or their distance be remembered veridically?—to mention only two instances where phenomenal properties obviously cannot be represented in this way. The existence of the perceptual constancies also further underscores the saliency of phenomenally perceived qualities, as contrasted with the specific nature of the proximal stimulus. If, in *perception* (of size for example), the visual angle is incorporated into a larger organization including registered distance, one can hardly expect visual angle to be a factor in *memory* for size. Therefore, in order to do justice to memory of prior phenomenal experience, it has not seemed fruitful to stress the idea that the trace is a copy of the proximal stimulus.

What I am proposing is that the specific features of the proximal stimulus are recorded in memory, and that these features become the signs of the associated phenomenal features which are also recorded in memory. The 3-mm. image (of an object at arm's length) leaves behind a record in the neural substrate of a specific size which is associated with the phenomenal impression "size of apple" or "size of hand" or "3 inches." The image of a straight line leaves behind a record of a certain shape that is associated with the phenomenal impression "straight." Thus subsequent stimuli are compared with these specific features of the trace; they are evaluated or interpreted in terms of their similarities and differences. A 10-mm. image (of an object at arm's length) immediately gives rise to an impression of a thing much larger than an apple, even when seen in isolation. A curved image immediately gives rise to an impression of a curved line, etc.

This raises an important question. How is a particular memory trace aroused? Ordinarily, when a familiar object is encountered, it is immediately recognized, which suggests that the *relevant* memory trace is evoked. The selection process in which only the relevant trace, among the myriad traces in the brain, comes to the fore would seem to be based upon a principle of similarity. The phenomenal properties of the stimulus object (for example its shape, color, etc.) constitute the model of search in a resonating or scanning process that leads to the selection of the relevant trace. This conclusion seems necessary because it can hardly be the case that the selection is made on the basis of identity of locus of stimulus and trace. Any and all regions of the retina and visual cortex serve as a screen, so to speak, on which is registered any and all stimuli encountered.[2]

[2] For a discussion of this problem, see W. Köhler, *Dynamics in psychology,* New York: Liveright, 1940; or I. Rock, A neglected aspect of the problem of recall: The Höffding Function, Chap. in *Theories of the Mind,* edit. by J. Scher, New York: Free Press, 1962.

Now how does this reasoning apply to the arousal of memories representing the physical properties of the stimulus? In the case of orientation, for example, the argument I have made is that only by virtue of traces that have a specific orientation in the neural substrate can we explain why the scene appears tilted on first looking through right-angle prisms. Here it cannot be the phenomenal impression yielded by the tilt of the stimulus that is the basis for trace selection, since it is the phenomenal appearance that we wish to explain. Instead, assuming that the physical tilt of the image on the retina is discriminated by the nervous system, memory traces specific to that physical tilt could be aroused by a present stimulus on the basis of similarity of orientation on the retina. The associated information stored in the trace concerning the phenomenal orientation of objects whose images yield that retinal orientation is then aroused.

There is, however, another way of explaining how the physical properties of the stimulus can be recorded in memory. When, for example, a specific orientation within the neural substrate is consistently associated with information as to phenomenal orientation, a neural link may be established between that physical orientation in the brain and the trace of the information concerning perceived orientation. Therefore, if at a later time a stimulus projects to the cortex in that same orientation, the associated content is directly aroused. The same would then be true for other orientations in the substrate each of which is associated with only one phenomenal orientation. According to this view, it is not necessary to believe that the relevant trace is aroused on the basis of similarity, because the physical property of the stimulus in question *can* be uniquely linked with only one trace. It is as if a new coordinate system of directions has been established in the neural substrate, such that a tilted direction is now the correlate of egocentric verticality, etc. Yet this new coordinate system entailing linkages between specific orientations in the substrate and specific phenomenal orientations is a product of prior experience and therefore has the status of a trace system. As suggested in Figure 8–1, one might think of such a coordinate system as being "etched" into the neural substrate during adaptation in the orientation shown. Adaptation entails a shift in an already established coordinate system. A model of this kind can also do justice to the problem of generalization, that is, the fact that it is not necessary to have experience with all possible orientations of objects during prism adaptation.

In the case of shape, I have argued that the process that underlies the perception of curvature entails the arousal by the stimulus of traces which contain information about the objective shape-properties of lines, but the arousal of the relevant traces depends upon the physical geometry of the stimulus. Here again, it is possible that the selection of the relevant trace is on the basis of a similarity principle, in which the physical shape of the image of the line is the crucial factor. But, strictly speaking, it is not simply the shape that is important. A curve concave to the right has the same shape as one concave to the left or concave up or down. Yet a person who has adapted to prismatically created curvature and now sees a line concave to the right as straight, does not see a line concave to the left as straight. In fact, the concave-left curve will lead to an impression of even greater curvature than it did prior to adaptation. Thus it seems that the nervous system would have to discriminate specific *orientations* of the image in addition to physical shape. Consequently it is not merely a

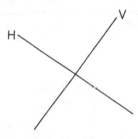

Figure 8–1

trace of a certain shape, even if shape is defined in terms of the physical geometry of the stimulus pattern, which is the sign of a certain phenomenal curvature. In other words, what is crucial is a specific direction of curvature in the neural substrate.

Therefore, the second sort of hypothesis presented above seems attractive, namely, that the locus of points within the neural substrate representing the projection of specific curvatures of the retinal image becomes associated with the corresponding information concerning shape; that is, linkages are established between certain coordinates in the substrate and traces containing information about shape. When an image of a certain curvature projects to the cortex, the relevant associated content is then directly aroused. Hence one might say that the spatial attributes signified by the coordinates in the substrate have undergone a transformation, but this transformation is a function of past experience. The hypothetical coordinate system representing the transformation in the neural substrate is illustrated in Figure 8–2. There were two experiments described in Chapter 6 which seem to call for an explanation along this line. In one, adaptation to prismatically created curvature was obtained, although only a random array of spots was visible; in the other, only a single dot was visible.[3] Therefore, in neither case were *lines* visible that could be said to yield traces faithful to the specific curvature of their retinal images. Nevertheless it must be presumed that the observer did learn that a point which stimulated the retina anywhere along a curved path, such as is depicted in Figure 8–2, was straight ahead of him. This suggests that there is a change in the coordinate system in the neural substrate as suggested

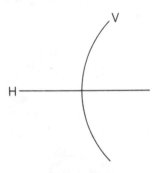

Figure 8–2

above. A similar explanation is possible for adaptation to optically produced change in the size of the retinal image. Here the new coordinate system would represent the altered "calibration" of distance across the neural substrate.

How Can Past Experience Affect the Way Things Look?

One of the weaknesses of empiricism in perception, correctly emphasized by Köhler and Koffka, has been the glib assertion that the world looks the way it does because of past experience. Not only has there been little concrete evidence to support this supposition, but there has rarely been any attempt to suggest a mechanism through which past experience could operate to affect appearances. To give just one example: It was claimed that size constancy was learned through commerce with the environment. The child finds out that distant things which at first look small are actually large. But how could mere knowledge of this fact affect per-

[3] R. Held and J. Rekosh, Motor-sensory feedback and the geometry of visual space, *Science*, 1963, 141, 722–723; M. Cohen, Visual curvature and feedback factors in the production of prismatically induced curved line aftereffects. Paper read at Eastern Psychological Assoc., New York, April 1963.

ceived size? Nowhere in perception does mere knowledge about a state of affairs alter the phenomenal content of what is seen (witness the illusions). Hence the empiristic theory is weak until it can suggest how perception comes to be affected by past experience.

Is the theory developed in the previous chapters open to this criticism? This theory proposes that features of the memory trace affect the way things will subsequently appear. To place this hypothesis in proper perspective, it is important first to emphasize that phenomenal properties such as orientation, size, and shape are a function of stimulus relationships and to that extent are directly given, without need of prior experience. That is to say, relative orientation of one thing to another, relative position, relative size, and shape insofar as intra-figural relationships are concerned, are held to be a function of the information contained in the retinal image. Nevertheless, memories are stored that are faithful both to the proximal stimulus and phenomenal features of all objects seen. As a result, the trace becomes an alternate source of information as to the phenomenal attributes of the stimulus. If, for example, an object is seen in isolation, so that its orientation is not given by its relationship to other objects or to the visible body, still its orientation can be perceived on the basis of the orientation of the cortical "image." Every orientation within the neural substrate has become the sign of a particular phenomenal orientation. Traces thus enrich or supplement that which could otherwise be perceived on the basis of the stimulus alone. Other instances in perception where there is reason to believe the trace enriches the perceptual experience were discussed in Chapter 1 (pages 4–6).

This is the kind of process I am suggesting is the basis of the memory effects discussed in this book. The trace contributes its phenomenal content to the stimulus. Under conditions where the phenomenal attribute is not immediately yielded by the information supplied by the total stimulus situation—for example, when an isolated object is seen—the contribution of the trace becomes important. Similarly, the trace plays a role under conditions where the entire retinal image is optically transformed. At the beginning of prism adaptation, a conflict exists between the determination of perception by the relationships within the image, which are not altered, and the determination of perception by the (wrong) traces, which are tapped by the distorted proximal stimuli.

In the earliest encounters with the environment, although the relationship of images to one another serves immediately as a basis for the experience of relative orientation, size, etc., still it would probably be incorrect to say that objects are initially seen to possess the kind of absolute properties they take on later. For example, the sense of the definite size of an object would not yet exist; neither would the sense that an object was upright or upside down, straight or slightly curved, or straight ahead. Such impressions are primarily a function of the manner in which the object relates to the self. Since the body, and in particular the head, is not as readily visible as other objects, a certain amount of prior experience is required before the phenomenal self is adequately represented in the total perceptual field. Memory traces entailing features that are copies of the proximal stimulus and are associated with phenomenal features relating to the body, are gradually built up from a variety of different experiences. For example, it takes time before the information is registered that images in the vertical retinal orientation are aligned with the head. Once that happens, however, a line can immediately be seen as "aligned" or "tilted." Prior to that it would make no sense to speak of egocentric orientation unless the head and body were clearly visible in the immediate scene.

Or, in the case of size, the concrete meaning could hardly be thought to exist prior to commerce with objects. As noted in Chapter 5, an apple would look smaller than a grapefruit at birth, but the fact that it was small in relation to the self would not yet be particularly evident. The fact that it has such a different size for a man and a mouse depends upon its size relative to the phenomenal body. In the case of shape, I have argued that there is an aspect of it that is not given by the geometry of image relationships, namely, the absolute feature of curvature of a line. That quality depends upon the relationship of the position of points on the line to the self and not merely on the relationship of the line to external objects. For reasons outlined in Chapter 6, experience is required before the specific curvature of lines can be appreciated. At the outset, then, it would be inappropriate to speak of a line as "straight" or "curved" to denote the sense of "straight" or "curved" familiar to the mature observer. When the image is optically transformed, the necessity once more arises for experience, so that the altered image can be associated anew with the properties of things given by their relationship to the self.

The trace, then, has the important role of contributing absolute properties to the perceptual experience. The enrichment or supplementation by the trace in the instances under discussion seems to be quite like that which occurs in *meaning*. An originally meaningless object begins to *look* meaningful after experience with the way in which it functions and behaves. An association between the perceived object and its mode of behavior develops such that later the perceived object is experienced as meaningful even when it is not "behaving." In the same way, the absolute impression of size, for example, is like that of a meaning accruing to the stimulus. From prior experience, an image of a certain size is associated with an object seen to be, let us say, the size of the hand. As a result, that image, in complete isolation, will subsequently convey the impression of being hand size.

The point is even clearer in the case of curvature. If it is asked why the curved image begins to *appear* straight for a subject wearing a wedge prism, the answer is that commerce with the optically transformed scene provides a good deal of information that the lines which yield such curved images have certain properties, or behave in those ways that are called "straight." That is to say, the curved image becomes associated with memory components, such as the fact that all points along vertically oriented lines of this curvature maintain their radial direction in the left-right axis of the observer when he moves his head up and down, or that lines of this shape do not alter their curvature when approached from opposite directions, etc. These contents define "straightness," so that by virtue of their association with the stimulus, they add perceptual meaning to it.

The conclusion we have been led to is that the perception of "straightness" is analogous to a meaning based on past experience. This is a rather disturbing conclusion. "Straightness" certainly gives the impression of being a sensory "given." It is difficult for most of us to imagine how a curved image can yield the impression of a straight line. Nevertheless, that is precisely what happens in adaptation to optically produced curvature. However, it is helpful to realize that initially the curvature of the image did not signify anything with respect to phenomenal straightness or curvature. This leads to the generalization that the kind of influence I am assigning to a trace is one of yielding perceptual qualities that initially do not exist at all or, if they do, exist only in a very primitive form. I refer to qualities such as egocentric orientation, radial direction, specific size, specific curvature.

The kind of explanation of perceptual adaptation I have offered is in many respects similar to the classical explanation of the perceptual constancies, in terms of interpretation of sensations based on past experience. I have said that the physical aspect of the proximal stimulus can be considered a sign of the experienced quality, based on associated contents, analogous to the relationship of a symbol to its meaning. However, I do not believe that the impression of the phenomenal quality, such as curvature, is merely interpretive. It is *perceptual* in that it concerns visual appearance, not merely knowledge as to the properties of the object. Furthermore, the sign, for example the physical curvature of the image, is *not* itself directly experienced. To illustrate—once adaptation has occurred, it is not the case that we continue to *see* the curved image as curved, but know it signifies a straight line. Rather we *see* a straight line, and we are not aware the image is curved.

"Why Do Things Look as They Do?"

The conclusions reached in this book are relevant to Koffka's famous question, "Why do things look as they do?" Koffka rejected the answer "because they are what they are" not only because perception is often non-veridical but because this answer is actually no answer at all. An explanation of perceptual experience must be based on events within the organism, not on the external world as such. He rejected the answer "because the proximal stimuli are what they are," because it is often false— perception often differs from what we might expect on the basis of the retinal image. His own answer was that "things look as they do because of the field organization to which the proximal stimulus distribution gives rise." [4]

Since only certain perceptual attributes were examined in the preceding chapters, I am in no position to offer a thoroughgoing reconsideration of Koffka's conclusions. On the basis of the areas studied, however, I would suggest that, if the second answer were reformulated to read "because the relations among proximal stimuli are what they are," it would explain why things look as they do in a great many cases. It is true that I am omitting any consideration of the question of the organization of the field into distinct and segregated objects. However, assuming the existence of bounded and shaped things (the determination of which is one use the Gestaltists made of the concept "organization"), the relationship of their images to one another corresponds very closely to the relationship of the things themselves to one another in the real world.[5] Thus relative orientation, position, and size and the intra-figural or object-relative aspect of shape are all directly given by the relationship of the retinal images of objects to one another (provided we restrict the analysis to two dimen-

[4] K. Koffka, *Principles of gestalt psychology*, New York: Harcourt, Brace, 1935, p. 98.

[5] In many cases the Gestaltists did emphasize stimulus relationships as the crucial determinant (for example, Duncker's analysis of movement perception), but subsumed relational determination under the broader category of "organization." Many have found the notion of organization vague.

sions; if we do not, variations in distance vitiate the correlation between object relations and image relations).

The fact that the relations among objects in the real world are reflected in the relations among their corresponding images provides, in my opinion, one major explanation for the veridicality of perception. Many psychologists feel that it is meaningless to say that perceptions are veridical, because we can never compare the real with the phenomenal world. We have no access to the real world, they say, so that all we can mean by veridicality is that there is a correspondence between our phenomenal experiences (for example, between vision and touch). I would claim, however, that what is meant by veridicality is simply this: that our experience of the world is in accord with all that we can discover about the external situation (admittedly via sensory operations). It is a useful concept in the field of perception because veridicality is often a rather remarkable achievement, since what we see is not necessarily in accord with the proximal stimulus or with proximal stimulus changes.

By focusing on the question of perceived relationships, we bypass the philosophical difficulties that are otherwise raised by assertions of veridicality. Since the substantive nature of the physical world is not commensurate with the content of phenomenal experience (for example, assemblages of electrons and nuclei separated by a lot of empty space versus subjectively solid "things"), the idea of perception being a truthful picture of reality has seemed naïve to modern philosophers. But if only external *relationships* are considered, it is perfectly legitimate to inquire whether the apparent size of *a* in relation to *b* corresponds with the physical size of *a* in relation to *b*.

Returning to the first answer which Koffka rejected, that things look as they do because they are what they are: It is true that this is no explanation. However, it turns out to be a very useful notion to keep in mind while considering certain problems. For example, in the case of viewing a straight line through wedge prisms, the curved image will behave exactly as the straight image would behave without prisms. It will retain the same curvature no matter what direction it is viewed from; it will project as a point when viewed head on, etc. It is a strange sight to witness some of these things, because curved lines do not usually behave in this way. But the point I am making is that the line is not curved, only its image is curved. Straight lines behave this way, and hence the curved image of a straight line must also behave this way. To consider one other example, in viewing the world through an optical device that tilts the image, it is surprising to discover in getting up from a seated position that successive points along an apparently tilted direction remain straight ahead (see Figure 2–4). Since, however, that locus of points is objectively vertical, successively seen points do remain straight ahead as the observer rises. Hence their images must behave accordingly. These examples illustrate the point that because things are the way they are, their images must reflect what they are, provided there is no alteration of the relationship between things within the image. Therefore, either the static retinal image or the transformations of the retinal image during movement must necessarily inform us accurately about the environment and its relationship to ourselves.

The evidence on adaptation suggests that there is a powerful tendency toward veridicality. One can safely formulate the rule for most cases of optical distortion that perception will tend to change in the direction of agreement with the objective state of affairs. The situational aftereffects are particularly dramatic illustrations of this rule. Not only do distorted images tend more and more to yield veridical perceptions, but differently distorted images simultaneously tend to do so, depending on phenomenal location with respect to the observer. One might well ask why these perceptual changes occur. I have shown that the information as to the objective nature of things is available, but it does not follow from this that perception must therefore change. That it does seems to reflect the tendency toward veridicality, the tendency for retinal stimuli to signify, or be perceptually interpreted in accordance with, whatever properties the corresponding objects have been ascertained to have.

This brings us to the perceptual constancies. If the rule that seems to operate in the adaptation paradigm held true in daily life, we would have to predict that constancy would prevail. Since visual information is available that objects do not change their shapes when tilted into the third dimension, or their sizes when viewed from varying distances, that information should accrue to the specific proximal stimuli associated with these conditions. An elliptical image, *plus* cues to the slant of the surface on which the ellipse is seen, will tap the associated traces containing the information that such an object is a circle.[6]

Based upon the facts of prism adaptation and the probability that

---

[6] I am considering here constancy effects based on a "taking into account" mechanism. There seem to be two types of mechanisms that yield constancy. Relational determination has been shown to operate in the case of achromatic color (Wallach, op. cit., 1948), speed (J. F. Brown, The visual perception of velocity, *Psychol. Forsch*, 1931, **14**, 199–232; H. Wallach, On constancy of visual speed, *Psychol. Rev.*, 1939, **46**, 541–552), and size (Rock and Ebenholtz, op. cit., 1959). But each of these constancies is also subject to "taking into account" effects.

learning is a factor in some of the perceptual constancies, it seems clear that veridicality also depends upon prior experience. In such cases, the trace yields the information that is responsible for the correctness of perception, and that information is derived from previous exposures to various proximal stimulus relationships. In the case of the situational aftereffects and the perceptual constancies, the taking into account of information about location, distance, and the like represents a supplementation by memory of what is given in the stimulus in the determination of veridical perception.

In the light of the strong tendency toward veridicality, what can be said about illusions that, by definition, are non-veridical perceptions? Many illusions are still not understood, but there are two types of illusions about which we do have some understanding. First, there are those that reflect the tendency to perceive perceptual qualities in terms of relationships, except that the environmental conditions are unusual. For example, if perceived achromatic color is determined by the proportion or ratio of light reflected by objects with respect to one another, then classical contrast (that is, the identical gray appearing lighter on a black than a white background) is to be expected, due to the physical arrangement obtaining. If the gray-black pair and gray-white pair are placed 180° apart under local illumination in an otherwise dark room, the two grays are now drastically different in appearance. The illusion in daily life is modulated by the effect of other surfaces in common to both and the effect of the surfaces of each pair on each other when they are placed close together. The luminous appearance of the moon against the totally dark surrounding of the evening sky is another example. Or consider the illusions of curvature shown in Figures 6–8 and 6–10. If one aspect of phenomenal curvature is the manner in which lines approach and recede from one another, it follows that special conditions in which the curvature of context lines differs markedly can yield illusions.

The other type of illusion we can say something about is based on the operation of learning effects when they are not appropriate. The moon illusion is a case in point. Various cues based on sight of the terrain yield a greater registered distance when the moon is on the horizon than when it is overhead. Taking this registered distance into account makes the horizon moon appear larger.[7] Emmert's law (to which the moon illusion is believed to be related) describes the illusory change of the apparent size of an after-image when it is viewed against surfaces at different distances. Just as all aftereffects of adaptation to optical transformation are

[7] See I. Rock and L. Kaufman, The moon illusion, II, *Science*, 1962, **136**, 1023–1031.

illusions, so many phenomena such as these size illusions can be thought
of as aftereffects of the adaptation that goes on in daily life. That is, if a
person has "adapted" to the changes of image size with changes of viewing
distance, for example if a smaller image of a distant object has come to
signify the same size as a larger image of the object when nearby, then
when the image does not change its size (for example, an after-image),
it would have to be seen non-veridically as getting larger with increased
distance. In conclusion, at least two types of illusion follow from, rather
than contradict in any way, the factors that ordinarily yield veridicality.[8]

Earlier I mentioned the criticism leveled against the empiricist who
attributes phenomena such as the constancies to past experience, but who
offers no mechanism other than knowledge about the environment.
Knowledge as such does not seem to affect perception. Yet it must be
acknowledged that perception seems to move in the direction of veridicality, reflecting what has been learned about the environment. This is a
problem that should not be glossed over. Still there is a difference between
perceptual change produced by certain specific experiences and perceptual change produced by mere knowledge. In adaptation to a tilted image,
for example, when the observer moves he acquires information that a
seemingly tilted direction in the field is in fact aligned with the vertical
axis of his head and body. This information is in the form of visual experience and is, therefore, stored in the form of visual traces. In the case of
situational aftereffects, informational content accrues to traces of specific
features of the proximal stimulus, including those defining the location of
the object, along lines suggested earlier. In the case of the constancies,
this informational content becomes associated with traces of specific
features of the proximal stimulus, for example, the size or shape of the
image and cues to distance or slant. The informational content in both
cases is such as to define clearly the phenomenal nature of the object.
The "compressed" object becomes less compressed when the head is
turned toward it; the initially distant object becomes large when it is near.
Hence in various ways the informational content is deposited in the form

---

[8] Another instance of non-veridical perception is that of camouflage, whether natural or created by man. Camouflage can best be understood as resulting from the operation of principles of grouping, such as were revealed by Gestalt psychology. Ordinarily,
the Gestaltists have argued, these principles of organization of the field, such as similarity, operate to yield veridical perception. This is so because (1) evolution has led to
perceptual laws that yield veridical organization of the field as it typically occurs in
nature (distinct objects have uniform and distinct coloration). (2) Man-made objects
are constructed to be readily visible in terms of the way we perceive. Camouflage then
represents the same principles but operating to render objects less visible.

of a trace which subsequently can be aroused. The core of the answer I am suggesting then is that when a concrete trace containing *visual* information accrues to a specific stimulus, it can affect the way it appears. This is not the same as "knowledge about the situation."

The Role of Awareness in Adaptation Studies

If a stationary observer views a luminous dot in an otherwise dark room through wedge prisms, he is hardly in a position to know that it is displaced. Hence one cannot expect adaptation to displacement to occur unless some other source of information is introduced. The same would be true if the observer looked at a luminous line through tilting prisms, or an optical device that alters the size of the retinal image. How is the observer to know that things are not where they seem to be, in the orientation they seem to be, and the sizes they seem to be, in these situations?

Does this mean that a prerequisite for successful adaptation is awareness by the observer of the optical distortion? Although generally the observer *is* aware of the effects of the optical device, there are two reasons for saying that such awareness is not necessary for adaptation—one empirical, the other logical. There are several studies where the subject does not seem to be aware of any distortion but nevertheless adapts. In the work on size perception, it was often the case that subjects were unaware of the diminutive size of objects seen through the minifying device from the first moment of exposure. Another case in point is that of adaptation to contradictory information from vision and touch. The subjects were generally completely unaware that anything was amiss and, because of the dominance of vision, this is not surprising. Still a third example is the immediate correction effect in looking across a room through displacing prisms. The observer at once sees a point as straight ahead which is quite displaced by the prisms.

The logical basis for saying that awareness of the distortion is not essential follows from the analysis of what *is* essential. What is necessary is that there be sensory information of some kind to the effect that a different proximal stimulus than heretofore is now associated with the relevant phenomenal content. An association must develop between the altered proximal stimulus and a phenomenal content that previously was associated with the unaltered proximal stimulus. For example, a curved image must be associated with information signifying straightness. If, for any reason, that curved image at the outset conveys an impression of straightness, then one might say adaptation is instantaneous and the requisite conditions for establishing a lasting association are already present. If minified images yield impressions of normal size from the outset, so much the better for the process of establishing a lasting association between these two things.

Ordinarily, however, such an *immediate* correction or adaptation effect does not occur, in which case adaptation is based upon information of one kind or another to the effect that things are not the way they at first appear. Is it generally the case that this information is consciously experienced? It clearly is, when the source of information is the sight of the body or familiarity with the objects in the scene. When, however, the information is based upon the manner in which the image displaces with movement of the observer, it would seem that the observer is typically not attending to such stimulus transformations and that even if he were directed to do so, it is doubtful that he would consciously appreciate its significance. For example, the subjects in the studies by Mikaelian and Held and by Held and Rekosh who saw only randomly placed spots or spheres were probably not aware of the nature of the altered direction of flow of the elements within the retinal image.

A clear example where there is no awareness of the information leading to adaptation is in an experiment by Wallach and Karsh, in which the modification of perceived depth yielded by a given retinal disparity was demonstrated.[9] The experiment created a conflict between two cues to depth, retinal disparity and the kinetic depth effect (KDE)—or, in another variation, disparity and perspective. By means of a telestereoscope, the magnitude of disparity of a three-dimensional wire figure was altered. At the same time the figure was rotated. The rotation alone would yield an impression of depth via the KDE. Hence disparity was altered, but the KDE was not. The observer perceived the figure distorting as it turned, which was a function of the increased disparity cue between any two points except between points lying in the frontal plane (where their separation was perceived veridically). The subjects were unaware that the KDE signified that the figure was non-distorting and shorter than it appeared. Yet adaptation occurred in the direction of changing the perception of depth based on retinal disparity. We must conclude, therefore, that the KDE information that the cube was not distorting and was not as deep as it appeared was assimilated despite the fact that there was no awareness of this information.

Perhaps, therefore, the safest conclusion to draw at this time is that the

[9] H. Wallach and E. B. Karsh, The modification of stereoscopic depth-perception and the kinetic depth effect, *Amer. J. Psychol.*, 1963, **76**, 429–435.

information relevant for adaptation must be registered in the nervous system but not necessarily phenomenally experienced. That being the case, an association can develop between the prismatically altered proximal stimulus and the registered information to the effect that that proximal stimulus signifies an object different than it did in the past. The reason adaptation would not occur in situations where the observer sees only an isolated object, and does not see himself or familiar objects, and does not move, is that the altered stimulation could be associated only with objects precisely where they seem to be or of the size they seem to be. Hence there is nothing new going on in the nervous system.

The Problem of Partial Adaptation

There is one problem that, to my knowledge, has not been the subject of discussion to date, namely, the fact that adaptation is a gradual rather than an all-or-none process. If adaptation is based on the formation of a new association between altered proximal stimulus and particular phenomenal content, what ought we to predict as to its course? At first there ought to be a few or weak traces containing this new association, and many or strong traces containing the old one. In terms of learning theory, one might translate the situation into an *A-B, A-C* transfer paradigm. The same stimulus is associated with different "responses." *A-C* should be quite difficult to learn, particularly since *A-B* is a strong association. The point I wish to focus on is this: When, after a brief exposure period, *A* is presented (say a straight line), what ought to happen? If pre-experimental traces of a straight image are tapped, the subject should see the test line as straight. If experimental traces are tapped, he should see a curved line. While frequency would favor the pre-experimental traces, recency would favor the experimental traces.[10] There are reports in the literature of peculiar "double" experiences which seem to reflect the influence of both traces. For example Held, in a study of adaptation to altered cues of auditory localization, reported that subjects often claimed to hear a sound in two different places at the same time.[11] Held and Bossom found

[10] I believe that only the operation of a powerful recency effect could explain the development of substantial adaptation within a matter of minutes, considering the lifetime of contradictory experience to be overcome. Recency has been shown to be a powerful determinant of trace selection in a situation where more than one trace is relevant to the stimulus. (See W. Epstein and I. Rock, Set as an artifact of recency, *Amer. J. Psychol.*, 1960, **73**, 214–228.)

[11] R. Held, Shifts in binaural localization after prolonged exposure to atypical combinations of stimuli, *Amer. J. Psychol.*, 1955, **68**, 526–548.

that some subjects who wore displacing prisms reported the presence of a secondary image of the target during the test period.[12] Effects of this kind are to be expected on the basis of a trace theory.

But what does a *compromise* between the two alternatives mean? And why does the compromise start by being closer to the pre-experimental trace and gradually, over time, move in the direction of the experimental trace? As yet we have no answer to this question. However, the same question can be raised concerning all compromise judgments in perception when there are two conflicting determinants. For example, in experiments on perception of the vertical of space where the visual frame of reference is tilted, the direction of gravity calls for one response and the direction of the main line of the visual scene calls for another response. Given such a conflict, why do most subjects compromise and select an orientation of the rod that lies somewhere between these two directions? Compromise judgments also occur in experiments on the constancies, namely, the typical response is one that lies somewhere between a match based on the proximal stimulus and a match based on the objective features of the standard. It is, therefore, possible that the nervous system reacts to conflicting determinants by a principle analogous to the resolution of divergent forces in physics, provided these determinants call for reaction on the same continuum. In that case, the stronger determinants would have the greater effect. If this were a fundamental fact about reaction to conflict in perception, there is no reason why the two determinants could not each be a function of memory trace systems.

In conclusion: I have endeavored in this book to relate what is known about various kinds of perception under normal conditions of observation to the problem of adaptation to optical distortion of the retinal image. For each topic considered, I have argued that there is good reason why the world ought *not* to appear distorted on first looking through the optical device, since the essential information conveyed by the retinal image would seem to remain intact (namely, relationships of components of the image to one another and to the self as object in the field). The explanation suggested as to why the world *does* appear distorted was that memories of the specific character of the normal retinal image have been established in the past and these memories influence what is now seen. This same explanation can serve as the basis for understanding perceptual

[12] R. Held and J. Bossom, Neonatal deprivation and adult rearrangement: Complementary techniques for analyzing plastic sensory-motor coordinations, *J. comp. Physiol. Psychol.*, 1961, **54**, 33–37.

adaptation; that is, memories of the specific character of the distorted image are acquired, thus establishing an altered coordinate system in the neural substrate. In either case, daily life or prism adaptation, the specific character of the retinal image becomes associated with information about spatial properties of objects, and, thus, the former becomes a sign of the latter.

I have tried to develop a theory that would do justice to the problem of how things *appear,* both before and after prism adaptation. While mere knowledge cannot influence visual perception, specific *visual* memory traces *can* do so by joining with the stimulus to form the underlying correlate.

Bibliography

Asch, S. E., and H. A. Witkin. Studies in space orientation I and II. *J. exp. Psychol.*, 1948, **38**, 325–337, 455–477.

Berkeley, G. *An essay towards a new theory of vision.* London: J. M. Dent, 1910.

Bishop, H. E. *Innateness and learning in the visual perception of direction.* Doctoral dissertation, Univ. of Chicago: Microfilm Thesis No. 4924, 1959.

Bossom, J., and R. Held. Transfer of error-correction in adaptation to prisms. *Amer. Psychol.*, 1959, **14**, 436 (abstract).

Brindly, G. S., and P. A. Merton. The absence of position sense in the human eye. *J. Physiol.*, 1960, **153**, 127–130.

Brown, G. G. Perception of depth with disoriented vision. *Brit. J. Psychol.*, 1928, **19**, 135.

Brown, J. F. The visual perception of velocity. *Psychol. Forsch*, 1931, **14**, 199–232.

Cohen, H. B. Transfer and dissipation of aftereffects due to displacement of the visual field. *Amer. Psychol.*, 1963, **18**, 411 (abstract).

Cohen, M. Visual curvature and feedback factors in the production of prismatically induced curved line aftereffects. Paper read at Eastern Psychological Assoc., New York, April 1963.

Cohen, W., and D. Tepas. Temporal factors in the perception of verticality. *Amer. J. Psychol.*, 1958, **71**, 760–763.

Czermak, J. Physiologisch Studien. III: Sitzungsberichte der kaiserlichen. Vienna: Akademie der Wissenschaften (Mathematische-Naturwissenschaftliche Classe), 1855, **17**, 563–600.

Day, R. H., and G. Singer. The relationship between the kinesthetic spatial aftereffect and variations in muscular involvement during stimulation. *Austral. J. Psychol.*, 1964, **16**, 200–208.

Dewey, J. *Psychology.* 3rd ed.; New York: American, 1898.

Dietzel, H. Untersuchungen über die optische Lokalisation der Mediane. *Z. f. Biol.*, 1924, **80**, 289–316.

Duncker, K. Über induzierte Bewegung. *Psychol. Forsch.*, 1929, **12**, 180–259.

Epstein, W., and I. Rock. Set as an artifact of recency. *Amer. J. Psychol.*, 1960, **73**, 214–228.

Ewert, P. H. A study of the effect of inverted retinal stimulation upon spatially coordinated behavior. *Genet. Psychol. Monogr.*, 1930, **7**, nos. 3 and 4.

Fantz, R. Form preferences in newly hatched chicks. *J. comp. Physiol. Psychol.*, 1957, **50**, 422–430.

———. Response to horizontality by bantam chickens in level and tilted rooms. *Psychol. Rec.*, 1959, **9**, 61–66.

Foley, J. P., Jr. An experimental investigation of the effect of prolonged inversion of the visual field in the rhesus monkey. *J. Genet. Psychol.*, 1940, **56**, 21–51.

Gibson, J. J. Adaptation, after-effect and contrast in the perception of curved lines. *J. exp. Psychol.*, 1933, **16**, 1–31.

——. *The perception of the visual world.* Boston: Houghton Mifflin, 1950.

—— and M. Radner. Adaptation, after-effect and contrast in the perception of tilted lines, I and II. *J. exp. Psychol.*, 1937, **20**, 453–467, 553–569.

Hamilton, C. R. Intermanual transfer of adaptation to prisms. *Amer. J. Psychol.*, 1964, **77**, 457–462.

Hay, J. C., and H. L. Pick, Jr. Visual and proprioceptive adaptation to optical displacement of the visual stimulus. *J. exp. Psychol.*, 1966, **71**, 150–158.

——, ——, and K. Ikeda. Visual capture produced by prism spectacles. *Psychon. Sci.*, 1965, **2**, 215–216.

Harrington, T. L. Adaptation of humans to colored split-field glasses. *Psychon. Sci.*, 1965, **3**, 71–72.

Harris, C. S. Adaptation to displaced vision: Visual, motor, or proprioceptive change? *Science*, 1963, **140**, 812–813.

——. *Adaptation to displaced vision: A proprioceptive change.* Doctoral dissertation, Harvard Univ., Ann Arbor, Mich.: Univ. Microfilms, 1963, No. 63-8162.

——. Perceptual adaptation to inverted, reversed, and displaced vision. *Psychol. Rev.*, 1965, **72**, 419–444.

Hebb, D. *The organization of behavior.* New York: Wiley, 1949.

Hein, A. Postural aftereffects and visual-motor adaptation to prisms. Paper read at Eastern Psychological Assoc., Atlantic City, April 1965.

—— and R. Held. Transfer between visual-motor systems of adaptation to prismatic displacement of vision. Paper read at Eastern Psychological Assoc., April 1960.

Held, R. Shifts in binaural localization after prolonged exposure to atypical combinations of stimuli. *Amer. J. Psychol.*, 1955, **68**, 526–548.

——. Exposure-history as a factor in maintaining stability of perception and coordination. *J. Nerv. Ment. Dis.*, 1961, **132**, 26–32.

——. Adaptation to rearrangement and visual-spatial aftereffects. *Psychol. Beitr.*, 1962, **6**, 439–450.

——. Plasticity in sensory-motor systems, *Sci. Amer.*, 1965, November, 84–94.

—— and J. Bossom. Neonatal deprivation and adult rearrangement: complementary techniques for analyzing plastic sensory-motor coordinations. *J. comp. Physiol. Psychol.*, 1961, **54**, 33–37.

—— and S. J. Freedman. Plasticity in human sensorimotor control. *Science*, 1963, **142**, 455–462.

—— and N. Gottlieb. A technique for studying adaptation to disarranged hand-eye coordination. *Percept. mot. Skills*, 1958, **8**, 83–86.

—— and A. Hein. Adaptation of disarranged hand-eye coordination contingent upon re-afferent stimulation. *Percept. mot. Skills*, 1958, **8**, 87–90.

—— and A. Hein. Movement-produced stimulation in the development of visually-guided behavior. *J. comp. Physiol. Psychol.*, 1963, **56**, 872–876.

—————— and A. Hein. On the modifiability of form perception. Chapter in *Symposium on models for perception of speech and visual forms*, edit. by J. C. Mott-Smith, W. Wathen-Dunn, H. Blum, and P. Lieberman. Cambridge: Mass. Instit. of Techn. Press, in press.

—————— and H. Mikaelian. Motor-sensory feedback versus need in adaptation to rearrangement. *Percept. mot. Skills*, 1964, 18, 685–688.

—————— and J. Rekosh. Motor-sensory feedback and the geometry of visual space. *Science*, 1963, 141, 722–723.

Helmholtz, H. von. *Treatise on physiological optics.* Trans. from the 3rd German ed.; J. P. C. Southall, ed. Vol. III. New York: Dover, 1962.

Hering, E. *Spatial sense and movements of the eye.* Trans. by C. A. Radde. Baltimore: Amer. Acad. Optom., 1942.

Hess, E. Space perception in the chick. *Sci. Amer.*, 1956, 195, 71–80.

Hochberg, J. On the importance of movement-produced stimulation in prism-induced after-effects. *Percept. mot. Skills*, 1963, 16, 544.

——————. *Perception.* Englewood Cliffs, N.J.: Prentice-Hall, 1964.

Holst, E. von. Relations between the central nervous system and the peripheral organs. *Brit. J. Animal Beh.*, 1954, 2, 89–94.

—————— and H. Mittelstaedt. Das Reafferenz-prinzip. *Die Naturwissenschaften*, 1950, 20, 464–467.

Howard, I. P., B. Craske, and W. B. Templeton. Visuomotor adaptation to discordant exafferent stimulation. *J. exp. Psychol.*, 1965, 70, 189–191.

Hubel, D., and T. Wiesel. Receptive fields, binocular interaction and functional architecture in the cat's visual cortex. *J. Physiol.*, 1962, 160, 106–154.

Koffka, K. *Principles of gestalt psychology.* New York: Harcourt, Brace, 1935.

Kohler, I. The formation and transformation of the perceptual world. Trans. by H. Fiss. *Psychol. Issues*, 1964, 3, No. 4, 1–173.

Köhler, W. *Dynamics in psychology.* New York: Liveright, 1940.

—————— and H. Wallach. Figural after-effects: an investigation of visual processes. *Proc. Amer. Phil. Soc.*, 1944, 88, 269–357.

Kottenhoff, H. Situational and personal influences on space perception with experimental spectacles, Part one: Prolonged experiments with inverting glasses. *Acta Psychol.*, 1957, 13, 79–97.

McCollough, C. Color adaptation of edge-detectors in the human visual system. *Science*, 1965, 149, 1115–1116.

——————. The conditioning of color perception. *Amer. J. Psychol.*, 1965, 78, 362–378.

Mach, E. *The analysis of sensations.* New York: Dover, 1959.

Matin, L., and E. G. MacKinnon. Autokinetic movement: selective manipulation of directional components by image stabilization. *Science*, 1964, 143, 147–148.

Mikaelian, H. Failure of bilateral transfer in modified eye-hand coordination. Paper read at Eastern Psychological Assoc., New York, April 1963.

—————— and R. Held. Two types of adaptation to an optically rotated visual field. *Amer. J. Psychol.*, 1964, 77, 257–263.

Mittelstaedt, H. Telotaxis und Optomotorik von Eristalis bei Augeninversion. *Naturwissen*, 1944, 36, 90–91.

Mortant, R. B., and J. Aronoff. Starting position, adaptation, and visual framework as influencing the perception of verticality. *J. exp. Psychol.*, 1966, **71**, 684–686.

―――― and H. K. Beller. Adaptation to prismatically rotated visual fields. *Science*, 1965, **148**, 530–531.

―――― and J. R. Harris. Two different after-effects of exposure to visual tilts. *Amer. J. Psychol.*, 1965, **78**, 218–226.

Mountcastle, V. B., and T. P. S. Powell. Central nervous mechanisms subserving position sense and kinesthesis. *Bull. Johns Hopkins Hosp.*, 1959, **105**, 173–200.

Peterson, J., and J. K. Peterson. Does practice with inverting lenses make vision normal? *Psychol. Monogr.*, 1938, **50**, No. 5.

Pfister, H. *Über das Verhalten der Hühner beim Tragen von Prismen.* Doctoral dissertation, Univ. of Innsbruck, 1955.

Pick, H. L., Jr., and J. C. Hay. Adaptation to prismatic distortion. *Psychon. Sci.*, 1964, **1**, 199–200.

―――― and ――――. A passive test of the Held re-afference hypothesis. *Percept. mot. Skills*, 1965, **20**, 1070–1072.

―――― and ――――. Gaze-contingent adaptation to prismatic distortion. *Amer. J. Psychol.*, in press.

Posin, R. L. *Perceptual adaptation to contingent visual-field movement: an experimental investigation of position constancy.* Doctoral disseration, Yeshiva University, 1966.

Riess, B. F. The relationship between the tilt of a visual field and the deviation of body position from the vertical in the white rat. *J. exp. Psychol.*, 1951, **40**, 531–537.

Rock, I. The perception of the egocentric orientation of a line. *J. exp. Psychol.*, 1954, **48**, 367–374.

――――. The orientation of forms on the retina and in the environment. *Amer. J. Psychol.*, 1956, **69**, 513–528.

――――. A neglected aspect of the problem of recall: the Höffding function. Chap. in *Theories of the mind*, edit. by J. Scher. New York: Free Press, 1962.

――――. Adaptation to a minified image. *Psychon. Sci.*, 1965, **2**, 105–106.

―――― and S. Ebenholtz. The relational determination of perceived size. *Psychol. Rev.*, 1959, **66**, 387–401.

―――― and S. Ebenholtz. Stroboscopic movement based on change of phenomenal location rather than retinal location. *Amer. J. Psychol.*, 1962, **75**, 193–207.

―――― and W. Heimer. The effect of retinal and phenomenal orientation on the perception of form. *Amer. J. Psychol.*, 1957, **70**, 493–511.

―――― and L. Kaufman. The moon illusion, II. *Science*, 1962, **136**, 1023–1031.

―――― and R. Leaman. An experimental analysis of visual symmetry. *Acta Psychol.*, 1963, **21**, 171–183.

―――― and W. McDermott. The perception of visual angle. *Acta Psychol.*, 1964, **22**, 119–134.

————, A. Mack, L. Adams, and A. L. Hill. Adaptation to contradictory information from vision and touch. *Psychon. Sci.*, 1965, **3**, 435–436.

————, E. S. Tauber, and D. P. Heller. Perception of stroboscopic movement: evidence for its innate basis. *Science*, 1965, **147**, 1050–1052.

———— and J. Victor. Vision and touch: an experimentally created conflict between the two senses. *Science*, 1964, **143**, 594–596.

Roelofs, C. O. Optische Lokalisation. *Arch. Augenheilk*, 1935, **109**, 395–415.

Schlodtmann, W. Ein Beitrag zur Lehre von der optischen Lokalisation bei Blindgeborenen. *Arch. f. Ophth.*, 1902, **54**, 256–267.

Senden, M. von. *Space and sight.* Trans. by P. Heath. Glencoe, Ill.: The Free Press, 1960.

Singer, G., and R. H. Day. Spatial adaptation and aftereffect with optically transformed vision: effects of active and passive responding and the relationship between test and exposure responses. *J. exp. Psychol.*, 1966, **71**, 725–731.

———— and ————. The effects of spatial judgments on the perceptual aftereffects resulting from prismatically transformed vision, *Austral. J. Psych.*, in press.

Smith, K. U., and W. M. Smith. *Perception and motion.* Philadelphia: Saunders, 1962.

Snyder, F. W., and N. H. Pronko. *Vision with spatial inversion.* Wichita: U. of Wichita Press, 1952.

Sperry, R. W. Effect of 180 degree rotation of the retinal field on visuomotor coordination. *J. exp. Zool.*, 1943, **92**, 263–279.

Stone, L. S. Functional polarization in retinal development and its re-establishment in regenerating retinae of rotated grafted eyes. *Proc. Soc. Exp. Biol. Med.*, 1944, **57**, 13–14.

————. Polarization of the retina and development of vision. *J. exp. Zool.*, 1960, **145**, 85–93.

Stratton, G. M. Some preliminary experiments on vision without inversion of the retinal image. *Psychol. Rev.*, 1896, **3**, 611--617.

————. Upright vision and the retinal image. *Psychol. Rev.*, 1897, **4**, 182–187.

————. Vision without inversion of the retinal image. *Psychol. Rev.*, 1897, **4**, 341–360, 463–481.

————. The spatial harmony of touch and sight. *Mind*, 1899, **8**, 492–505.

Tastevin, J. En partant de l'expérience d'Aristote. *L'Encephale*, 1937, **1**, 57–84, 140–158.

Taylor, J. G. *The behavioral basis of perception.* New Haven: Yale Univ. Press, 1962.

———— and S. Papert. A theory of perceptual constancy. *Brit. J. Psychol.*, 1956, **47**, 216–224.

Teuber, H.-L. Perception. In J. Field, H. W. Magoun, and V. E. Hall, eds., *Handbook of physiology. section 1. neurophysiology,* Vol. 3, Chap. 65, Washington: Amer. Physiol. Soc., 1960.

Victor, J., and I. Rock. An experimentally created conflict between vision & touch. Paper read at Eastern Psychological Assoc., Atlantic City, April 1962.

Wallach, H. Brightness constancy and the nature of achromatic colors. *J. exp. Psychol.*, 1948, 38, 310–324.

——— and P. A. Austin. Recognition and the localization of visual traces. *Amer. J. Psychol.*, 1954, 67, 338–340.

——— and E. B. Karsh. The modification of stereoscopic depth-perception and the kinetic depth effect. *Amer. J. Psychol.*, 1963, 76, 429–435.

——— and J. H. Kravitz. The measurement of the constancy of visual direction and of its adaptation. *Psychon. Sci.*, 1965, 2, 217–218.

——— and J. H. Kravitz. Rapid adaptation in the constancy of visual direction with active and passive rotation. *Psychon. Sci.*, 1965, 3, 165–166.

———, J. H. Kravitz, and J. Lindauer. A passive condition for rapid adaptation to displaced visual direction. *Amer. J. Psychol.*, 1963, 76, 568–578.

———, D. N. O'Connell, and U. Neisser. The memory effect of visual perception of three-dimensional form. *J. exp. Psychol.*, 1953, 45, 360–368.

Walls, G. L. The problem of visual direction. *Amer. J. Optom.*, 1951, 28, 55–83, 115–146, 173–212.

Weber, C. O. Visual-motor coordination in concave and convex mirror space. *Amer. J. Psychol.*, 1931, 43, 254–260.

Weinstein, S., E. A. Sersen, L. Fisher, and M. Weisinger. Is re-afference necessary for visual adaptation? *Percept. mot. Skills*, 1964, 18, 641–648.

Weiss, E. *Memory for size.* Thesis research paper, New School for Social Research, 1961.

Werner, H., S. Wapner, and J. H. Bruell. Experiments on sensory-tonic field theory of perception: VI. Effect of position of head, eyes, and of object on position of the apparent median plane. *J. exp. Psychol.*, 1953, 46, 293–299.

——— and S. Wapner. Studies in physiognomic perception: I. Effect of configurational dynamics and meaning-induced sets on the position of the apparent median plane. *J. Psychol.*, 1954, 38, 51–65.

Wertheimer, M. Experimentelle Studien über das Sehen von Bewegung. *Z. Psychol.*, 1912, 61, 161–265.

Werthheimer, M., and A. J. Arena. Effect of exposure time on adaptation to disarranged hand-eye coordination. *Percept. mot. Skills*, 1959, 9, 159–164.

Witkin, H. A. Perception of body position and the position of the visual field. *Psychol. Monogr.*, 1949, 63, No. 7.

Wooster, M. Certain factors in the development of a new spatial coordination. *Psychol. Monogr.*, 1923, 32, No. 4.

Worchel, P. Space perception and orientation in the blind. *Psychol. Monogr.*, 1951, 65, No. 332.

Wundt, W. Zur Theorie der raumlichen Gesichtswahrnehmungen. *Phil. Stud.*, 1898, 14, 11.

Zimmermann, R. R. Analysis of discrimination learning capacities in the infant rhesus monkey. *J. comp. Physiol. Psychol.*, 1961, 54, 1–10.

Zuckerman, C. B., and I. Rock. A reappraisal of the roles of past experience and innate organizing processes in visual perception. *Psychol. Bull.*, 1957, 54, 269–296.

Index

absolute curvature, 189–190

absolute size of retinal image, 145, 146, 155, 163

accommodation, 133, 164, 165, 240

achromatic color constancy, 214 *n.*, 263

active exposure, 55–58, 60, 120–122, 164, 194–195

active movement(s), 56, 81, 98, 99, 113–114; adaptational role of, 116–119; body, 90; head, 89; informational aspect of, 120–121, 199–200, 215; passive movement vs., 116–119, 199–200; *see also* movement(s)

Adams, Laurence, 230

adaptation, awareness and, 207, 265–267; basis of, 102–111; classical sensory, 13–14; color, 187, 203; complete, 1; configurational, 9, 58, 113 *n.*, 194; to contradictory visual-tactual information, 225–235, 243, 244, 252, 265; definition of, 1; to displacement, *see* displaced image; genuine, 11, 84; instantaneous, 265–266; to inverted image, 1, 6, 7, 10, 15–19, 28, 34, 39–43, 48, 53, 54, 61, 99, 240; to magnification, 1, 146, 148, 156, 158 *n.*, 163; meaning and signifi-

cance of paradigm of, 13–14; measure of magnitude of, *see* tests; to "miniature world," 159–164, 173, 251–252; to minification, 1, 92, 96, 97, 146, 148, 150–153, 156–158, 160–161, 163–175, 192, 224, 226, 227, 234, 240, 248–249; motor, 25–26, 44, 46, 48, 50, 52; to movement, *see* movement(s); partial, 54, 63, 267–269; prism, *see* prism adaptation; proprioceptive, 122, 132–138, 140, 244; to reinverted image, 6, 8, 18–29, 43–53, 62–63, 240; in stationary observer, 39, 58–59, 63, 102 *n.*, 104 *n.*, 128–132, 140, 160, 163, 171–172, 181, 186, 195, 202–203, 241, 242; to tilt, 1, 7–9, 12, 39–43, 54–62, 67–76, 96, 97, 193, 201 *n.*, 202–203, 208, 209, 211, 222–223, 238–239, 251–252, 262; visual, *see* visual adaptation, wearing off of, 12

adaptive change, 70, 89, 96, 134

afferent change, 79–81, 86, 117

afferent feedback, 110, 117, 138, 198

afferent information, 79

aftereffect(s), 4; compression-expansion, 201–203, 207–208, 211–212, 264–265; conditioned, 204; configurational, 9, 58,

277